COMPENDIUM OF PASTORAL MEDICINE

Compendium of Pastoral Medicine

by

Albert Niedermeyer, M.D., Ph.D.

translated by

Fulgence Buonanno, O.F.M., Ph.D.

NEW YORK CITY

JOSEPH F. WAGNER, INC.

Imprimi Potest:

FR. CELSUS R. WHEELER, O.F.M.
Minister Provincial

Nihil Obstat:

DANIEL V. FLYNN, J.C.D.
Censor Librorum

Imprimatur:

✠ FRANCIS CARDINAL SPELLMAN, D.D.
Archbishop of New York

The *Nihil Obstat* and *Imprimatur* are official declarations that a book or pamphlet is free of doctrinal or moral error. No implication is contained therein that those who have granted the *Nihil Obstat* and *Imprimatur* agree with the contents, opinions or statements expressed.

English rights have been granted for this translation of *Compendium der Pastoralmedizin* by Verlag Herder & Co., Vienna, Austria.

Second Printing, October 1961

Preface

The object of this study is to review the most important problems of Pastoral Medicine. Because of this, the treatment is limited to what is strictly necessary. Hence there is no place for a discussion of controversial matters, and provision has therefore been made only for an objective explanation of established facts.

Because of the nature of this work, the so-called scientific apparatus, consisting of notes from and remarks on the literature on the subject has been omitted. It is not the function of a survey like this, but of a scientific Handbook of Special Pastoral Medicine and a treatise on General Pastoral Medicine, to investigate in detail the controversial problems of the day and to explore the literature on the subject.

Hence the object of this volume is to supplement the scientific works on Pastoral Medicine, making their ideas accessible to a greater number of people.

A modern survey of Pastoral Medicine should not be written exclusively for the theologian but should offer something to the person whose field is medicine or is related to medicine. If this is not so, then the book has failed in its purpose.

Finally, such a survey should serve as an introduction even for the educated laity in various professions, such as teachers, lawyers, sociologists, and biologists who have need of knowledge of this subject in their work.

—ALBERT NIEDERMEYER

Contents

PART II

SPECIAL PASTORAL MEDICINE

PART III
RELIGION AND THERAPEUTICS
(DEONTOLOGY)

PART I

FUNDAMENTAL

PRINCIPLES

1. Basic Concepts

~~~~~~

1. MEANING AND NATURE OF PASTORAL MEDICINE

Pastoral Medicine, taken in its broadest sense, comprises the entire sphere of contact between Theology and Medicine. This includes, first of all, Pastoral Theology, Moral Theology, and Canon Law, as well as the other branches of theology.

Pastoral Medicine is of special importance to Canon Law in the matter of conjugal rights and in regard to the role of the medical expert in the canonical marriage process. In this respect, Pastoral Medicine manifests a certain similarity to Forensic Medicine.

a. The twofold starting point

Just as the questions of Forensic Medicine can be considered under a twofold aspect—namely, from the standpoint of the lawyer and that of the medical expert—so also can those of Pastoral Medicine, insofar as they can be seen from the viewpoint of the theologian and that of the medical expert.

We speak of the "theologian" and the "medical expert," in whom theory and science are manifested, in order to distinguish them from the "spiritual adviser" and the "practitioner," in whom are manifested the practical aspects of their profession.

This twofold starting point does not bring about a distinct difference of view on individual questions but, rather, a difference in the selected subject matter. The viewpoints and formulation of questions found in one field of knowledge are not only of interest to the other, but also enlarge the knowledge of the other.

3

b. Universalistic interpretation

In the earlier positivist manner of treating medicine and hygiene, the biological viewpoint prevailed. In time medicine and hygiene were enlarged in their scope through recourse to the social viewpoint, which led from consideration of the individual to the concept of effects extending beyond the individual.

The universalistic mode of considering the subject matter enlarges the view by introducing moral and religious elements.

Ethical and metaphysical knowledge remains in the sphere of the natural knowledge of reason. Morality and religion are established on supernatural knowledge, which is based on revelation.

Where misunderstanding is excluded, the specification "metaphysical" can be used without hesitation to designate "behind the visible world" (μετὰ τὰ φυσικὰ), the elements of the supernatural realm. In using the universalistic method in medicine, positivist knowledge should not be repressed but enlarged and expanded.

There has been for years in modern medicine a slow but constant progress toward a universalistic approach. If the modern tendencies of *médicine de la personne*, and psychosomatic medicine, are to convey more than merely a new slogan, they must necessarily flow into a "universalism" as understood and found in Pastoral Medicine. So understood, Pastoral Medicine can represent the crowning point of medical science.

c. The object of Pastoral Medicine

The purpose of Pastoral Medicine is determined, in the first place, by the need which the spiritual adviser has. And Pastoral Medicine is of no less importance to the doctor since he needs a guide in his practice. Practical treatment is based on the fundamentals of a scientific theory: *Without correct theory, there cannot be correct practice.* Hence the knowledge of scientific theory is indispensable. Pastoral Medicine is a very important part of medical science and a very important branch of Pastoral Theology. Its importance for both branches of knowledge becomes more clearly evident as time goes on.

Pastoral Medicine stands and falls with the notion of science, which alone makes a universalistic consideration possible and guarantees a complete view of the matter. The former positivist concept of science is for it altogether too narrow.

d. Medical science and medical practice

Medical science includes the theory, research and presentation of the collective branches of medicine and hygiene. The scientific basis proceeds from the theoretical branches, such as Anatomy, Physiology, Pathology, etc., as well as from the auxiliary natural sciences, such as Biology and Genetics, and serves as a basis for the practical clinical branches, such as Internal Medicine, Surgery, Obstetrics and Gynecology, Psychiatry, Neurology, Pediatrics, Dermatology, Venereology, etc.

Medical practice entails the treatment of sick people. Its basis is, in the first place, medical science. It also touches on a certain non-rational basis ("medical skill") and moral values (humaneness and love of neighbor). The difference between humaneness and love of neighbor (charity) is the difference between purely natural and supernatural motives.

e. Medicine and hygiene

(a) *Definition*

By medicine (the art of healing) we mean the branch of practical clinical medicine. Its object is sick mankind and its task is to heal.

By hygiene (the science of health) we mean the science of human health and its preservation, especially the preventing of needless injuries (prophylaxis). Its object is, above all, the healthy person; its task is to preserve his health.

(b) *Individual and social viewpoint*

Medicine and hygiene can be considered from the viewpoint of the individual or of society. According to this classification, we have the distinction of individual and social medicine, individual and social hygiene.

By social medicine we mean the whole of the practical clinical branches as seen in their social aspect. Every clinical branch has a social aspect, even if only from the standpoint of "social well-being" and expert medical opinion for the various divisions of that well-being. This aspect of social medicine is perhaps the most important branch in practice but not the only one. The entire field of "labor medicine" is a branch of social medicine.

It is therefore not correct to restrict the concept of "social medicine" to social well-being or to the problems related to the protection of labor, as has been the case in the literature since 1918.

Social medicine should not be confused with social hygiene, as has sometimes been the case.

(c) *Individual and social hygiene*

Hygiene comprises the science of the health of the *individual* (individual hygiene) and *human society* (social hygiene). Regarding the concept of social hygiene, there is no complete agreement among authors. It is understood here only in the universalistic sense, as the hygiene of human society. As such it includes the hygiene of exogenous conditions of life (hygiene of environment), as well as that of endogenous health factors (hereditary predisposition, constitution, etc.); accordingly, the science of hereditary health, eugenics, and hygiene of the constitution and personality.

(d) *Moral and cultural hygiene*

Alfons Fischer was the first to demand that social hygiene, understood in his time as hygiene of the social environmental factors, should, through the inclusion of moral factors (moral hygiene), be extended to include cultural hygiene. This justified demand is fulfilled by the universalistic meaning of social hygiene as the hygiene of human society.

From this we have succeeded, especially in agreement with the concept of mental hygiene, in attaining a suitable definition of Pastoral Hygiene.

(e) *Mental hygiene*

If hygiene has as its object human health, it is evident that this task must not limit itself merely to physical health but must also extend to mental health. That which is the purpose of psychosomatic medicine in the realm of practical medicine—namely, of showing the manifold correlation between bodily and mental factors in the genesis of disease—is likewise the purpose of mental hygiene.

(f) *Concept of health*

It is necessary to start off with a correct and comprehensive definition of the meaning of "health." Up to a short time ago, the concept of health was stated merely in a negative manner—namely, health was the absence of any morbid abnormality. Positivism adopted this negative definition. When Alfons Fischer demanded that a life "worthy of a human being" be made a characteristic of health, the anatomical pathologist Aschoff countered with a pure positivist view that it is not feasible to introduce in science a concept which, like that of "human dignity," implies social and moral values. In the meantime, progress favored a more extensive concept of health. The World Health Organization declared in its statute of 1947 that "Health is not merely the absence of disease but a state of complete physical, social and moral well-being." From this concept also resulted the need of a revision in the direction of a universalistic meaning of the terms "normality" and "abnormality."

(g) Hygiene as a descriptive and normative science

Hygiene is a science which not only describes things, establishes facts, and indicates, but also confirms causes and associations. It seeks to establish general laws, pointing out the causes of injuries to the health of the individual and society and how they are to be avoided. One side of hygiene has a preponderantly biologico-natural scientific aspect; the other has more of a sociological-ethical character, and hence assumes a more rational scientific aspect.

Accordingly, it is not enough merely to establish what hygiene is (descriptive hygiene); we must also know what it should be, and what it should not be (normative hygiene).

The norms of standard hygiene contain a positive and negative characteristic insofar as they regulate what should be or what should not be. The same goes for the resulting practical measures. The positive (furthering) measures seek to bring to a realization what is desired (should be); the negative (restrictive) measures seek to suppress what is not desired (should not be). To this belongs also the prevention of injury to health (preventive hygiene, prophylaxis) —for example, legislation concerning epidemic diseases. The tasks that are to be fulfilled in the fields of public health, medical politics, health guidance, health care, social care and social charities, public and private welfare work; their limitations and the medico-pastoral view and treatment of them, are reserved in a special manner to Pastoral Hygiene.

B

(h) *Hygiene as a natural science—its place in relation to the philosophical sciences*

There is not the slightest doubt that hygiene is, above all, a science and primarily makes use of natural scientific methods of research. After the concept of health had received a wider and more universalistic meaning, it was definitely established that hygiene is not only a descriptive but also a normative science, which also has a sociological-ethical side. The result is that hygiene, in this sense, is no longer merely a natural science, nor can it be considered a strict natural science. What is more, there are important phases of hygiene, above all, of mental hygiene, that border on the philosophical sciences. Under this viewpoint, natural sciences and philosophical sciences no longer exclude one another but complement each other and lead to the knowledge of truth.

f. Hygiene and ethics

The relationship of hygiene to ethics results from the normative aspect of hygiene. Ethics as a science is the study and justification of moral law on the basis of the natural knowledge of reason.

Moral theology as a science is the study and justification of moral law on the basis of the supernatural knowledge of revelation.

The realization or application of this knowledge is designated as practical or moral ethics. From the agreement between natural and supernatural knowledge it follows that there can never be insurmountable opposition between science and doctrinal theology. The same is to be said concerning the relation between hygiene and moral philosophy.

g. Basic law of Pastoral Medicine

From this knowledge arises the basic law of Pastoral Medicine and Pastoral Hygiene: *Nothing pertaining to health can be correct if it is morally wrong.* The characteristic criterion of Pastoral Medicine and Pastoral Hygiene—the universalistic point of view—manifests itself more clearly in its application to ethics. This specific medico-pastoral manner of considering problems is not content to investigate the biological, at best the social aspect, of the problem, but goes beyond to the ethico-metaphysical view, and here is found the crowning point of the complete outlook.

h. The scientific character of Pastoral Medicine

The objection has been raised that Pastoral Medicine is not a science because it is not free from postulates and because it is subject to an ideology. Pastoral Medicine is free from postulation in the sense that it concerns itself with a *method* of research; to the extent that it establishes facts beyond a doubt by means of a purely descriptive and objective method. Insofar as it is a *normative* science it cannot be conceived of without the use of *moral* standards, without a positing of *values* and the taking of a stand in regard to the latter.

In this respect, Pastoral Medicine must free itself from the traditional form of positivism which recognizes only the "positive establishment of facts" as a science.

If, moreover, science is a knowledge of truth, then subjection to an ideology is not a hindrance but rather a requirement for the knowledge of truth, as long as that ideology corresponds to truth.

Standards and values are decidedly affected according as we acknowledge merely a natural order or both a *natural* and *supernatural* order. The universalistic viewpoint must include the supernatural order as a given state, as a reality. It need not consider the supernatural itself as an object of scientific research; rather, research must take the supernatural into account in order to produce a knowledge of truth.

The two orders of being, as recognized by perennial philosophy in its metaphysics of being (ontology): the order of nature and that of the supernatural, possess a true corresponding relation (*analogia entis*). The supernatural order is not perceptible to the senses; it is not a source of the knowledge of sense perception and experience, but does not because of this possess a lesser but, rather, a greater degree of reality of being (reality). God as *Actus Purus* is at the same time absolute reality: *Ens a se, Ens realissimum.*

i. Physical and metaphysical phenomena

According to this view, for every *physical* phenomenon in the natural order of being, there is a corresponding *metaphysical* phenomenon, which is behind the physical (μετὰ τὰ φυσικὰ); hence, for the most part, something in the realm of the supernatural.

In order to avoid confusion it must be made clear that the terms "metaphysics" and "supernatural" are not to be interchanged or confused. Metaphysics, like ethics, belongs to the realm of pure, natural knowledge obtained through reason, yet both border on the realm of revealed supernatural knowledge.

j. Postulates of Pastoral Medicine

We have demonstrated the limits within which it is possible to have a science without postulates. Now we have to consider the most essential postulates which Pastoral Medicine must acknowledge as immediate data in order to attain a successful knowledge of the relationship among beings. These follow naturally from the universalistic interpretation.

The essential and indispensable postulates of this universalistic interpretation are:

1. The fundamental truth of the existence of God as Creator and Preserver of the universe;
2. Man as a creature—his place in nature as a creature of God;
3. The fallen nature of man (*natura vulnerata*).

Without an acknowledgment of these postulates, essential problems will remain unsolved and insoluble.

From these postulates the following necessary basic principles result:

From the fact of the fallen nature of man arises the need of redemption. The recognition of this fact, as well as that of a supernatural order, brings about an essential change of attitude toward physical death.

The purely positivist view presents physical death as the end of all vital functions and the definite termination of individuality and personality. From the standpoint of practical ethics this would make every sacrifice, every renunciation of earthly goods and pleasures of life, absurd; consequently, the result would be one of absolute practical materialism.

The question of death appears entirely different when we see in death a consequence of fallen human nature; when we acknowledge the creation of the human soul (*creatianismus*) and its immaterial substantiality. From this follows not only the future life of the soul after death (immortality), but also the resurrection of the body; above all, the realization that the true meaning of life finds its fulfillment not in the visible world but in the supernatural order.

The importance of these ideas for medicine, and especially for the doctor in his relations with the sick, is incalculable.

k. Norms and values of life

The biological interpretation (practical medicine, individual hygiene) derives its norm from the welfare of the individual (*bonum privatum*). The main consideration is that pertaining to physical welfare. This is expressed in the axiom *Salus aegroti summa lex*.

The social interpretation (social hygiene, social medicine) derives its norm from the welfare of natural societies (*bonum commune seu publicum*). The principal but not exclusive consideration is that pertaining to physical welfare. Whenever spiritual and moral values are considered, it is ordinarily from a merely natural viewpoint.

The ethico-metaphysical interpretation derives its norm from the concept of moral laws and the relation of man to his source of being.

This leads to a comprehension of his place in a supernatural community and considers the final end of man's life, the *summum bonum*.

Based on this viewpoint, not only the present life or *vita temporalis*, but also the *vita spiritualis*, is to be taken into consideration.

A true estimate of the hierarchical order of values will be of great help toward the proper orientation and attitude in practical cases, as, for example, in the importance of reception of the sacraments by the sick. (Cf. *Deontology*.)

It would be misleading to explain the above dialectical distinctions in the sense that there is an opposition of values, an absolute precedence of the *bonum publicum* to the *bonum privatum*. "Common good takes precedence over private good," should not mean that private welfare should without discretion be sacrificed for the common welfare. Moreover, rightly understood, *bonum privatum* is normally arranged and subordinated to rightly mean *bonum publicum* without conflict or opposition.

Finally, the *bonum publicum* is only rightly adjusted when it is directed toward the norms of the *summum bonum*.

In a truly understood hierarchy of values the lower degrees are absorbed and surpassed by the higher degrees but never destroyed (principle of arrangement, subordination and elevation).

Pastoral Medicine and Pastoral Hygiene stand and fall with the universalistic scientific concept already explained.

l. Definition of Pastoral Medicine and Pastoral Hygiene

Accordingly we arrive at the following definitions:

1. By Pastoral Medicine we mean the complete bordering sphere between medicine and theology: In the first place Pastoral and Moral Theology, including their dogmatic basis, which results from the common need found in the practical work of both the spiritual adviser and the physician.

2. By Pastoral Hygiene we mean the large field of hygiene as a science, which comes about by an increase of perspective and progressively, from the biological aspect, toward the social, and finally to the ethico-metaphysical phase, and ends with a complete view, considering man not only as a member of a natural but also of a supernatural society.

The above-developed universalistic interpretation is essential and specific, both for Pastoral Medicine and Pastoral Hygiene.

2. BORDERLAND SPHERES, AUXILIARY SCIENCES

The universalistic character of Pastoral Medicine implies a relation to numerous other fields of knowledge. The following have been of great importance to Pastoral Medicine:

a. Naturalistic medical branches

General biology

Of essential importance are the questions concerning the biology of reproduction, heredity and the theory of evolution. The treatment of these belongs to an introductory study of medico-pastoral problems.

Physics and chemistry

Various authors have dealt with the questions of Pastoral Chemistry—e.g., Olfers.

Anatomy and physiology

Embryology (the history of development, ontogeny of man).

Ethnology (study of races)

This is of great importance for the science of the missions (missionology).

Anthropology

Anthropology, understood in its customary, former meaning, had to do with prehistoric human findings. It offered only a part of a universalistic anthropology and could more accurately be called paleo-anthropology. Hence the great need for a universalistic form of anthropology.

Among the introductory branches of medicine, the history of medicine is here brought to attention. Of the clinical branches there are two which have a relation to Pastoral Medicine:

1. Gynecology and obstetrics;
2. Psychiatry, with emphasis on psychopathology and psychotherapy.

The importance of Forensic Medicine has already been discussed.

b. Spheres of contact between the natural and the philosophical sciences

In this category are to be mentioned: first of all, sociology, then psychology, and finally pedagogy. Because these branches are assigned to the sphere of contact between the natural and philosophical sciences, this is not to be taken as an adherence to a more or less materialistic "biologism." These belong essentially to the philosophical sciences but must be associated with knowledge of the natural sciences.

c. Philosophical-theological branches of study

Metaphysics, ethics (practical philosophy, moral philosophy)
Fundamental theology

Here the fundamental truths and their proof (apologetics) are considered (dogmatic theology). The fundamentals of dogma are as essentially important for Pastoral Medicine as they are for obtaining a clear knowledge of the ultimate questions of life.

Moral and Pastoral Theology—Canon Law

We realize the importance of these from their preliminary definition. The importance of Pastoral Medicine for the science of Canon Law is based on the role of the doctor as medico-legal expert in the canonical marriage process, especially in reference to the question of impotency and that of inability to give consent because of mental disease or mental debility.

Asceticism and mysticism

The importance of these theological branches for Pastoral Medicine is manifest from the following topics: Physical culture and mortification; fasting, phenomena bordering on the supernatural; ecstasy, etc.; distinction of psycho-pathological ("pseudo-mystical") phenomena and genuine mystical phenomena; wonder healings, etc.

Science of the Missions

The significance of this topic to Pastoral Medicine is most clearly seen in connection with the question of ethnology and of medical missionary care.

The science of Social Charities

Here is found a relationship with practically all fields of social welfare and health care, or public welfare.

The above summary shows that Pastoral Medicine is associated not only with Pastoral and Moral Theology, but with practically all the principal branches of theology.

3. SUMMARY OF THE SUBJECT MATTER

a. General principles of Pastoral Medicine

Besides general abstract fundamentals and basic scientific problems viewed according to their nature and purpose, and the suppositions of a universalistic science, the introductory observations must include the history of Pastoral Medicine, as well as general biological fundamentals and the most important problems of sociology and moral theology.

b. Special Pastoral Medicine

The topics of Special Pastoral Medicine are grouped principally around the following branches of medicine:

1. Medical psychology, psychopathology and psychotherapy;
2. Questions concerning human sexual life (sexology);
3. Obstetrics and gynecology; surgery and general therapy.

The first-named branch belongs predominantly to psychiatrists and neurologists; the third, predominantly to obstetricians and gynecologists. The second assumes an intermediary position between the first and the third.

c. Pastoral Hygiene

The questions of Pastoral Hygiene correspond essentially to those of social hygiene, the principal spheres of which are the following:

1. Hygiene of human conditions (nourishment, clothing, home and work);
2. Hygiene of human reproduction;
3. Mental hygiene and general cultural hygiene.

We here find in the foreground questions concerning the hygiene of human reproduction, eugenics and mental hygiene; then, questions concerning the nature of public health; and finally, the hygiene of the clerical state as well as that of ecclesiastical institutions.

To Pastoral Medicine as well as to Pastoral Hygiene belong the complex problems pertaining to defining the relationship between spiritual director and physician, between physician and patient, and the science concerning medical duties (deontology).

d. Medico-pastoral casuistry

A casuistry whose method resembles that of medical casuistry more than that of moral casuistry seems of basic importance for Pastoral Medicine. Its worth is based on proof that the principles of Pastoral Medicine are not just theoretical and subtly reasoned principles, but directly manifest their full worth in life and in practical cases.

B*

4. FURTHER PRINCIPLES OF CLASSIFICATION

In many works on Pastoral Medicine, especially in the treatment of questions in which the pastoral aspect predominates, the approved classification based on the viewpoint of Moral and Pastoral Theology is recommended, namely:

a. *De praeceptis;*
b. *De Sacramentis.*

In the above classification, the following are of primary interest:

a. *De praeceptis*

(1) With regard to the fifth commandment: the questions concerning the right to life; preservation of health; protection of one's life and the life of others; bodily injury; sterilization, euthanasia, craniotomy, abortion, as well as the other questions relating to obstetrical and surgical intervention.

(2) With regard to the sixth commandment: the questions concerning sexual abuse, *abusus matrimonii;* and among others, the important questions concerning the *observatio temporum* (Knaus, Ogino, and others).

b. *De Sacramentis*

(1) Regarding the Sacrament of Baptism: the necessity of baptizing feeble and apparently dead infants.

(2) Regarding the Sacrament of Matrimony: requirements concerning the ability to give consent, both in the mental and physical realm; the question of *impedimentum impotentiae,* etc.

(3) Regarding the Sacrament of Holy Orders: requirements regarding bodily and mental health; principles to be followed in deciding suitability or unsuitability of candidate.

(4) Regarding the Sacrament of Extreme Unction: the duty of the doctor regarding the reception of the Sacraments by the sick, etc.

In order that the subject matter may be made suitable and practical, this study will select the most necessary and practically important questions of Pastoral Medicine and Pastoral Hygiene and will present these in the most concise and systematic form.

2. Fundamentals of a Universalistic Anthropology

1. GENERAL CONCEPT

The object of medicine is man—principally sick, suffering, needy and help-seeking man. Thus arises the primary and essential duty of the doctor: to help suffering man through means of healing made possible by a knowledge of medical science.

The object of Pastoral Medicine is likewise man, but not only sick and health-seeking man, but man in relation to his complete nature; not merely his biological nature and social relations, but also his ethico-metaphysical nature; in respect to his place in nature as well as his supernatural destiny; consequently, as a "citizen of two worlds."

If a positivist medicine could formerly be satisfied with an "anthropology" which considered man simply in an evolutionist manner, as a transitory terminal member in a series of subhuman developments, and which held, above all, that there were degrees of transition between man and the anthropoid ape (anthropo-paleontology), so Pastoral Medicine can be satisfied only with an anthropology which presents a true doctrine of man, in his complete nature, hence a universalistic anthropology.

Since the former positivist anthropology was based on evolution and positivist genetics and on a more or less monistic-materialistic psychology, it will be our task to critically examine the same.

17

At this time, we will consider the place of man in nature.

2. THE PLACE OF MAN IN NATURE

It makes quite a difference whether man is considered, according to revelation, as a creature of God or whether this fact is denied.

The acceptance of man as a creature must also entail the recognition of a fallen human nature (*natura lapsa seu vulnerata*); for a consideration of the evil found in nature and the wickedness of man shows that this could not be created by an almighty, all-wise and all-good Creator. Hence, evil calls for another cause, and there is no other suitable explanation than that brought out by revelation—namely, the original fall of man, the revolt of man against his Creator.

The acceptance of the fact of original sin brings with it immunity from two basic philosophical errors, which assume an absurd position in regard to the evil in the world—namely, optimism and pessimism.

Optimism claims that the world as it is, is the best of all possible worlds and that man is by nature good (Rousseau). It is blind to the fact and reality of evil. It rejects the tenet that the world as it is could not possibly be created by an almighty, all-wise and all-good Creator.

Pessimism, on the other hand, does not reject the reality of evil but inevitably leads either to a denial of a Creator or to primitive dualism, by considering the principle of evil as existing from the beginning, being as eternal and mighty as the Creator. Actually pessimism attributes to evil the role of Creator (Demiurge—" world architect ").

If these primary and necessary postulates of a universalistic anthropology are denied, then there remains only one possibility—the assumption that man developed " of himself," i.e., without the intervention of a supernatural power and intelligence, from lower beings, which in turn developed from inanimate matter. This assumption is definitely associated with the system of materialistic monism. Materialism and the system of evolution are inextricably united to each other.

The materialistic-evolutionary interpretation of the place of man in nature has received from Haeckel in his " Cosmological Perspective," the following classical expression:

1. The universe is eternal, infinite and boundless.

2. The substance of the universe with its two attributes of matter and energy fills the infinite space and is in perpetual motion.

3. This motion passes into endless time as a uniform development, with alternating periods of birth and death, of evolution and involution.

4. The countless heavenly bodies are all subject to the law of substance.[1]

5. Our sun is one of innumerable heavenly bodies, our earth one of the numerous transiting planets.

6. The earth went through a slow cooling process before fluid could originate on the earth and with it the primary conditions for organic life.

7. The then-following biogenetic process, the slow development and transformation of countless organic forms required millions of years.

8. The type of vertebrates has surpassed in development the other types of animals.

9. One of the most important branches was that of the development of mammals.

10. The most complete class is that of the primates, which first came into existence in the beginning of the tertiary period (also called the age of mammals).

11. The youngest is man, who was developed from the anthropoid ape at the end of the tertiary period.

12. Accordingly, universal history is a short vanishing episode in the history of the earth which, in turn, is a small part of the history of our planetary system. As the earth is a particle of the sun in the endless universe, so the individual man is a tiny granule of plasm in transient organic nature.

These twelve theses present the creed of absolute unbelief and are in opposition to the teaching that man was made to the image and likeness of God, and instead advocate an absolute futility and worthlessness of human life.

In this philosophy of life, which ruled supreme as " scientific "

---

[1] By " the law of substance " Haeckel means a synthesis between the " law of conservation of energy " and that of the " conservation of matter "; the idea of " substance " is understood not philosophically but materially: namely, as " that from which something subsists " and not that " which subsists of itself " (*in se subsistens*). This, therefore, involves a falsification of the concept of " substance."

for almost a century, there was no place for free will, responsibility and human dignity.

What is remarkable about this concept of the universe is that according to its tenets an inconceivable period of time is required for the origin and development of the universe. Haeckel spoke of "millions of years," but at the present time this amount, merely for our solar system, is increased to billions and trillions.

The recent development of natural science, above all, of physics and astronomy (Quantum theory), atomic research, theory of relativity, principle of indetermination), which are associated with the names of Planck, Niels Bohr, Einstein and Heisenberg, have shaken the edifice of this primitive materialism; so that at present, it has at least lost its nimbus of modernity. It is no longer considered modern to openly advocate scientific materialism. It is advocated more in a masked, sublimated and, because of this, perhaps, more dangerous form, but one no longer openly admits one's dedication to materialism.

The thesis concerning the infinity and eternity of cosmic space already has been completely rejected by science. Since the world had a beginning, it also must have an end; and since the world has had a beginning, this must be understood as an act of creation. The boast " by itself " which the autonomy of evolution claimed and to which it gave impetus, has been silenced.

As primitive materialism has been overthrown in the fields of astronomy and physics, so likewise has mechanism in the field of biology.

Since the time of Driesch, vitalism again has come into discussion. Modern biology, under the leadership of Uexkuell, Woltereck, André, Portmann, and Schubert-Soldern has succeeded in acknowledging order and design.

3. BASIC QUESTIONS CONCERNING THE THEORY OF EVOLUTION (THEORY OF DESCENT)

a. Historical note

The first great period of a systematic natural science extends from the time of Aristotle up to the time of the two great systematizers Linné and Cuvier.

Both were, in the advancement of their famous system concerning the plant and animal realm, directed by the idea of the "constancy of species" and their origin through an act of creation. Linné stated: *Tot numeramus species, quot diversas formas ab initio creavit infinitum Ens.* Cuvier in his treatise on types held the idea of a general plan of structure; this necessarily presupposes a planning intelligence. The first criticism of this system opposed the assumption of an "affinity" of species on the basis of pure, logical, systematic categories (species, genus, family, order, class and type). It sought to have the affinity based no longer on the idea of a structured society, but rather on the idea of a genuine affinity of types based on common descent (genetically). So the demand for a "natural" system was raised in opposition to Linné and Cuvier.

Simultaneously with the idea of descent that of transformism also was accepted and brought into the field in opposition to the "constancy of species."

The following are precursors of the theory of evolution: Étienne Geoffroy St. Hilaire, Erasmus Darwin (the grandfather of Charles Darwin) and Goethe.

It was J. B. de Lamarck who gave the essential impetus to the further development of transformation and to the shattering of the theory of the constancy of species.

In the famous disputation of August 2, 1830, St. Hilaire shook the standard authority of Cuvier. The main points of the controversy pertained more to the field of geology and paleontology; Cuvier supported the so-called theory of the cataclysms against the theory of a slow and continuous evolution.

In the fields of zoology and botany, the opposing opinions can thus be formulated: Cuvier considered the individual species as changeless and as individual creative acts of God. He explains the adaptation of form to function in a teleological manner—i.e., by means of the principle of finality.

Lamarck rejected the teleological view as unscientific, theological and anthropomorphic. He designated the species as variable and inconstant. The species form varieties which further develop into new species. Lamarck considers the external conditions of life, environment, as the cause of the variation.

Active adaptation to environment, the use and non-use of organs, play the chief role in variation.

Lamarck did not, during his lifetime, receive public recognition, but the recognition that would have been his was later given to Charles Darwin. Darwin could never have attained his worldly success without the work of Lamarck. Darwin followed Lamarck completely, even if he did seek to prove his theory of descent with entirely different principles. Darwin not only reaped what Lamarck had sowed, but also made use of factors which the history of the theory of descent tends to overlook: in the first place, the spiritual atmosphere which the revolution of 1848 had created; and secondly, the theory of Malthus in the economic field.

In 1798 Malthus advanced his theory concerning the disproportion between population increase and the means of subsistence.

The " means of subsistence " theory became the basis for Darwin's theory of the "struggle for life." It is even today advocated as the " scientific " basis of the demand for birth control (neo-Malthusianism).

In his theory concerning the origin of species by natural selection, Darwin holds that in nature the struggle for life plays the same breeding, selecting (eliminating and preserving) role as that of breeders of domestic species. This leads to the survival of the fittest. In this process, the great propelling force is not adaptation but selection.

On the basis of these ideas, Darwin's view concerning the mode of evolution can be called selectionism.

The system of selectionism has caused disastrous effects not only in the biological but also in the ethical and social realm. In recent times, it has led to a race hygiene which seeks to eliminate " the inferior " by sterilization and euthanasia.

August Weismann has carried the ideas of Darwin in regard to selectionism to their extreme consequences. Weismann considered hereditary dispositions as the ultimate material units (genes, idants, determinants). He distinguished between the germ plasm and the soma, and made this the basis of his theory of the continuity of germ plasm, which later was developed into the theory of the germ track. He definitely rejected the supposition of Lamarck regarding inheritance of acquired characteristics.

Thus Weismann has become the leader of the formerly prevalent selectionistic heredo-biology (genetics).

A difficulty arose in regard to the theory of descent because of its static interpretation of an immutable hereditary disposition. Since it postulated a concept of variable and inconstant species, it was difficult to associate with this a static and constant hereditary disposition.

De Vries maintained that the change of species did not come about through a gradual and constant adaptation and hereditary transmission of acquired characteristics but rather through a sudden change of " hereditary structure " (mutation); mutations are accordingly " firmly hereditary " and effective " hereditary changes."

Although both the theory of evolution and that of selectionism were considered secure, it is worthy of note that de Vries, by means of his theory of mutation, succeeded in reverting to the hypothesis of a constancy of species.

b. Ideological consequences

The theory of evolution was extremely well received during the nineteenth century, when its consequences began to be proclaimed.

Of greater importance than Darwin himself, in the popularization and propagation of theory of evolution, were his contemporary Thomas Huxley and his pupil Ernst Haeckel.

Around 1880 Huxley, while on a sea expedition, believed that he had discovered the preliminary degree of life in the most primitive " original slime," and he named it Bathybius Haeckeli. This Bathybius proved to be a deposit that could be artificially reproduced; nevertheless, its effects were enormous. Huxley unsparingly applied the conclusions of the theory of evolution to the ideological realm. He stressed that " the question of all questions " was opened and definitely answered : the question of the origin of living beings, in contrast to the doctrine of creation which was formerly held; the question of the position of man in nature, in the sense of a development of man from ancestral animals and, especially, from anthropoid apes. It was Huxley, rather than Darwin, who first expressly taught the origin of man from the ape. Haeckel disseminated the " natural scientific concept of the world " in two popular works, " Weltraetsel " (" The Enigma of the World ") and " Lebenswunder " (" The Miracle of Life "), which met with great favor. In addition, he projected a phylogenetic system of zoology. With his " natural history of creation " Haeckel was convinced he had conclusively refuted the theory of creation.

In the field of science, the great influence of Haeckel was based on his fundamental biogenetic law. He reduced this to a concise formula: Ontogenesis (the developmental history of the individual organism) is an abbreviated recapitulation of phylogenesis (the history of the species). The theory of evolution with its various tendencies was one in that it had rendered unnecessary the supposition of a Creator and that it had conclusively refuted the "creation myth." From this we have two trends which have come down to the present time.

The Lamarckian trend held fast, afterwards as before, to the basic importance of adaptation and environment as well as to the doctrine of the inheritance of acquired characteristics. It corresponds ideologically with the postulates of socialism.

The Darwinian trend holds fast to the influence of environment on hereditary predispositions and to the exclusive omnipotence of selection; consequently it leads to the postulates of race hygiene and the theory of race. The practical effects of these theories already have been pointed out.

c. Arguments of the theory of evolution

"Proofs" for the theory of evolution—more correctly, arguments for it—are divided into the following principal groups:

1. Argument from paleontology
2. Argument from systematics
3. Argument from comparative anatomy
4. Argument from embryology
5. Argument from zoogeography and phytogeography.

It is clear from the findings of the first four groups that they do not conclusively confirm a real ancestral affinity—i.e., genetic descent through a series of generations; but they at least attest in favor of an affinity in structural plan. In other words, they do not prove the genetic correlation but often indicate merely that violence is done to the facts.

(a) Paleontology

Paleontology is able, on the basis of findings of the remains of animals and men, to establish merely a certain series of typical fossils. The fact that this succession shows a definite agreement with a hypothetical "phylogenetic system"—in other words, that a genetic origin is imaginable in the corresponding series—is still, by far, not a positive proof that this really took place through a series of generations. There is no doubt that the order in which the remains are found in the corresponding geological strata is impressive; but, so far, paleontology has not given proof of an actual genetic transformation and never will be able to do so.

It shows merely, in the most convincing manner, the transformation of a plan of structure according to a determined scheme. Still more impressive are the remains which manifest, in a certain manner, a missing link between two different groups, as, for example, reptiles and birds (archaeopteryx, ichthyornis, etc.). But this very thing proves nothing more than a typical transformation of a plan of structure. This holds also, in like manner, for the "battle horse" of the theory of "descent," the series of variations undergone by the foot of the fossil horse from a foot with five toes up to a foot with one toe, protected by only one hoof.

(b) *Systematics*

Systematics is a method, valuable in zoology and botany, of imposing order upon numerous living forms, combining the related and distinguishing the different. '

Evidence of homogeneity is found in common characteristics of body structure and form (morphology).

The classification into systematic categories (species, genus, family, class, order, etc.) is a logical process of arrangement. It is based on the affinity of the plan of structure. The idea of a "natural system" based on a genetic affinity of lineage has introduced more confusion than order in systematics.

(c) *Comparative anatomy*

Comparative anatomy teaches us to realize that certain organs, despite the difference of external form, are homologous and that others, despite likeness in form and function, are only analogous. Accordingly, the following are homologous organs: the wings of birds and anterior extremities of mammals, the hands of man and the fins of a whale; all of them transformation forms of the anterior extremity of the vertebrate type.

The wings of birds and of insects would be analogous organs. Comparative anatomy has been of great importance in regard to rudimentary organs, which have been considered a first-class proof

in favor of the theory of descent. For a long time it was believed that the rudimentary organs could be explained, exclusively, on the basis of the theory of descent; that they had lost their function and had become superfluous and useless—as for example, the *appendix vermiformis* found in the caecum. Thus the pineal gland (epiphysis) also has been considered as an outgrowth of the epithalamus (sphenodon, hatteria). That this is a mistaken notion will be shown in another part of this study.

(d) *Embryology*

For a long time certain data from embryology seemed to present convincing proof: for example, that even the human embryo, in a certain stage, shows branchial fissures on both sides of the neck.

From this, it was believed that it could be concluded that man must have descended from aquatic ancestors. Haeckel bases his "biogenetic basic law" upon similar data from comparative embryology. Accordingly, ontogenesis (history of the individual organism) would only be an abbreviated recapitulation of phylogenesis (ancestral history), resembling the way the series of findings in paleontology corresponds to the series of classes in the phylogenetic system. The error of this argumentation lies in this: that this series is explained phylogenetically, i.e., in the sense of a genetic descent, which fact still has to be proved. What is to be proved is considered as already proved and this, logically, results in the error of *petitio principii*; moreover, the thesis to be proved is used as a basic proof and this results in the error of the vicious circle (*circulus vitiosus*).

The only thing that embryology can prove, through an unbiased evaluation, is a certain parallelism in the series, progressing from a most simple and general to a most complicated and special plan of structure; such a progression is still far from being a genetic "development" and is only a logical consequence.

(e) *Zoogeography and phytogeography*

A further argument posited by the theory of evolution is based on the distribution of animals and plants over the surface of the world according to determined laws.

The argument is thus formulated: If animals were placed on

earth by an intelligent act of creation in conformity with a plan, it is to be expected that every species, from the beginning, would be placed where it would find the conditions of life suitable to its nature. Now authors must admit that the facts of animal distribution agree with this requisite. Moreover, it is thought that much more is to be admitted—namely, that every land really received all the animals which could live in that very place. According to this, it is expected that all lands which have the same climate also would produce approximately the same fauna and flora. But this requisite indeed has not been fulfilled.

A critical examination will bring out the weakness of this argument. Actually, animals and plants need not live wherever they " can " live.

From the standpoint of logic, it is nothing more than the inadmissible inversion of the burden of proof. According to geographical arguments, it is to be noted that even the animal kingdom of the polar regions plays a definite role. The Arctic and Antarctic have approximately the same conditions of life. One would therefore expect the same fauna. But the immense beasts of prey found in the Arctic are not to be found in the Antarctic. Tropical South America has approximately the same climate as tropical Africa. Despite this fact, the fauna found in each are basically different.

The presence of common and related forms is explained by the assumption of a submerged continent forming a bridge between Africa and South America (Atlantis theory); the change of related forms is explained through genetic evolution.

The correct deduction is that the climate of itself cannot explain the laws that regulate the diffusion of animals. When, from this, the conclusion is drawn that animal distribution speaks against the theory of creation and favors the theory of evolution, the logic is unintelligible, since the one idea does not oppose the other.

d. The origin of man

The critical question of the theory of evolution is that of the origin of man. Of special note is the question of a missing link between man and the anthropoid ape. There has been an attempt to destroy the idea of the unity of the human race through the assumption of a polyphylectic descent: the assumption that the human race had developed from ape ancestry and from, at least, two and perhaps still more entirely different lines of descent.

In 1881, it was believed that the long sought missing link had been found when Dubois discovered fossils in Java, which he designated *Pithecanthropus erectus*. Other discoveries followed. Here we mention only those of the *Neanderthal*, the *homo Heidelbergensis*, the *homo Mousteriensis*; the *homo Rhodesiensis* and the *Sinanthropus*.

On the basis of certain apelike characteristics in the Neanderthal (receding forehead, massive brow ridges, projecting lower jaw, so-called prognathism, and receding chin), such characteristics have been designated as "primitive" and the lack of the same as "recent."

Thus far even human fossil remains have furnished no proof of a genuine descent from apelike ancestors; we find rather that whenever there is a question of certain discoveries pertaining to man, clear signs of human activity are present and these characterize man as *homo sapiens* (burial, ritual, use of fire, etc.). There is no such thing as *homo insipiens*; much less of a *homo primigenius* in the sense that he has not, as yet, become man in the full sense of the word.

This is best perceived in the research of ethnology, which was able to establish the fact that the "primitive" and even "most primitive" man always manifested a full use of human reason along with a surprising religiosity and high standard of morals (Wilhelm Schmidt, Koppers and others). The supposition, for example, of Levy-Bruhl, of a "pre-logical stage" in the primitive, to whom the laws of thought found in logic were not yet accessible, has proved itself a phantasy and fable.

There is still another argument which the theory of evolution has introduced in favor of consanguinity between man and the anthropoid ape: the precipitating reaction of blood, according to Uhlenhuth. It has been established that the blood or human serum provokes a precipitate in the serum of animal blood. But this was not so when the human serum was put into the serum of anthropoid apes.

On the other hand, in more recent times, Rosina Zdansky has shown that the blood and serum reactions are strongly specific to the species and that this strong specificity speaks more for the constancy of species than for the theory of evolution.

e. General critique of the theory of evolution

From the vast data interpreted in favor of evolution, of which we can mention here only fragments, there remains in an accurate scientific critique nothing that can constitute a real proof in favor of a definite genetic evolution.

The facts permit, rather, a more liberal interpretation in the sense of an affinity in the plan of structure.

There is no actual proof for the evolution of man from the animal realm and for the gradual, progressing, spontaneous development of most primitive to complete forms of life. But if such a proof were or would be given, this would not, in the least, be a proof against the theory of creation. H. Muckermann and Mitterer have stated rightly that the idea of evolution does not in any way necessarily exclude that of creation. They merely estimated the theory of evolution to be more scientifically confirmed than it really is and believed that they could demonstrate its compatibility with the doctrine of creation. But even were it proved or were it possible to demonstrate that man, according to his corporeal nature, descended from animal ancestors, this would not demonstrate anything contrary to the doctrine that the *anima rationalis* is conferred only by means of a creative act of God (creationism).

There is absolutely no need for a compromise between the theory of creation and that of evolution. If there is any evolution in the sense here specified, i.e., inconstancy of species and transformation, then it can only be a matter of an evolution in conformity to a plan.

To attain such a result, there was no need for expending such enormous scientific effort in favor of the theory of evolution to demonstrate its incompatibility with the theory of creation.

For a century man has been led astray by the unprecedented triumph of evolution into a spirit of intoxicated progress, which seemed to leap over all the boundaries.

If a spontaneous evolution " from primitive animal to man " were possible, why should not even a further, no less fantastic, future evolution be possible?

If, on the other hand, a man is a creature, then he is limited by boundaries which he may not and cannot overstep.

4. BASIC QUESTIONS CONCERNING THE THEORY OF HEREDITY (GENETICS)

a. Concept

Every living being is subject to the law of reproduction. Every living being has come from a living being (*omne vivum e vivo*—Pasteur). We can add to this: Every living being comes from a living being of the same species (law of identity of species).

In these two basic laws lie the fact of heredity and its close connection with reproduction.

Heredity consists in the conformity of descendants (filial generation) with ancestors (parental generation) in regard to essential characteristics.

This brings out clearly the close connection between the problems of heredity and those of evolution; at the same time, it shows the difficulty of bringing the modern theory of heredity into accord with the theory of evolution.

If heredity consists in conformity between ancestors and descendants in regard to essential characteristics, the question arises: Which characteristics are to be considered " essential "?

There are variable characteristics which allow the greatest margin for individual variation. On the other hand, there are characteristics pertaining to the character of species which do not allow for any variability and which remain constant. If race characteristics have been considered constant and essential, so must this be said, in still greater measure, for the characteristics of species. It is therefore absolutely not possible to speak of the term " constant " in regard to race; and on the other hand, of the term " transformation " in regard to species. The one excludes the other.

The basic concepts regarding the biology of reproduction, the questions concerning the relation between reproduction and growth, as well as between reproduction and cell division, must be studied at greater length in connection with the general problems of sexuality.

In cell division, the process that takes place in the nucleus of a cell, especially in the dark-staining, rod-shaped bodies (chromosomes), plays an important role.

In recent times, chromosomes have been considered the " bearers of heredity " and bearers of physical characteristics (gene theory).

The totality of genes was designated as the genome, the hereditary mass, and with regard to its structural arrangement, the hereditary aggregate.

According to B. Steiner, the chromosomes are not considered absolutely as the bearers to heredity but as the physical basis for, merely, the variable characteristics and not for the "hereditary trunk," which is constant (matrix).

On the fact of the quantitatively equal supply of chromosomes in the paternal as well as the maternal germ cell the parity theory is based; and in every respect this gives the two sexes the right to be judged with perfect equality from all points of view.

This does not take into account the fact that in the process of fecundation and heredity there is no such thing as complete equality, since the important centrosome is contributed only by the paternal germ cell. (Cf. page 60.) The number of chromosomes is fixed according to the species and is constant in certain species (the law of constancy in the number of chromosomes). Within the chromosome and its subdivision (chromomere), a certain arrangement of genes is assumed (gene topography—Morgan).

There is an essential difference between germ cells and body cells (somatic cells): germ cells continually originate only from germ cells, somatic cells only from somatic cells (continuity of germ plasm—Weismann), so that a germ tract is clearly distinguishable from a somatic tract.

The individual is, according to this idea, carried in a certain manner with all his soma as an appendage of the germ tract (germ tract theory).

Under chromosomes, the sex chromosomes (X and Y chromosomes) are distinguished and these are decisive for the determination of sex (heterochromosomes). The egg cell always contains the factor X; the sperm cells are different: some manifest the factor X the others factor Y. If two germ cells (gametes) unite so as to form a fertilized cell (zygote), the combination XX is homozygote, the combination XY is heterozygote. A female results from a homozygote and a male from a heterozygote union.

If there are certain hereditary characteristics coupled with the heterochromosomes, there will arise a heredity related to sex; i.e., certain characteristics will be inherited only by the male and others only by the female descendants.

The facts thus far learned do not make it decisive that the chromosomes are the exclusive bearers of hereditary characteristics. Without doubt, they play an important role in heredity but, in no case, the exclusive role which a too simplified materialistic system would claim. Chromosomal inheritance presents only a partial event within the complete hereditary processes. We must reject the monopoly of chromosomes in heredity in favor of a complete comprehension of the matter. The basic concepts must be held firmly if one wishes to overcome the former mechanistic-materialistic interpretation of the phenomena of heredity and arrive at a universalistic comprehension of the problem of inheritance.

It is absolutely inadmissible to assume, in the inheritance of mental characteristics, exclusive dependence on the physical chromosomes. Such a tenet would be equivalent to an absolute denial of free will; it would bring about a determinism in the system of heredity. The tracing back of all characteristics to physical, hereditary factors would, at the same time, make this heredity of determinism one of absolute Materialism.

Contrary to the former gene theory, there already prevails in genetics the opinion that the object of heredity is not so much the individual, developed characteristic as the distinct predisposition, i.e., a possibility (potency), which can, but not necessarily must, develop into a corresponding characteristic. We have thus much less to do with unequivocally determined physical genes than with heredity potencies, which are polyvalent and pluripotent; i.e., in a predisposition there are many possibilities from which, at any given time, the one or the other can become actual.

With this idea, the basic concepts of genetics would be placed upon a new basis.

b. The laws of heredity

(a) *The Mendelian propositions*

Besides the theory of mutation, the rediscovery of the Mendelian heredity propositions by de Vries, Correns and Tschermak, and the Mendelism founded on these propositions, contributed essentially to the reconstruction of " selectionistic " genetics.

Gregor Mendel had, in his famous experiments with plant hybridization, made some very important conclusions, based on systematic experiments in hybridization. These conclusions were deduced from experiments dealing with the crossing of plants having different characteristics—pairs of simple and easily observable characteristics being used.

It was not the intention of Mendel to designate his conclusions as laws of heredity; much less to overestimate them as laws of human inheritance.

In applying the Mendelian conclusions on inheritance to man, the neo-Mendelists have deviated far from the original theory of Mendel and have thus brought undeserved discredit to it, even in regard to those aspects which are clear, valid and in conformity with law. We remain closer to the truth, and more in accord with the meaning of Mendel, when we speak of the Mendelian rules concerning heredity instead of referring to the same as the Mendelian laws of heredity.

It is customary to distinguish three Mendelian rules:

1. The rule of uniformity;
2. The rule of separation;
3. The rule of independence.

The rule of uniformity means that all individuals of an F1 (first filial) generation of pure-bred parents are homogenous. The rule of separation distinguishes two possibilities:

1. That of the intermediary hereditary succession (uniform mixed color);
2. That of the dominant and recessive succession.

If the rule of the dominant (in case of dominant hereditary succession) prevails, then the recessive characteristic recedes and is overcome by the dominant character. It is, however, latently present and can reappear.

The recessive succession is, at times, sex-linked; i.e., according to the predominant view, the corresponding gene is linked to the X or Y chromosome.

The main idea of the rule of independence is that many independent characteristics can, in turn, reappear independently of one another and can be crossed, if the one or the other pair of characteristics follows the rules of the intermediary succession or of the dominant or recessive succession.

The theory of dominance and recession has led to a distinction between genotype and phenotype. This distinction can be important in practice in regard to the inheritance of morbid predispositions as seen in heredo-pathology. A morbid predisposition can be recessively present and not be recognized; thus the bearer of this predisposition would be, according to the phenotype, free from hereditary disease, and according to the genotype, afflicted with hereditary disease.

(b) *The so-called higher Mendelism*

The above rules present only the fundamental basis of the formerly prevailing system of Mendelian genetics. Since the matter is very complicated and a great number of deviations from the simple basic schema appeared, in time the exception to the rule occurred more often than the course corresponding to the rule. Hence it was necessary to seek an explanation for the deviations in a schema involving the system of selection. This attempt at explanation is at present included in the unsatisfactory collective name of " super-Mendelism."

Here belong the phenomena to which genetics has given the following designations: polyhybrid, pleiotropia, multiple allele, polymer, uniting and crossing over of factors, change of dominant and manifestation variation; penetration and expression; sex-linked heredity; chromosome topography, etc.

In any case, the frequent complications in attempts toward clarification show that the deviation from the normally expected hereditary succession according to Mendel is so diverse and numerous that there is no such thing as a definite computation of hereditary succession, at least as regards man (hereditary prognosis).

(c) *Empirical hereditary prognosis*

A definite heredo-prognosis would be of great value to heredo-pathology; and since Mendel fails in this regard, one has, since Ruedin, been content with a purely empirical heredo-prognosis concerning the most important hereditary diseases. This, by a straight statistical method, computes the percentage of descendants who, in the case of a given disease, actually inherit it and the percentage who are free from it. In this way, because of a movement to do away with the diseased, there has been a tendency to interpret the diagnosis of hereditary diseases as extensively as possible. Hence a very important point should not be overlooked: namely, that the necessity for creating the concept of an empirical hereditary prognosis suffices to show on what a weak basis heredo-pathology stood until recent times; that a definite knowledge of this field is still very meager, and entirely insufficient to establish with any certainty practical measures of negative selection.

c. Hereditary predispositions and environment

(a) *Formulation of the question*

The realization that for the actualization of a morbid disposition there is required a co-operation of the endogenous factor of disposition with the exogenous factors of environment brings to view the problem of environmental effect. The former concept of the problem as "hereditary predisposition or environment" must be considered both one-sided and false.

Behind the formulation of the question there are powerful ideological forces which should not be underestimated in order that we may truly evaluate the importance of the question.

(b) *The hypothesis concerning twins*

The method of research concerning twins has been of decisive importance in specifying the effects of predisposition and environmental factors.

The research with twins starts with the hypothesis that twins originating from two different ova can be hereditarily different, but that those originating from the same ovum are of necessity hereditarily the same; that is, they possess exactly the same hereditary structure.

Accordingly, whenever there is conformity of behaviour between twins, this fact must be attributed to heredity; and discordance or difference of behavior can, on the contrary, be explained only by environmental effect.

The twins-hypothesis with its very important consequences is based, at least as regards man, on an unproved supposition: *de facto* there is still no certain proof that "concordant" human twins actually stem from a sole fertilized ovum the division of which comes about after fertilization—i.e., after the fusion of the nucleus.

It will perhaps be possible to find other explanations for the great concordance of many twins, when it is realized that findings concerning the membrane can no longer be used for the diagnosis of uniovularity nor for the numerous vascular communications (anastomosis) between the two placental circulations. As long as uniovularity has not been surely proved, then all important conclusions deduced from the twins-hypothesis and concerned with the effects of predisposition and environment must be considered somewhat rash.

(c) *The opposing factors in present-day heredo-biology*

In the controversial questions here considered, the great ideologico-political opposition of the present time manifests itself. In the foreground are the controversial scientific questions behind which lies a powerful spiritual struggle. The heredo-biology of selection, once centered in Germany and the northern countries, has, under the leadership of Morgan and Muller, developed into a strong but one-sided form, characterized by concepts such as the gene theory, the topography of chromosomes, etc.

We should not omit mentioning either the unilateral nature of this trend in genetics, which has overrated the part of a hereditary predisposition, or the basic materialism of its ideas. Opposed to this is the new trend of genetics which has developed in Russia under the direction of Mitschurin and Lysenko. This trend has emphasized the almost abandoned environmental factor. In opposition to the trend of selection, it has revived Lamarckian thinking on the inheritance of acquired characteristics, and made it the center of the issue.

This recent biosocial genetics based on experimental material in the field of practical cultivation of plants is primarily practical, applied genetics. Utilizing the results of wide experience in this field, the work of Mitschurin and Lysenko has met with outstanding success. This success in cultivation is based on the utilization and influence of all imaginable exogenous factors.

Under the influence of political tension in recent times, the opposition was intensified and brought about the formula of "Occidental" and "Oriental" genetics. Predominating in the East has been the rejection of Mendelism and the gene theory, the labeling of them as idealistic and reactionary. It has assigned to "Oriental genetics" the terms "progressive" and "truly materialistic"; i.e., biology is adequate to the demands of dialectical materialism.

In reality, the so-called Occidental genetics is by no means less materialistic than Oriental genetics.

The genetics of Mendel and Morgan is based on an exaggeration that overestimates the role of the physical " bearer of heredity "— that is, on the gene theory and characteristics of the system of selection as found in Weismann; it also places exaggerated emphasis on the factor of hereditary predisposition.

A universalistic doctrine of heredity in the question of predisposition or environment cannot have the one-sided viewpoint of " either-or," but must give attention to the united effect of all concurring factors; and beyond this, must consider the importance of psychospiritual factors and finally, the fact of *natura vulnerata* as well as the power of grace and the supernatural. Only in this way will the great antithesis of the present epoch be turned into a fruitful synthesis.

"Biosocial " genetics according to Mitschurin is based on a one-sided over-estimation of environmental factors, as well as upon the principle of descent according to Lamarck, without which evolution could not endure, and on the exaggerated estimation of hereditary acquired characteristics, which for this trend is the main question.

d. Heredity of acquired characteristics

It is impossible in the space of this short presentation to go into detail concerning the extraordinarily complex problem of the hereditary transmission of acquired characteristics.

Important here is the fact that it is a central problem or the central problem of genetics. For a decade it was the cause of a bitter struggle between the followers of Lamarck and Darwin. The battle was intense since political trends and ideologies entered the controversy.

The hereditary transmission of acquired characteristics presents a central problem for genetics only as long as the theory of heredity is closely united with the theory of evolution. Once the theory of evolution is dethroned from the position it held as a dogma of modern biology, and the constancy of species norm and the plan of structure type are again recognized, the question of the hereditary transmission of acquired characteristics declines from its former towering place to that of a special question that is both secondary and peripheral. It is by no means so important that the existence of a fundamental doctrine of genetics depends on its resolution.

As already stated, for a universalistic genetics, a simple "either-or" view when treating of hereditary predispositions and environment is impossible. Both endogenous as well as exogenous factors must be taken into account, so that besides the effective biological and social elements the powerful effect of the ethico-metaphysical factors is also to be considered.

e. Norms of a universalistic system of genetics

Depending on the knowledge acquired in the study of the problems of evolution, it is important above all to liberate genetics from a too close union with evolution. If we admit up to a certain point an evolution of organisms we admit it only in the sense of a regulated evolution and one conforming to a plan. If we acknowledge that a spontaneous development of living beings is an impossibility, then we acknowledge with Agassiz the presence in all things of the creative thought of God.

This is reflected in the archtypes in the plans of structure; conformity with a plan is manifested in the norm of the species. The norm of the species as such is incontestable; the constancy of the norm of the species is, at least within a historically computable space of time, imperative.

In the theory of the plan of structure, the morphological characteristics of the primitive type can be recognized.

As such, the Aristotelian concept of entelechy seems closer to reality and more realistic than the idealistic Platonic concept of "idea."

In this manner, we discover anew the reality of the universal, which was lost through nominalism. This was the attack which ultimately led to the errors of materialism in the so-called century of natural science.

In opposition to the normal constancy of the species we must advance the principle of plasticity at least as regards the individual hereditary predisposition. Only in this way and not in the inverse manner which the system of selection has offered, is a solution of the problem of heredity and variability possible.

From the principle of plasticity of the (individual) hereditary predisposition arises the polyvalence (having more than one interpretation) and pluripotentiality of predisposition. It is hence better to speak of hereditary potencies rather than hereditary tendencies or predispositions, since *de facto* there is reference only to possibilities (potential) which can, but must not, become a reality (*actus*).

In this way, the complicated genes theory becomes weak and superfluous. The chromosome theory would then return to its true and acknowledged worth. The chromosomes are only the physical substratum for that part of the heredity potencies which belong to the individual, variable elements of heredity. They therefore present only the physical basis for the individual impression of the species norm (*principium individuationis*).

The variability of these elements of heredity has effect only within the species norm. Thus the basis for race formation is to be found within the species norm and in this variability. Here the variable portion or aspect of heredity is the place where the Mendelian rules have their basic value.

The super-individual, general, constant elements of heredity, on the contrary, do not vary and are not subject to Mendelian rules. They present that phase of "hereditary stratum" in which the species norm and the higher plan of structure arrangements and systematic categories (genus, family, etc.) are manifested. These have no connection or relation with the chromosomes but, rather, are found unalterably in all of the life substance. (Matrix type of heredity, Steiner; "heredity stock," Plate.)

In like manner, there arises the return of the Mendelian rules to their actual field of activity; to the rules of hybridization in the crossing of simple, variable and united elements. Thus the complicated hypothesis and complicated concept formations of higher Mendelism become superfluous. In this way too are removed all the other obstacles that necessarily accompanied the system of natural selection as long as that theory was to avoid conceding the possibility of hereditary transmission of acquired characteristics.

Moreover, this question no longer appears so important and central for the whole of genetics as it did for Lamarckianism when explaining descent through adaptation and environmental effect.

Even this central problem of the theory of heredity has lost its towering importance for us and can be reduced to its true intrinsic value now that it has been removed from evolution.

With this, all stirring controversial questions between the principal opposing trends of genetics which are designated as "Occidental " and " Oriental," as " pessimistically reactionary " and " progressively optimistic," are brought to an end.

The much controverted hereditary transmission of acquired characteristics takes place within definite spheres, inasmuch as it has to do with physical characteristics within the species norm, the principle of plasticity of the germ plasm and the polyvalence of hereditary potencies; from that point on it appears as a common foregone conclusion and logical necessity. There is no longer any difficulty in acknowledging this fact.

With regard to the hereditary transmission of psycho-spiritual characteristics, and especially with regard to the influence of hereditary qualities through corresponding mental adaptation, all difficulties which in recent times opposed the idea of the hereditary transmission of acquired characteristics vanish.

On the contrary, the possibility of the hereditary transmission of a psycho-spiritual disposition (not " characteristics ") appears as a self-evident conclusion from the tenet of the substantial body-soul unity in man, from the body-soul correlation, from the primacy of the ethico-spiritual realm.

All these facts follow as a necessary consequence from the Thomistic principle of *anima forma corporis*. In correspondence with the principle of the unity and indivisibility of the human soul, the spiritual soul as a unitive principle (*forma substantialis*) regulates all formative processes within the entire organism, including the vegetative process. Its effect is found in every individual body cell and in their ultimate vital elements.

We do not need to admit with Duns Scotus, and in opposition to St. Thomas, a special *forma corporeitatis* (an *anima corporea* in opposition to an *anima spirituale*) and a plurality of forms, nor need we postulate a special " cellular soul " as a cytodynamic principle.

We acknowledge the *anima rationalis* as the supreme vital principle of man, which includes, comprehends and surpasses the inferior principle of the *anima vegetativa* and *sensitiva*, which are common to man, animal and plant.

On this basis, the hereditary transmission found in man cannot basically remove freedom of the will. In this regard, not even the hereditary transmission of psycho-spiritual characteristics can ever be coercive. We have already explained that in this phase not characteristics are inherited but, at the most, dispositions, tendencies (inclination). What man does with his inherited predisposition and how he brings to reality the given possibilities, is the product of his freedom and responsibility. The action itself, the *actus humanus*, is free as long as one does not produce culpable inclinations through irresistible habit. Habit (*consuetudo*) transforms an innate disposition (*habitus innatus*) into an acquired disposition (*habitus acquisitus*), so that such can become an impediment to moral freedom. But freedom is primarily present even in those cases of which it can be said: "The first time we are free; with the second we become slaves." The typical example of this would be addiction. The acquired habit can lead not only to a tendency toward degeneracy, but also to a tendency toward regeneration.

Accordingly, heredity can be a hindrance to freedom of will; in the case of inherited disposition to mental disease, it can even do away with freedom of will, as with an obstacle (*obex*). At any rate, the meaning of free will, especially of free moral decision and the moral personality of the individual, is preserved.

Basically there also remains the possibility that a free moral decision of the will can form, in a reversible manner, processes of hereditary degeneracy and, through a decisive reversion of direction, lead to regeneration.

The "law of irreversibility" (O. Abel) can be valid in regard to the processes of transformation in the animal and plant realm; regarding man, and inasmuch as it refers to the ethico-spiritual realm, it is not valid.

Such a science of heredity leaves the moral responsibility of man and the directing of human life toward a supernatural end, inviolable. It takes into consideration the fact that human nature is a fallen nature and thus regards the impact of original sin in all the phases of life and in all the manifestations or vital expressions of man.

On the other hand, it will evaluate the supernatural effects of grace in regard to regeneration. In the light of such a universalistic comprehension of the problem of hereditary transmission, all the difficulties which an atomistic view of hereditary materialism inevitably brings, are removed. All problems are easily resolved, and instead of the former confused complication, there arise a pleasant simplicity and clarity. The return in the field of genetics to the clear and solidly established concepts of Scholasticism shows itself to have a genuine value. Through the fruitful application of Scholastic principles to the problems of modern heredo-biology,

Thomistic philosophy proves itself a genuine *philosophia perennis*.

A true scientific, universalistic solution of the problem of heredity could only be accomplished on the basis of the presented principles. In this way a truly universal anthropology is also attained, which reveals to us the true place of man in nature, his relation to the supernatural and, at the same time, the meaning and purpose of his life. In this way, science is never opposed to supernatural revelation and is enriched by an abundance of added knowledge.

PART II

SPECIAL

PASTORAL

MEDICINE

1. Questions concerning Sexual Life

A. GENERAL BASIS

Preliminary Remarks

General view and division of subject matter

The scientific presentation of human sexual life can be made under a threefold viewpoint:

1. The biological viewpoint;
2. The social viewpoint;
3. The ethico-metaphysical (moral-religious) viewpoint.

Only through the integration of all three points of view will there result a universalistic interpretation, which is the criterion of Pastoral Medicine.

If a general biological basis of sexual life is sought, it would seem best to present first normal, healthy sexual life. The physical aspect is treated under sexual physiology, and the mental aspect under sexual psychology, or the psychology of sex. The abnormal deviations discussed under sexual pathology touch on the physical as well as the psychic aspect (sexual psychotherapy).

The study and application of scientific knowledge derived from sexual physiology and sexual pathology lead to the subject of sexual hygiene.

As hygiene has its descriptive and normative aspects, so we find that sexual hygiene has a close relation to sexual ethics. Particularizing further, one may say that the ethical aspect leads to education in the normally directed sexual life (sexual pedagogy). On the other hand, hygiene leads from the individual (individual hygiene) to society (social hygiene); and from this to problems of sociology.

It is from the sociological viewpoint that one is led to the question of the meaning and nature of sexuality (sexual philosophy) and to that of the metaphysico-religious aspect of sexual life; and finally to the ultimate and deepest meaning to be attributed to human sexual life according to the natural and supernatural order of being: *sub specie aeternitatis*. This leads to a division of the subject matter as follows:

1. Sexual Biology
2. Physiology of sex
3. Psychology of sex
4. Sexual Pathology
5. Sexual Hygiene
6. Sexual Pedagogy
7. Sociology of Sex
8. Sexual Metaphysics

1. SEXUAL BIOLOGY

a. General viewpoint

The problems of general sexual biology group themselves primarily around the concepts of growth, reproduction and heredity. These are the basis for the generative functions common to all living beings. We can only speak, then, of sexuality in the strictest sense when sex differentiation (sexual dimorphism) has a place in the plan of bodily structure. If, first of all, mention can be made of asexual propagation in the lower classes of living forms, this brings up, in the differentiation of sexual propagation, the topic of sexual reproduction.

Accepted in the science of general biology is the interrelationship between the aptitude for reproducing—that is, the aptitude common to all living beings—and the general vital phenomena of growth, which in turn are associated with the vital functions of nutrition or metabolism.

Accordingly, we have the definition: " Reproduction is a growth beyond the measure of the individual." This definition does not seem to emphasize the essential element. Growth is limited to the formation of the species norm; reproduction is a new individuation of the species norm. It therefore seems more correct to say that "Reproduction is that general function of living beings by which they are able to reproduce living beings of the same species by providing a part of their own bodily living substance."

In general, the principle of biology holds fast: *omne vivum e vivo, omnis cellula e cellula*. With this principle, the possibility of spontaneous generation (*generatio aequivoca seu spontanea*) is eliminated. A spontaneous generation in the sense of a "spontaneous" origin of life-forms from non-living matter seems also incomprehensible from the standpoint of a universalistic science.

The original genesis of each singular life-form seems to be sufficiently explained only through an act of creation on the part of God. With the birth of a living being there was given, from the moment of the creative act, the faculty to reproduce beings of the same species, just as, in the *fiat* in the Biblical account of creation, there is directly contained the delegation of a part of the creative power through the command to propagate: *Crescite et multiplicamini*.

b. Asexual reproduction

Asexual reproduction in its most primitive form occurs as a process of fission (fission fungi, gemmiparous fungi—schizomycetes, blastomycetes). Here the process appears still very much associated with growth and manifests itself as a growth beyond the individual measure proper to the species. It manifests a profound affinity with the process of regeneration and the reproductive neo-formation of bodily substance, a process found in large measure in undifferentiated forms of life and becoming more limited with the increase of differentiation.

In regard to the primitive mode of reproduction through fission, it has been said that the unicellular organisms (Monera, Protista) which are reproduced in this way are "immortal," since in them it is not possible to establish the death of the individual according to the normal conditions of life. Yet the idea of the "immortality" of the unicellular organisms is misleading. Actually, their life as individuals ends at the moment of the division into two parts (in a certain sense, the division of the "in-dividuum" is a *contradictio in adiecto*) to give place to two new individuals of the same species. The first individual has ceased to exist as such. For the unicellular

C*

organism, individual death coincides with the moment of the generation of two new living beings.

c. Sexual reproduction

(a) *Isogamy*

In the next step, we find reproduction associated with the reunion
of two cells which are completely similar and do not yet present any
differentiation of sex (isogamy).

In this phase, despite the lack of a morphological differentiation,
we can establish a fundamental difference of function: one of the
two cells is inert (passive), and the other is mobile (active).

With the differentiation of cells into somatic and sexual cells, and
with the process of amphimixis, there develops a fundamental
difference in cell division. In the division of somatic cells it always
happens that every daughter cell receives from the mother cell the
same and complete group of chromosomes (diploid). But in the
sexual cells there is a reduction of the group of chromosomes to
half the amount (haploid), so that in the copulation of germ cells
(gametes), the new cell (zygote) resulting from amphimixis presents
anew the complete group of chromosomes but in a new mixture:
proceeding in part from the active cell and in part from the passive
cell.

(b) *Heterogamy—Sexual differentiation*

There arises in the next phase a wider functional and—what is
more—a morphological differentiation between the still, passive
(female) germ cells and the numerous mobile active (male) cells
(heterogamy).

The difference between the behavior of the germ cells, some active
and some passive, can already be established in the phase of
isogamy, thus before the morphological differentiation is manifest.
The difference between the active and passive germ principle
extends to the most primitive stage of the organic world.

With the progressive differentiation of living beings, the germ
cells are differentiated further, especially as regards number, size
and movement, by means of which the way to greater morphological
differentiation is indicated.

The female germ cell (egg cell, *ovulum*) progressively develops
into a great spherical cell with nutritious substances of reserve

(deutoplasm), while the male cells become small, more numerous, more mobile but with less matter and generally assume a flat and pointed form.

The union of the male and female germ cell is known as fecundation. Only when this takes place can we speak of sexual reproduction in the strict sense.

d. Alternation of generation—Parthenogenesis

If by a progressing form of organization sexual reproduction tends in general to prevail more and more over asexual reproduction, it is still far from being the exclusive form.

Sexual reproduction can exist along with asexual reproduction, either simultaneously, as is the case with many plants (reproduction through seed, and at the same time through sprouts, bulbs, buds, etc.), or in the form of alternation of generations, in which sexual and asexual generation alternate at regular intervals.

There is also reproduction without fecundation, even where there is a complete difference of sex (parthenogenesis). With many living organisms even an artificial parthenogenesis can take place by means of definite (chemical, thermal, electrical) stimuli. This has, so far, not been successful in the realm of higher forms of animals.

In man and in the higher forms of animal life, parthenogenesis never occurs naturally. Hence the only virgin birth, that of the Son of Man, can never be compared to natural or artificial parthenogenesis, since it was a miraculous and supernatural birth and not subject to natural law or the laws of human life.

The capacity for sexual reproduction can be modified and produce grotesque effects or can even be annulled through a parasitic mode of life.

e. Germ cells and body cells—Germ track

With the increasing shaping of the body structure into multicellular organisms (metazoan), there takes place an increasing differentiation of the somatic cells conserving the individual and the germ cells conserving the species (sexual cells).

Weismann's theory of the "continuity of the germ plasm" and of the "germ track" has led to the opinion that the "soma" is only an annexed formation, transitory, mortal and subordinate to the "immortal" germ track and that the individual life is thus entirely unessential in comparison with the life of the species. If one holds that, for the reproduction of man, the same biological laws as for the other organisms prevail exclusively, then there will arise unacceptable conclusions concerning the value of the individual. On the contrary, it is to be admitted that, for the reproduction of man, the same general biological laws prevail as for the reproduction of plants and animals; but these laws do not present for man the entire and exclusive content of the process of reproduction, in the sense that no laws beyond these operate.

f. Human sexuality: its individuality

An unbiased comparison of the sexual life of man and of animal will show that in addition to the vast areas of likeness in the somato-physiological realm, there is a basic difference that manifests something completely new. Sexual phenomena in animals occur at the time of reproduction (heat, oestrum) coercively and with the irresistible force of a purely natural process. In man, however, the phenomena are possible at any time from puberty to its expiration (although libido is not equally strong at all times); but the phenomena can also be controlled by reason and will.

There is another and more important difference between human and animal sexuality. Man is born in a state of absolute need, and has for a longer period of time need of the care and help of his parents.

On the other hand, physical and sexual maturity, despite its slow development, is achieved before the mental and moral maturity necessary for the human form of sexual life: matrimony and the establishment of a family. Strains and difficulties arise which must be mastered. These difficulties cause what is designated by some as the "sexual necessity" of youth. It is, however, clear that this state cannot be given free rein and allowed to become a part of the normal human state, but must be brought under the control of reason and will. This is the important, the specific human task.

Human sexuality, then, is placed under the domain of reason and moral law. Accordingly, man is capable of abusing sexuality, a condition not found in animals (excluding the occasional analogous manifestations of degeneracy or of domestication in domestic animals).

Biology has, up to the present time, often too little evaluated this difference between human and animal sexuality. It is closely related to that fundamental difference found in the realm of mental life: the possession of the *anima rationalis* in comparison with the lower degrees of mental life in plants and animals, i.e., *anima vegetativa* and *anima sensitiva.*

Just as, in the realm of mental life, the lower degrees are necessarily presupposed for the development of the higher degrees, and the laws for the course of mental functions which exist for lower degrees are not suspended in the higher degrees but are expanded and directed by other laws, so too the biological laws for the sexual life of plants and animals apply also for man, but only in the lowest levels of the human personality, and never exclusively.

This viewpoint also makes it easier to prove that, with the higher development of the human personality through reason and free will, and through a supernatural aim in life, the relationship between the individual and the germ track has shifted far more in favor of the individual than in the lower forms of life.

2. PHYSIOLOGY OF SEX

a. Primary and secondary sex characteristics

Sexual dimorphism, namely, the clearly manifested morphological differentiation between the male and female conforming to the essence of the species, prevails in man and the higher animals. This difference is not limited to the external and internal sexual organs themselves (testes, ovaries), and the organs of copulation (*membrum virile,* scrotum, vulva, and vagina), that is, to the primary sexual characteristics, but extends to the entire bodily structure.

The emphatic differentiating characteristics of the bodily structure are the secondary sex characteristics: thorax and pelvic structure; type of pilosity; distribution of adipose tissue; development of the breast, turgor, larynx, voice, etc. The profound differences in bodily structure also correspond to the profound differences in mental life. (Cf. below, *Psychology of sex.*)

b. Origin of sex

It is generally held that the origin of sex in man and higher animals is determined through syngamy at the moment of generation. According to this opinion, both germ cells contain the so-called X chromosome, or only one contains it, while the other contains a Y chromosome. In other words, the fertilized ovum (zygote) corresponds to the formula XX or that of XY. In the first case, a female individual is formed and, in the second, a male individual.

Sex, therefore, in this opinion, is determined by the sperm cells which in distinction to the constant X character of the ovule may contain either an X or Y chromosome. Hence, if the fecundated ovule is homozygote (XX), a female is born; if, on the other hand, it is heterozygote (XY), a male is born. Although this experimental, apparently well-founded theory has never been refuted, there is a possibility that it is not the last word on the origin of sex. Apart from the fact that no theory concerning the determination of sex has been confirmed (Schoener), the hypothesis of the origin of sex determined purely by the chromosomatic method is with difficulty compatible with the history of development (embryology). Above all stands the fact that, in the initial grades of embryonic development, the sexual disposition is still not differentiated and is the same for both sexes (phase of bisexuality). If the differentiation does not take place distinctly and definitely—that is, if the development remains still, at an " intermediate " stage—it can lead to the formation of intermediate sexual grades. These facts are only with great difficulty compatible with the supposition of a differentiation of sex through chromosomes.

Sex determination is more easily and naturally explained by supposing that, besides " syngamic " sex differentiation through chromosome factors, programic and gamic factors come into play— that is, internal (endogenous) dispositions in the germ cells and external (exogenous) " prenatal " influences, which become effective after fecundation. Hence, normally, at birth the sex is completely differentiated and clearly recognized. If this does not happen, it is then a matter of deformity. (See below, *Sexual pathology*.)

c. Sexual development

At one time the newly born, the suckling and even the child were considered as completely indifferent from the sexual standpoint in the sense that excitations of any kind, which could be interpreted as a *libido sexualis*, were not manifested in them.

However, psychoanalysis maintains that the most simple, vital gestures of an infant, sucking at its mother's breast or its own fingers, may be interpreted as expressive manifestations of infantile libido.

Thus, in regard to the child, there is mention of an oral, anal and genital phase of eroticism as well as a phase of auto-eroticism (narcissism).

As controvertible as an exaggerated interpretation of the libido concept is, as suspicious as the exaggeration of one-sided pan-sexualism is, and as disputable as the theory of the polymorphic perversity of the infant is, yet a certain kernel of truth must be admitted in the theory of infantile sexuality. In regard to sex, the child is not a " blank sheet of paper " that receives the sexual content only when it attains sexual maturity. Instead, the child is prepared in a latent manner a long time before puberty. The more undisturbed this prepuberal period is, the better will the future period of maturity be. Hence infantile sexual trauma often exercise, as psychoanalysis had properly acknowledged, a disastrous influence upon later mental development.

The full and conscious awakening of the sexual instinct takes place at the time of puberty. At first it is a case of processes which normally are unconscious or subconscious. At puberty, the secondary sexual characteristics become more manifest; in temperate zones they attain their full expression in man not before his twenty-fifth year and in woman, not before her twentieth year. (In the tropical zone this development takes place sooner for both sexes.) It is the important task of sexual pedagogy to protect the sexual development from any harm so that the period of puberty takes place safely and becomes a solid basis for a harmonious development of character.

In the male the sexual instinct is wont to manifest itself more or less tempestuously; but in the female, it manifests itself more in the form of mental tension and vague nostalgia. The time of puberty, with its accompanying sexual tensions, can be a dangerous crisis in psychopathic persons.

d. The sex instinct in man

The sex instinct or drive in man has in various ways been placed in analogy with the rutting of animals. But this analogy is only partial. In animal, this rutting appears only at a certain time and then with irresistible force. During the remaining interval, sexuality is completely at a standstill. On the other hand, the human sex drive is never at a standstill from the time of sex maturity up to senile involution, and consequently it has been termed a "persistent rutting." This must be qualified in regard to the female, in whom *libido sexualis* is subject to definite cyclical variations. The male is, of course, theoretically speaking, always libido-capable and as regards the female, *congressus* can, theoretically speaking, always be consummated.

An attempt has been made to divide the sex instinct into many components or partial instincts.

So there has been a distinction made especially between the instinct of tension and the instinct of relaxation. The theory of partial instinct was introduced to explain the origin of certain sexual anomalies which are supposed to be derived from the absolute or relative predominance of a partial instinct, as, for example, happens in fetishism. It would be better if the components were interpreted, not in the sense of a disjunctive difference, but under the aspect of completeness and unity whereby the emphatic appearance of a certain phase appears merely as an expression of a non-harmonious development.

e. Internal secretions—Hormones

The theory of internal secretion has attributed an important role to the products of the sexual glands and other endocrine organs (hormones).

Important as the knowledge of endocrinology has been for a deeper understanding of sexual processes, there has been a one-sided overestimation in this field which can lead to serious errors.

The hormones have been considered as the exclusive formative factors which ultimately affect even mental processes. (*Propter ovarium solum mulier id est, quod est.*) Thorough research on the centers affected by the endocrine glands shows that the principle *anima forma corporis* has its place and value even in this realm.

The endocrine glands of the entire organism (sex glands, thyroid gland, pituitary gland, pineal gland, suprarenal gland, pancreas, etc.) are in closest association with one another and form the endocrine system.

It is not yet conclusively clear whether, or to what degree, the *hypophysis cerebri* (pituitary gland) is an activator of sexuality. There is still a question too whether the pineal gland (epiphysis) is a control and restraint organ, or whether there is a general sexual center in the brain stem, especially in the diencephalon (in the *tuber cinereum*).

This last hypothesis, with the reservation that such a sexual center constitutes the supreme but not ultimate impelling motive for the corporeal processes, is entirely probable. All body organs are, in the last analysis, instruments of the soul and provide the bases of activity for the soul, whose primacy prevails in this sphere also.

f. Maturity processes

The productive function of the sex glands begins at maturity. In the testes the process of producing spermatozoa takes place; in the ovaries, that of the maturing of the ova (follicle formation), which occurs at this time with full intensity. In the maturing of the spermatozoa, cell division takes place under the thrust of the chromatin substance according to the principle of "reductional division." In the maturing of ova, the Graffian follicles develop from an ordinarily solid mass of cells (primordial follicle), within which the maturing egg cells rest in the liquid-filled hollow.

At full maturation the follicle bursts and allows the egg cell free passage to the outside (ovulation). If the egg cell is not fertilized it will be spoiled and will be cast out. With the human being and the anthropoid ape this takes place in a bloody expulsion of the premenstrually swollen mucous membrane that lines the cavity of the uterus.

Occurring in the case where fecundation has not taken place, this function (menstruation) is currently held to be the "breakdown" in the cyclical rebuilding process which prepares for fecundation.

The follicle ruptured at maturation and transformed into an endocrine organ, the "yellow body" (*corpus luteum*), plays an important role. During menstruation it remains in blood, later to degenerate and shrink (false *corpus luteum*). However, in the case of the impregnated ovum, this component (true *corpus luteum* or the *corpus luteum* of pregnancy) grows and must fulfill an important protective function for the embryo until the placenta is formed.

g. Cyclical processes

The cyclical processes here mentioned are not limited to these immediate functions but involve all the female organs of generation (the breast, hypophysis, etc.) and have in addition a profound mental effect. This is the basis for the well-known cyclical variations. Corresponding to the occurrence, even the *libido sexualis* is subject to cyclical variations and is strongest during the time of ovulation, when the possibility of fecundation is greatest.

The recent theory concerning the cyclical variations of female fertility (Knaus, Ogino) is based, on one hand, on a deep knowledge of the relation between ovulation and menstruation, and, on the other hand, on the research concerning the life span of the germ cells.

According to the most recent outstanding opinions, the life span of the ovum after the rupture of the follicle takes place is only a few hours, whereas that of the sperm cells within the female body lasts at most two to three days.

It is assumed that the short life span of the *germ* cells is due to the fact that, following the maturation divisions (i.e., the reduction division), they, being haploids, will comprise a total of only half the chromosome number as compared with the other, *somatic*, cells.

The possibility of advance calculation of this process is by no means absolute; and because of this, the practical application of this physiological knowledge is complicated and difficult. (Cf. *Facultative sterility*.)

h. Copula carnalis

Sexual union ("cohabitation,"[1] *copula carnalis, coitus seu congressus*) is consummated by the *immissio membri virilis intra vaginam*, whereby during the first intercourse of the woman the thin membrane of the hymen is torn. The hymen, although intimated in some anthropoids, is found only in the human being. Only through the *penetratio vasis debita* and *effusio seminis intra vas* is a *copula perfecto* consummated, which fulfills the *fieri unam carnem*—as the essential characteristic of *matrimonium consummatum*.

[1] It is better to avoid the use of the term "cohabitation" since it has various meanings. It signifies not only *coitus*, but also the living together of couples as a right and a juridical duty.

Canon Law requires, according to the predominant opinion, as a characteristic mark of an *actus per se aptus ad prolis generationem*— the ability to produce a *verum semen*—that is, a semen which is a *testiculis elaboratum*. If this is lacking, so also is the required *potentia coeundi* and not merely the *potentia generandi*.

In this point, the canonical interpretation is stronger and more logically correct than that found in forensic medicine, even in cases concerning the distinction between *potentia coeundi* and *potentia generandi*.

The *effusio seminis* (ejaculation) takes place at the crisis of sexual excitement (orgasm). Physiologically, it is most favorable if the orgasm of the female is synchronous (occurring at the same time as that of the male); this is the most favorable condition for fecundation, since in the female orgasm complete loosening and relaxation of all contractile parts occur, especially the opening of the mouth of the womb (*orificium uteri*) under the influence of the slightly protruding round drop or plug of mucus (Kristeller). Hence the orgasm of the female has a special importance for the facilitation of pregnancy, yet this can take place, circumstances permitting, even without orgasm. It is even possible to have fecundation in the case of *eiaculatio ante introitum*; also in the case of a *hymen illaesus* and even in unconsciousness. Yet these cases are indeed exceptional ones.

i. Situs in copula

In view of the physiological importance of orgasm, cases can arise in which a certain modification of the *situs in copula* can be conducive to fecundation. There is reference here more to cases in which there is present an axial deviation of the vagina, so that, through a normal position, a sufficient friction of the clitoris, which is often the most predominant of the exogenous zones, cannot be had. Normally the entire vagina should participate in sexual excitation. The exclusive localization of sexual stimulus in the clitoris is very frequent but not according to norm. It often complicates the synchronous congruity of the partners. To modify the *facie ad faciem* position does not, at most, exceed a venial sin provided the grave danger of ejaculation outside the vagina is excluded. Without a just cause, it is a venial sin to choose a position with the intention of rendering conception more difficult. In confession, no questions about *situs* need be asked.

j. Fecundation

(a) *The germ cells*

Human sperm cells (sperm, spermatozoa, zoosperm, nemasperm) were discovered by Hamm of Leyden in 1677 and were described in detail by Swammerdam in 1680. The human egg cells were first discovered in 1827 by K. E. von Baer.

(1) *The sperm cells*

The individual sperm cell is the smallest of all body cells. The entire length is 0·05–0·06 millimeters, of which the greatest part belongs to the whip fibers (tail fibers). The essential portion of the cell, the head, with the middle piece measures 0·003–0·005 millimeters. The head consists for the most part of the nucleoplasm (karyoplasm). Of greater importance is the tiny " middle piece " found between the head and the tail.

(2) *The egg cells*

The mature egg cell is about 0·2 millimeters in diameter and linearly almost 100 times, and in volume a million times, greater than the sperm. Its cell nucleus, the " germinative vesicle " (*vesicula germinativa*), has a diameter of 0·03–0·045 millimeters.

(b) *The process of fecundation*

The process of fecundation, the union of the germ cells, is in human beings connected with the act of sexual union (*copula carnalis*). This is one phase of the fecundation process and depends on the active action of man and his conscious will (*actio humana*).

The second phase of the fecundation process—the essential part of fecundation itself—consists in the fusion of both germ cells within the female organism. This element is, according to its nature, completely independent of the conscious will of man; it is a pure *actio naturae*; it can, through the will of man, be hindered *contra naturam*, but can never of itself lead to such unnatural hindrance. This consideration permits a surmise regarding the moral significance of an attack of man *contra naturam*, through which the marriage act is robbed of its natural creative power.

In the normal sexual act, at the *effusio seminis* (*eiaculato*), about five cubic centimeters of spermatozoa are given off and this amounts to about three hundred million spermatozoa. By means of a biochemical influence (the turning away from the vaginal secretions containing too much acid—negative chemotaxis), and the turning towards the alkaline secretion of the cervical canal (positive chemotaxis), these succeed in reaching the cervical canal and from there, by their own active power, the *cavum uteri* and the oviduct (tube), where the meeting with the ovum takes place, presuming that such is present. This is regularly the case at the time of ovulation. The transport of the ovum from the ovary, from the follicle to the tubes and uterus, unlike the active self-movement of the spermatozoa, is purely passive.

In the process of spermatozoa fusion, only one of the millions of spermatozoa succeeds in penetrating the ovum. The ovum arches itself with the so-called pregnancy crest (*colliculus germinativus*) toward the pressing spermatozoon upon which "choice" has fallen (germinal selection). In this position of least resistance the cell membrane of the ovum is thrust through by the spermatozoon, the head and neck of which break through and the tail of which is thrust off as superfluous. In the moment of penetration, the ovum encloses itself from the outside, by means of a solid membrane (*membrana vitellina*), against the penetration of any other spermatozoa. The so-called "impregnation" has then been completed.

(c) *Further development*

(1) *External processes*

The further external processes of embryo development, from impregnation and the implantation of the fertilized ovum in the *cavum uteri* (nidation) up to full maturity of the fetus and to birth, take place in pregnancy (gravidity).

(2) *Internal processes*

In further and extremely important internal processes, the head of the spermatozoon, having penetrated the ovum, rapidly enlarges until equivalent to the nucleus of the ovum. There ensues a fusion of nuclei of spermatozoon and ovum in a union of mutual chromosome substances; the haploid substances of each chromosome are thus again united to the diploid substances. The "middle piece" of the spermatozoon is an intrinsic part of this blending and the process of all division which follows. Having penetrated the ovum, it becomes a small body (centrosome) within a highly active center of energy. It is the dynamic center for the collective internal processes which lead to cell division and through this to growth and bodily development. It is from the centrosome that the so-called polar radiation is released affecting and activating the entire cell. The centrosome is therefore the activating cytodynamic center which qualifies the formerly passive ovum for the process of cell division.

Before every cell division the centrosome divides itself into two parts; each part pulls on the opposite pole of the cell and now each becomes an outlet for polar radiation. Apparently both parts, now known by the name "centrioles," work as an attraction center for the two daughter nuclei developed from the common fertilization nucleus by means of untying and dividing: the polar rays apparently work as "pulling fibers" which pull apart both nuclei until the final untying of both new daughter cells takes place. This process repeats itself with every new cell division up to the time the body is completely developed; up to the end of all cell division, a time which coincides with the death of the organism. This process continues, therefore, during the entire lifetime of the individual.

k. The theory of parity and difference

Until recently, little value was attached to the fact that the centrioles, the activating principle in every cell division for the duration of life, were a part of the sperm cell which at the time of fecundation penetrated the maternal ovum.

In the past, there was much more consideration of the fact that, in the fusion of the egg and sperm nuclei, the nuclei are of equal size and basically have the same share of chromosomes. (We can here overlook the difference in regard to the so-called "X chromosomes.")

The overemphasis on the less important process of nucleus fusion and combining of chromosomes has been in part to blame for the erroneous conclusion that in fecundation both sexes perform the same biological function, especially in regard to their contribution to the "hereditary mass." The parity or equality theory, if the contributions in question were purely material, would be correct provided the theory of purely chromosome inheritance plays a part. But if, besides the chromosomes a plasmatic heredity plays a part, then the material contribution of the female cell must be considered greater than that of the male cell.

But if it is a question of the degree of participation of the two germ cells in the process of fertilization then the fundamental functional difference of the tasks entrusted to them cannot be disregarded. The female germ cell is characterized by its passive, "calm expectation" and the male germ cell by the active function of aggression. With complete success the activity of the male germ cell manifests itself in the definite contribution of the activating cytodynamic center in the centrosome, from which are derived the centrioles for all body cells of the female and male organism. Hence the parity theory must be rejected in favor of the difference theory. These long-known but underestimated facts, the old distinctions made by Scholasticism between the *principium generationis activum et passivum*, now form one of the unshakable fundamentals of biological knowledge. Up to the last detail of cell structure, this distinction of an active and passive principle effects a knowledge whose importance to different fields cannot be sufficiently estimated until it is successively perfected by deeper psychological knowledge.

3. PSYCHOLOGY OF SEX

a. General view

Nietzsche has said that the kind and degree of sexuality possessed by man makes itself felt in the most elevated spheres of his intellectual life. This is exact, since no man can avoid the effects of his belonging to a definite sex in regard to his mental life. The question of what is the primary cause—the question whether the soul is even here the *forma corporis* or whether the mental character of the sex is conditioned by the influence of the endocrine, organic functions, demands a definite clarification.

The formulation *propter ovarium solum mulier id est, quod est* (Chérau) implies a materialistic concept. Instead, from the principle *anima forma corporis* the following results: *propter animam feminilem mulier facta est, quod est,* or *organa habet, quae habet.*

This again attributes to the soul a definite sex, a view seemingly incompatible with its immaterial nature and with Christ's teaching on the state of the soul after death (*neque nubent*). It could be deduced from this that sexuality is only an attribute of the mortal body, which, after the resurrection, will be reunited to the soul. The question is therefore resolved when sexuality is understood as merely an accident but an *accidentia inseparabilis*.

In any case, the evident fact that man, in this life, belongs to a definite sex, is basically important for sexual psychology. Deviations from this rule belong to the sphere of sexual pathology. The question whether this belonging to a sex is perpetual, even surviving earthly life, or only a phenomenon of a transient order, belongs to the field of sexual metaphysics.

b. Mental differences between the sexes

We will now consider mental differences between the sexes. There is a tendency to consider only the effects of bodily sex differences on the mental sphere. It is here important to know that the psychic flow of the subconscious, the "depth personality" accompanying sexual life, has a greater part than consciousness. This is especially the case with women.

(a) Polarity

The relation of male-female presents itself in the physiological and psychological sphere as that of polarity, in which concept is found both the element of contrariety as well as the effort tending toward compensation.

From the principle of polarity it has been concluded that the relation of the sexes is one of struggle (the theory of the "struggle of the sexes"). In this theory, because of the prominent position of the male, his power and suppression of the female, there has gradually developed a concept of social and mental inferiority of the female, which some authors (Moebius, von Rosen) have characterized as physiological—i.e., corresponding to the natural order. In this sense Moebius spoke of a "physiological," K. von Rosen of a "moral feeblemindedness" of the female. There has also been an attempt to base the "biological inferiority" of the female on the theory of evolution, in that the difference of bodily structure has been interpreted as a hindrance to development, as a stop or halt at an undifferentiated stage. In opposition to what was formerly considered the inferiority of woman, the purpose of the radical trend of the modern movement concerned with woman is not only the emancipation of woman and her independence, but also a position of pre-eminence for woman.

On the other hand, it is to be stressed that the concept of polarity is based not only on the recognition of a difference but the recognition also of a basic equivalence. In the sense of right order, the natural sex differences must be admitted instead of denied, as was the case with the early emancipation movement in that it aspired to an unnatural "resemblance to man" (biological and social mimicry). The "battle of the sexes" is to be understood only in relation to the fact of *natura vulnerata*, as a disturbance of the original harmony.

(b) *Activity and passivity*

It is fairly obvious that the mental differences found in the sexes have their roots in the biological realm. Of the many formulations of this contrast, that of "activity" and "passivity" come closest to the essence.

The distinction between *principium activum* and *passivum* is actually based on the differentiation of the germ cells in respect to structure and function. Aggression, the essential male characteristic, and receptivity, that of the female, are the direct outcome of this.

The function of protection is not merely essential to the proper sex. Even psychologically the distinction between the active and passive principle seems to be basic, yet the mental distinction cannot be reduced to such a simple formula. It can be that in certain circumstances, because of an internal, impulsive and mental force, greater activity may be manifested in the female. Hence it is proper to proceed with motherliness as the normal mental principle of the female. Here lies the basis for the protective function toward the child and, at the same time, the need for protection and support from man.

The function of protection for wife and child and the spiritual and social function of leadership have their basis in the essence of paternity. If the burden of biological responsibility rests more on the shoulders of the mother, so the greater social and ethico-metaphysical responsibility rests with the husband.

(c) *Differences in the norm of reaction*

From the character of sex arise further, deeply rooted differences in mental structure. The manner of thinking and the norm of reaction is vastly different in the male and female.

It has been stated that the male is more productively—the female more receptively—gifted: strong logical thought is more characteristic of the male, while the female has more of an intuitive grasp; rational consciousness prevails in the male, in the female the more nearly non-rational, the subconscious and the unconscious; in the male, understanding and will, in the female, more feeling and emotion; in the male is found a greater capacity for abstraction, in the female, the meaning of the concrete; in the male, principles prevail—often with rigid inflexibility, in the female, human, sympathetic understanding in the individual case; in the male is found more of a stable, in the female, more of a "transient," mental capacity sometimes increased to the point of distraction and inability to "stick to the point."

c. Heterologous elements

While these differences are generally typical, there is danger in any schematic generalization. Certain traits peculiar to the opposite sex do not necessarily indicate that a man is effeminate nor that, in the case of a woman, she is a "man-female" (*virago*). A deeper understanding of the psychology of sex is based on an awareness that every individual has, *in potentia*, the characteristics of the opposite sex (heterologous elements) which, during the course of the individual life, can manifest themselves.

Sexual biology shows that in its early stages the embryo possesses the structural elements of both sexes (bisexuality of the embryonic disposition) and that the later differentiation is arrived at through the suppression of one set of characteristics and the unfolding of the dominant set. Repressed rather than eliminated, the secondary characteristics remain as recessive and *in potentia*. It is on this that the theory of Weininger is founded. This theory attributes to every man the components of male (M) and female (F); the proportion of M and F traits representing the individual "sexual formula." However, he did not sufficiently stress that this mixture does not present some unalterable, fixed "formula," immutable and constant for an entire lifetime. What is more, emerging from latency, the heterologous element may develop and assume control, a phenomenon that can lead to dangerous discrepancies and crisis and, in some cases, even to fatal psychosexual deviations. Yet the fact should never be overlooked that even pathological distortion always corresponds to a physiological normal process (*pathologia physiologiam illustrat*).

Jung with his theory of the "change of mental dominance" in the "critical period" has explained the matter better than Weininger. According to Jung, with this crisis, which in general arises when the biological and social task of differentiation between the sexes is fulfilled, the elements of mental life which pertain to the other sex assume a strong predominance: in the male, the female mental forces manifest themselves more intensely and evidently (*anima*); in the female, the masculine mental forces (*animus*) make themselves more evident.

This development has been seen to be thoroughly true. It can take place in a twofold direction; in the sense of the mental "downward development" or the "upward development," the greatest development at the time of greatest maturity. In the first case, the male becomes with increasing age " womanish "; the female becomes "mannish" to the point of being a contentious and power-seeking tyrant. If the development tends upward, it means for both the greatest enrichment and perfection as regards internal formation.

In often-observed cases of aging married couples of similar development, the expansion and penetration can manifest themselves in each partner; the *fieri unam carnem* of many years has even found its analogy in the mental sphere: it is perhaps an emphatic example of the formative powers of the soul and also of the meaning of the *mutuus fovendus amor*, as one, even if the secondary, end of marriage. For those reaching the greatest maturity, this can mean sublime perfection.

4. SEXUAL PATHOLOGY

a. General view

Sexual pathology concerns itself with morbid deviations either in the structure or function of sexual organs—with venereal diseases and abnormality of the sexual instinct (perversions). The latter are the object of sexual psychopathy in the strict sense (Krafft—Ebing).

b. Organic anomalies

(a) *Deformities*

The deformities of genital organs are numerous and varied. From the original bisexual germ character there can arise various kinds of deformities that are due to a retardation of development and a lack of differentiation. In extremely rare cases both original sex characteristics reach a full development (*hermaphroditismus verus*). The theoretical "ideal case"—uniform functioning and full development of both characters—has as yet not been established.

There are instances when there is a diverse development of the sexual parts (*hermaphroditismus bilateralis*), but rare is the case of the formation of a bisexual gland (*ovotestis*). Much more frequent and of greater import are the cases of " apparent hermaphroditism," subdivided into pseudo-hermaphroditism (external and internal) according to whether the external genital organs or the internal genital organs predominate; and into masculine and feminine pseudo-hermaphroditism according to the exterior character of the genitals. The nature of the gonad, and the predominant sex characteristics as manifested in the general habit of the individual, are the decisive factors in establishing the exact sex. There have been instances too of doubtful cases in which the actual sex of the individual is verified only later, while at birth it was diagnosed falsely (*erreur de sexe*).

In the male the sexual deformities of practical importance are: kryptorchismus, a development defect in which one or both testes remain in the abdominal cavity; hypospadia and epispadia (anomaly of position of the urethra aperture: deviation of the ventral and dorsal part of the member). In the female they are: aplasia (incomplete or defective development of tissue); atresia (imperforation, absence or occlusion of a normal opening) as, for example, aplasia of the vagina and of the uterus, atresia of the hymen and vagina, furthermore, double deformities (*vagina duplex* or *duplex uterus*) and their forms (*vagina septa, subsepta, uterus septus, arcuatus*, etc.).

The double deformities arise from the defective union of the original bilateral sex characteristics (Müller's ducts); this retardation of development can be either complete (*duplex uterus cum vagina duplici*) or only partial.

(b) *Constitutional anomalies*

In a wide sense, under retardation of development are also included cases in which the primary sex characteristics are clearly manifested, but, in the secondary characteristics, indications of the other sex are discernible and even predominant. There are cases of intermediate sexual stages, which come under the classification of intersexual constitutions. Even here the numerous gradations or degrees extend from the trivial forms apparent only to the expert, to those that are predominant, constitutional defects. It is easy to see how these latter affect even mental life. Moreover, the stopping at the infantile phase of development (*hypoplasia infantilis*) is to be interpreted as a retardation of development. In the mental order it manifests itself as psychosexual infantilism.

Among the instinct anomalies to be considered, there are cases in which definite signs of intersexuality or organic defects, characterizing true or pseudo-hermaphroditism, make the instinct anomalies appear as definitely pathological. Even infantilism can cause various functional disturbances.

(c) *Endocrine disturbances*

In addition, mention can here be made of the anomaly of sexual development as found in sexual precocity (*pubertas praecox*) and retarded puberty (*pubertas retardata*), which partially have an organic basis but whose chief cause is the disturbance of internal secretions. In *pubertas praecox* it is often a case of a defect of the adrenal cortex; namely, of the "interrenal system" (interrenalism) and, at times, unnatural sexual development and even pseudo-hermaphroditism can be associated with it.

The constitutional anomaly designated as *dystrophia adiposo-genitalis* is due to a defect of the hypophysis. In most cases it is associated with excessive obesity and a defective development of the genitals.

In this connection, mention can also be made of eunuchism, which is partly based on the defect of the hypophysis and is often associated with the anomaly of growth (eunuchoid gigantism or eunuchoid dwarfism). These nervous disturbances are to be distinguished from the endocrine disturbances produced by surgical removal of the gonads; i.e., the effects of castration.

c. Functional anomalies

(a) *Potency disturbances*

Under functional anomalies the first to be considered are disturbances regarding the intensity of the sexual instinct, especially regarding the capacity for performing the sexual act (*potentia coeundi*). This is primarily a quantitative anomaly. Here to be mentioned are the various forms of potency disturbances found in the male. A distinction is to be made between organic and psychical forms of impotency; as also between absolute and relative impotency, insofar as the impotency refers to all persons, or only to a certain person in the life of the subject. Knowledge concerning impotency is of great importance for the medical expert in the canonical matrimonial process (canon 1068, # # 1-3, CIC). Hence it merits a detailed presentation.

The milder forms of potency disturbances are *erectio insufficiens* and *eiaculatio praecox*. Lack of erection implies a great degree of potency disturbance. In the female, the disturbances of sexual feeling correspond to the potency disturbances in the male. Complete lack of sexual feeling (*anesthesia sexualis*) is rare; frigidity (sexual indifference) is less rare; and most frequent is *dyspareunia*, the lack of orgasm—often brought on by a lack of understanding on the part of the male. A serious form of impotency in the female is *vaginismus*, largely a psychotic, conditioned sexual neurosis, which makes the consummation of marriage impossible. This form also plays an important role in the matrimonial process.

The habit of resorting to inadequate sexual stimulus (*abusus sexualis*), as well as a premarital mental or sexual reference to a third party, plays an important part in the origin of potency disturbances. Often inhibitions caused by these connections have roots that are deep in the subconscious rather than the conscious. Consequently, it is sometimes difficult to determine whether the case is one of lack of consent or a lack of potency; consciousness will be a decisive guide in the first case, and in the latter, the subconscious.

(b) *Hypereroticism*

In contrast to the cited anomalies—which do not of necessity depend upon a quantitative weakness of the instinct, for they are often a matter of a disproportion between libido and potency—there are anomalies which arise from an exaggerated sexual excitability: satyriasis in the male and nymphomania in the female.

d. Venereal diseases

Sex diseases (venereal diseases) are so called because they are commonly transmitted through sexual intercourse. In lues (syphilis) there is an extragenital infection (*lues insontium*), and with *lues congenita* there is an intrauterine infection. In general, however, it must be held that there is no venereal disease if there is no extramarital sexual intercourse.

This ideal requirement may not be completely fulfilled; but without at least its proximate fulfillment, the fight against venereal diseases will remain ineffective. Because of this, other ways have been sought up to now to combat venereal disease. This problem is closely connected with that of prostitution.

e. Instinct anomalies (perversions)

Here we consider the qualitative anomalies pertaining to the direction of the instinct which deviates from the normal sex object, i.e., from a person of the opposite sex (heterosexual), and tends either toward oneself (auto-erotic) or toward a person of the same sex (homo-erotic), or towards objects (fetishism) or paradoxical venereal sensation or feeling (algolagnia). In the first cases we speak of paraphilia, and in the latter of parapathia (Stekel).

(a) *Homosexuality* (*Sodomia ratione sexus*)

Sexual love toward those of the same sex (homo-eroticism) often leads to a homosexual activity. The question often arises whether homosexuality is a constitutional abnormality, and therefore incurable, or a vice that can be remedied. This question cannot be decided in general by a simple *aut-aut*. There are doubtless intermediate sexual degrees (pederasty) in which the instinct anomaly arises from an endogenous, primarily pathological constitution. These cases manifest clearly distinctive bodily characteristics. But there are other cases in which homosexuality is only exogenous and acquired through seduction. In such cases, an inversion toward the normal in the direction of the instinct is possible. It is then merely a case of "facultative" homosexuals who are also capable of heterosexual relations (so-called "bisexuals"). The perverted direction of the instinct even when exogenously and secondarily acquired can become so fixed through habit in such an unequivocal way that these persons are as absolutely impotent toward the opposite sex as are primary and endogenous homosexuals.

We can therefore divide homosexuality into:

(1) Primary (original) and secondary (accidental), or endogenous and exogenous;

(2) Facultative and compulsive homosexuality.

In cases of a homosexuality which has been acquired through seduction and fixed through habit, the pastoral view of imputability regarding the individual act is the same as that pointed out in reference to ipsation. (Cf. pages 95ff.)

The spread of homosexuality even among females (*amor lesbicus, tribadism*) is greater than is generally assumed. Many times it is only a case of a passing eroticism "of compensation," but even here there is the danger of acquiring a habit of inadequate sexual stimulation. Even more serious is the danger of corrupting children and adolescents (pederasty), and the committing of unnatural acts of impurity (*paedicatio—coitus in anum*). In feminine homosexuality the danger lies in the fact that in selecting her friends the active Lesbian also attracts married women into her circle, and this can become a disturbing element for the marriage state.

Homosexuals, even when some physical potency exists, are unfit for marriage, at least mentally, and should be advised against it. In many cases, homosexuals see in marriage material advantages as well as a "covering mantle" for their anomaly and thus cause unhappiness to the other party.

(b) *Fetishism*

In fetishism, the libido is not aroused by the person of the sexual partner but by a member of the body or object which has some relation to the other. In a certain sense the part is taken for the whole (*pars pro toto*). Certain grotesque fixations which are somewhat like monomaniacal mechanisms can here arise: so-called "abnormal love conditions." There has been at attempt to explain fetishism as the independence, predominance and relative evaluation of the "partial instincts." With fetishism, there is associated at times the instinct of looking, peeping in a specific direction, which can also be overestimated as a partial instinct (*voyeurs*); the instinct, of exhibiting oneself, which works in the opposite manner, can become pathological and fatal as a form of exhibitionism. It is easy to see that these anomalies contain a pathological element. But even in this regard, there are cases in which the morbid fixation did not become predominant without the individual's co-operation.

(c) *Grotesque sensual feeling*

The arousing of venereal pleasure through pain (algolagnia) is the most common type of grotesque sexual feeling. Insofar as there is reference to an active procuring or passive endurance of pain, we speak of sadism (active algolagnia) and masochism (passive algolagnia). Sadism entails the striving for complete submission of the sexual object, mostly through bodily punishment. In masochism, the relation is inverted (submission, self-abasement, etc.). These anomalies can combine with the anomalies of the partial instincts, for instance, fetishism, and in certain circumstances, with the grotesque libido in relation to human excretion (coprolagnia). Lustful homicide presents the horrible extreme of sadism. It is important to know that there is a purely psychical masochism and sadism also. The former is apparently more frequent than the latter. Falling into the same category are abnormal fixations of instinct directed toward children (pedophilia) and toward the old (gerontophilia) and animals (zoophilism, bestiality, *sodômia ratione generis*). The last-mentioned is often manifested in imbeciles. For the most part, the psychological correlations of these aberrations have not been fully explored.

f. The discoveries of depth psychology

In order to explain the origin of sexual anomalies, psycho-analysis has adopted the theory concerning infantile sexuality and sexual trauma. There has been an attempt, by means of the theory concerning infantile oral and anal eroticism, to explain the origin of sexual deviations such as *cunnilingus*, *fellatio*, etc., from the standpoint of the independent "partial instinct." Psychoanalysis points out that all these possibilities in infantile sexuality are to be interpreted as a deviation of the dormant or "partial instinct"; in

D

consequence it designates the infant as a " polymorphic pervert."
In all, however, this much is true; that in every person there is *in
potentia* the possibility of aberration. To what point it is brought
into actuality is, however, a matter which depends not only on the
endogenous factors of predisposition, but also on those exogenous
factors of environment (seduction or good influence), and finally,
whether the moral will becomes effective or not, inasmuch as these
matters concern persons who are capable of responsibility. It should
not be forgotten that sexual psychopathy concerns itself with
psychopathy and not with mental disease.

g. Metaphysical outlook

The problem of the nature of sexual psychopathy will remain
unsolved so long as we fail to explain the depth and darkness of
human life in the fact of original sin. Only then will the theory of
infantile sexuality, the polymorphic perversion of the infant, assume
its true meaning: only thus can the element of truth found therein
become fruitful. Only on the basis of original sin can it be understood how everyone is *in potentia* capable of falling into any sin,
and how it does not always depend on mere personal merit if this
potentiality does not become an actuality. This reflection can and
should lead to humility and preserve us from selfrighteousness. On
the other hand, it is evident that not all cases can be declared merely
pathological. There remain original sin and personal guilt, and
without recognizing sin and personal guilt there cannot be any
genuine cure. Finally, here, as in every form of psychopathy, the
limits between the purely pathological causal factor and the
demoniacal factor, even if it is merely a concomitant factor (*casus
mixtus*), can scarcely be clearly traced in the individual case.

5. SEXUAL HYGIENE

If one of the principal objects of hygiene is the prevention of
avoidable damage to health, the same can be said of the hygiene
of human sexual life. It would be a fatal error to believe that the
damage to health which is verified in the realm of sexual life can
be avoided merely by hygienic means. Sexual pathology has already
shown how profound are the strata in which the deviations of the
instinctive life can be rooted. It has also indicated that these can

never be properly understood and only rarely cured by mere medical means without considering the fact of fallen human nature.

The realization that hygiene alone is not sufficient does not render it superfluous—just as medical therapy is not superfluous in the case of pathological sexual anomalies—nor does it diminish its value and worth. It merely makes us aware of the limitations of purely natural means. The individual questions of sexual hygiene will be expounded in connection with the general hygiene of human reproduction in a work on pastoral hygiene which the author plans. Here we show merely the general connection which sexual hygiene has with sexual pathology on the one hand and with sexual ethics on the other.

It can be said of sexual hygiene what can be said of hygiene in general: namely, that it has not only a descriptive element, but also a normative one. It must not only establish " what is," but also what " is right "; namely, norms of conduct. There thus arises the relation with morals. Finally, what has been defined as a fundamental law of pastoral hygiene and every genuine hygiene is applicable to sexual hygiene. Whatever is morally false can never be hygienically right. An objective scientific investigation and one free from prejudice will, by logical necessity—provided these problems are fully considered—lead to agreement between hygiene and morals.

6. SEXUAL ETHICS AND PEDAGOGY

a. Sexual ethics

(a) *General view*

In the treatment of sex problems, hygiene emphasizes the necessity of moral obligations and norms, and sees in these the most reliable guarantee of health. It is therefore a direct step toward ethics, toward the establishment of moral norms in the light of natural reason. It finds its culmination in moral theology, which obtains its law from a supernatural source and is based on love of God.

(b) *Absolute and relative ethics*

In the sexual life of man, far beyond the purely biological limits of the animal, the principles of responsibility, freedom and control prevail. This is intended as a general statement and without exception. Hence there is no place here for "relative" ethics, but only for an "absolute," universally binding and unconditional morality. Apparent limitation arises only when imputability is removed, when an infraction of the law does not constitute personal guilt. But the law as such still holds even here, and even the pathological cases constitute, for the thinking person, a clear confirmation of the norm.

(c) *Double standard in morality*

Even the so-called double standard in morality is basically nothing else but a form of ethical relativism. In reality, the norms of sexual morality bind both male and female absolutely, in the same manner and in all respects.

Even the biologically and psychologically founded distinction between the *principium activum seu passivum generationis* cannot change the equality of the two sexes. In spite of the difference in role and responsibility, male and female are equally liable in respect to moral duty and universally binding norms. If from the biological standpoint the female bears the greater burden and greater responsibility, the male bears the greater burden and responsibility from the social and ethico-metaphysical standpoint.

(d) *Marriage, one and indissoluble, as the norm* (*Monogamy*)

The one and permanent marriage is the basic norm for the sexual life of man. No conceivable participation in sexuality that is free of guilt and remorse is possible, in the long run, outside this basic norm: *Tertium non datur*.

Sexuality brings blessings only when it takes place and unfolds within the natural order. This natural order already has in itself a divine consecration ("natural matrimony"); it has been raised by Christ to a sacrament and thus united to the supernatural order.

(e) *Conscience and the sense of shame*

All deviations from the natural order evoke in man an inner reaction as long as he reacts in a natural manner. Such a reaction is conscience. Recent depth psychology has, since the time of psychoanalysis, gathered without doubt knowledge capable of showing impressively how wounded conscience can avenge itself.

In sexual matters the sense of shame is closely connected with conscience. It is absolutely false to represent this sense of shame as artificially brought about and as absent from the uneducated natural man. Where such persons exist, and they do exist, the uneducated natural man has not only a sense of shame but a highly developed one. If its external expression is not so manifest, it is because an offense of the natural order is unknown or inconceivable to him.

Comparative ethnology and sociology can confirm this fact very impressively and definitely whenever remains of primitive mankind are anywhere discovered. It must not be forgotten, however, that we are not dealing with man from paradise, but with fallen man.

(f) *Pure culture—"Sexual reform"*

From what has been said it is clear what the judgment should be concerning the efforts of "pure culture" and the countless attempts at a "sexual reform" which, in place of the traditional order, try to establish a new and allegedly more natural and better order.

If there is in the established order so much corruption, this condition is not in the order itself, but in individuals within it who are not prepared to realize the established order in a truly just manner. That is the reason for the development of hypocrisy and the explanation why prudery and inflexibility took the place of true and incorruptible shame. The true sense of shame is indissolubly connected with the dignity of man and constitutes a protection of the intangible sphere of the human personality. Any disturbance of the latter, as proved in collectivistic forms of life, results in the depersonification of the individual.

b. Sexual pedagogy

(a) *Explanation*

A purely rational explanation based only on the alleged biological and hygienic viewpoints will never guarantee a proper order of sexual life. Statistics on venereal disease taken from several German universities, for example, showed the highest percentage of cases to be among medical students. Although this group possessed the most comprehensive knowledge, they were apparently equipped with the weakest counterbalancing ideology.

Neither the purely naturalistic, orientated sexual pedagogy nor the naturally motivated "system of sexual ethics" can lead to internal perfection. They can, for example, show, on a rational basis, that continence is absolutely possible and even necessary, but cannot give the strength to put this idea into practice.

(b) *Supernatural sources of help*

Only the supernatural can give and maintain strength against temptations for long duration. Subordination to God is the basis for the subordination of the flesh to the sovereignty of the spirit: *Tu Deo, tibi caro* (cf. "Casti Connubii, N. 104). Christ speaks of those who have become eunuchs—in spirit—out of love for the kingdom of heaven: "Let him accept it who can" (Matt. 19: 12).

Under certain circumstances, for purely natural-ethical reasons, where, for instance, there is the probability of defective progeny or where the life of the mother is endangered, sexual activity is renounced. The necessary strength and motivation for such a renunciation can be discovered in the example of those who voluntarily abstain for supernatural reasons. On this basis we can realize the great significance that celibacy has even for the natural order, even in protecting the sanctity of matrimony, and we get an idea of the social and pedagogical values inherent in it, though the ultimate mystery has not yet been completely comprehended.

(c) *The purpose of education*

From what has been said, we can deduce directives for the fundamental principles of sexual pedagogy. Every pedagogy has to orientate itself toward an educational end. The educational end of Catholic morality is, in the ultimate analysis, the unfolding of the supernatural life, an education directed toward Christ.

Education toward a sexual life in conformity with the norm must be adjusted to this idea. The difficulties interposed by the disordered life of instinct and the impetuous desire to "give oneself to life" can become fruitful, and lead to greater security during the critical period of puberty.

We have examined the inadequacies of the sexual pedagogy which is based only on the rational, and have described how a natural sense of shame, as the expression of conscience, is a safeguard of the personality and is in consequence a moral force of the highest value. Lastly, the ideal model of chastity, virginity, particularly when motivated by the supernatural, has been of supreme pedagogical-moral value.

As the encyclical of Pius XI on the Christian Education of Youth ("Divini illius Magistri") is an official norm for pedagogy in general, so the encyclical "Casti Connubii," together with the "Arcanum Divinae Sapientiae" of Leo XIII which preceded it, represent the basis and norm for sexual pedagogy in particular and for the enunciation of the moral end of education in this sphere. The reading and study of the encyclical "Casti Connubii" in the higher classes in school will be of inestimable value for sexual pedagogy. The encyclical "Casti Connubii" is without doubt the magna charta of human dignity; and corresponding to it, in the social field, are the encyclicals "Quadragesimo Anno" and its predecessor "Rerum Novarum." The encyclicals "Casti Connubii" and "Quadragesimo Anno" are indissolubly united: the first calls to mind the dictates of morality, and the latter indicates the way to establish this in human society.

7. SOCIOLOGY OF SEX

a. General view

The sexual instinct found in man is a basic element of society, and from this important function the instinct receives its sacred nature. Through it, to the extent that the instinct does not deviate, becoming self-seeking, egocentric lust, but rather expresses a true love faculty, the individual progresses beyond the " I " to the " you."

From this bond between two persons arises the family as the first germ cell of society (not of the " state," as is often taught; for we are to distinguish between state and society: the family exists before the state, but society arises contemporaneously with it).

Hence, out of the sexual instinct, there develops, in the proper order, a natural bond linking the individual to the community and incorporating him in it. And in the proper order, the family is the unit in which individual interests and those of society as a whole find their most facile expression of compatibility. From this standpoint, the one and indissoluble marriage immediately appears as the basis of all social order, a basis which results from the very nature of man.

b. The naturalistic-evolutionary theory

Strange must the attempts appear which from the evolutionary viewpoint strive to invert this order and to represent it as the final link (purely arbitrary) of a social evolution which has its starting point in absolutely distinct forms of life. The naturalistic evolutionary interpretation proceeds from the following assumptions:

1. That man is not essentially different from the animal.
2. That the oneness and permanency of marriage did not prevail from the beginning of the evolution of mankind, but instead, a "primitive" state of general "promiscuity," i.e., an indiscriminately changing sexual society of all men with all women. From this there developed, with the "right of the stronger" as a consequence of the "struggle for existence" and "natural sexual selection," the plunder and purchase marriage, in which first the stronger, then the richer and mightier, possessed many women; and gradually there developed the one and permanent marriage. According to the tenets of evolution, this cannot be the last phase and hence in recent times proponents of the naturalistic-evolutionary doctrine have not failed to demand under the most diverse motivation a new social sexual order.

c. The reform of the sexual order

Many proponents of naturalism hold the opinion that monogamy does not correspond to the nature of man, and some, especially those adhering to a "double standard of morality," maintain that man is by nature polygamous. The socialistic advocates of feminism (Bebel, Ellen Key and others) have advocated free love; others, from the standpoint of race hygiene, have advocated multiple matrimony (V. Ehrenberg) and the respective "colonies of selection" (Midgard—Bund), etc. Moreover, institutions such as the "trial marriage" have been proposed (Lindsey, Sanger), as well as the "juvenile marriage," the "temporary marriage" (Buchow— Homeyer), and the "tripartite marriage" (Anquetil), etc.

The first revolutionary legislation of Soviet Russia represented a decisive attempt to establish a new social order in which marriage and the family were basically abolished. It can now be said that this attempt toward a " society without families " has not been able to survive as originally planned. The natural order has necessarily re-established itself.

d. The matriarchal theory

Related to the above evolutionary theories which consider the primitive social order to be one of " promiscuity," are the theories of Bachofen and Morgan concerning matriarchy as the original form of society. These theories have been disproved by the theological research of Wilhelm Schmidt and his school, and also by the " doctrine of the cultural cycles " of Schmidt and Graebner, which, on the basis of comprehensive ethnological and sociological research, inform us that wherever primitivity is found in the original form, sexual morality manifests an extraordinary high standing and the one and permanent marriage is considered holy and inviolable. Recent research on pygmies carried on by Koppers and others has fully confirmed this point. On the contrary, where this order does not exist among alleged primitives, it can be demonstrated that the existing order is not truly a case of primitive origin, but a secondary form of deterioration.

Thus ethnology confirms the doctrine of Christian sociology and disproves evolution in marriage. An elementary example of the erroneous doctrine is found in the opinions, rectified by Christian scholars, concerning the *ius primae noctis* (Oesterle, Schmidt), as well as in the assertions of Darwin concerning the alleged lack of religion among the inhabitants of the land of fire and that of Levy—Bruhl concerning the culture of the " primitives."

e. The question of woman: Feminism

The theory of evolution has given impetus to the radical demands contained in the movement of feminism. Without doubt, the question of woman in the present day is part of the general social question, and the solution of the latter will also bring about the final solution of the former.

Insofar as the economic side of the question of woman is concerned, the excessive number of women will be posited as the biologically basic cause; the disarrangement of the normal " sexual

D*

proportion" of the numerical relation between the male and female. Among the newly born, the relation amounts to the ratio 106:100. The relation becomes especially disproportionate through war and social influences so that, disadvantageously for women, in recent times there has resulted a surplus of women, especially of marriageable and child-producing age. Wherever there is an excess of women in a large degree, the effects on the social and ethical sphere are disastrous. In courtship the natural order is easily changed to its opposite. The state of virginity is deprecated and this has an effect on the social order. It should therefore be evident that virginity, especially that manifested in the social and sacrificial life of women in religious Orders, has an important meaning and influence during times when women are in excess numbers, and this is so without regard to the spiritual value contained in such a form of life.

In any case, "emancipation" has not truly freed woman. It is the woman who has suffered in all attempts to bring about her greater "sexual freedom" or to include her in the labor force. The latter has not brought her independence but only an oppressing dependency, and has caused an almost insoluble conflict with the twofold duties of home and family. Hand in hand there arise a disastrous lack of appreciation of the role of the homemaker and a destruction of family life.

Among the causes of birth decline, besides the primary moral cause, social relations play an important secondary and often prevalent role. The effects of birth decline in the eugenic realm are known. In order to solve these questions, it appears of decisive importance that woman be restored to her natural place in the home.

It must, however, be understood that the formula "The woman belongs in the home" cannot easily be followed unless there is a true home in which the woman finds internal and external security, and where there is the possibility of complete development and, above all, the position by which, in serving, she rules. The woman is neither a slave of man nor merely a "breeding animal." There is no greater degradation of woman than such depersonalization.

Among those advocating rights only for the husband, an opinion which ultimately terminates in the slavery of the wife, we find the advocating of a "double morality," which encourages complete freedom for the husband as regards sexual matters and imposes every burden and obligation on the wife. The solution of the question of woman is not to be found in a "battle of sexes," not in the one-sided oppression of the woman by stressing only the rights of the man, not in the refusal of woman to take on responsibility (*non serviam*). Rather, the solution must be in accordance with the words of the encyclical "Casti Connubii" that the husband is the head, and the wife the heart, of the family.

If the natural authority of the husband in the home and family is removed, the basic cause is to be found in the fact that the husband has detached himself from the authority of God. It is thus that all earthly authority has become questionable.

f. Reform of conditions and improvement of morality

Without a thorough reform of conditions in the social and economic order, the necessary improvement of morality cannot be accomplished; this also holds in reverse. Hence the encyclical "Quadragesimo Anno" advocates for the working man, as an unconditional "just wage," a "family wage," i.e., one in accordance with the unequivocal definition of Catholic social science, a wage which is sufficient to guarantee the adult full-time workman the support of a wife and a family of average size computed according to the times (at the present time, about two children).

From these requirements of commutative justice, there arises a demand for the establishment of institutions from which the socially burdened father of a family receives by way of compensation whatever he needs when his family exceeds the average size. This compensation would come from those whose social burden remains less than average.

The basic importance of this social claim made by Catholic sociology has not been recognized. Its importance, however, is incalculable. Thus, for example, the problem of social security will find its satisfactory solution in the family wage. Even the former apparently insoluble problem of the illegitimate child, and likewise the old wound of human society, prostitution—these will never be completely removed from the world, just as poverty will never be completely removed. Hence, side by side with social justice, there will always remain a wide field for social charities—charitable work that is closely allied to the cause of social justice. But the solution of social problems will at least be made more possible when their main causes: namely, pauperization, negligence and the social state of misery, are removed; and this solution will come about through sacrifices which are small but measured according to the greatness of their end. Eliminating evil effects from human social life will also be of benefit in removing from sexual life its disastrous scourges. So actually, the two great encyclicals "Casti Connubii" and "Quadragesimo Anno" represent the two supporting columns of the reconstruction of the human social life.

8. SEXUAL METAPHYSICS

a. General view

In order to get closer to the ultimate meaning of human sexuality (complete fathoming of this mystery is certainly reserved to the state of "vision"), a complete philosophical view is indispensable, a view which accepts biological and sociological knowledge but which at the same time accepts the supremacy of the metaphysical consideration. By metaphysics in this context we mean what is "behind the physis." There is reference here to the meaning of sexuality. The meaning of plant and animal sexuality is essentially exhausted with reproduction; it serves this end exclusively: namely, the preservation of the species. That is the "immortality" of this phase of life: for this the germ track, the "genotype," is all; the individual, the "phenotype," is nothing. These ideas, transferred to man without discrimination, imply a complete surrender of the value of personality and necessarily lead to a purely earthly, materialistic meaning of life.

On the contrary, in man there is something basically new, specifically human: reason, free will and moral responsibility. Human sexuality comes under this law. Even the sexuality of man comes under this law. He presents himself as an individual only in sexual differentiation. The nature of male and female has been designated from the beginning and this in the plan of creation: *Masculum et feminam creavit eos* (Gen. 1 : 27).

b. Sexuality and original sin

Thus man also has a part in the polar span which prevails in the realm of the living as a preserving and formative force of the instinct germinating power; a span which in man can either be

effectively preserving or fatally destructive. That the latter is possible
—i.e., that man is capable of abusing sexuality—is understandable
on the one hand from the fact of free will, and on the other, from
the fact of fallen nature. Without original sin, man would still be
sexually differentiated and predestined to reproduction. Reproduction would also be connected with pleasure, but this pleasure would
be entirely pure and innocent and would bring about greater happiness. (St. Thomas, *Summa theol.*, I, qu. 98.)

There is an erroneous opinion still propagated, that the nature of
original sin consisted in sexual union as such. On this opinion is
based the reproach that Christianity is "inimical to the body, to
sex and feeling." In reality, this is an old error which has nothing
in common with Christianity, but has, above all, received its deepest
expression from Manichaeism.

c. The doctrine of "Androgyny"

We also find similar ideas in the doctrine of "androgyny," manifested in many theosophically esoteric doctrines and based on
gnosis. Since, from the biological standpoint, the separation of the
sexes seems to be an expression of higher differentiation, these
notions merely depict a division and incompleteness. Every sexually
differentiated being feels itself to be only a part of a past and lost
complete unity; hence the desire toward completion and unity.

Man was androgynous in the complete and primitive phase, as
God is androgynous (thereby many systems hold that the holiness
of God consists in the permanent activity of this androgyny—a
blasphemous interpretation of the notion *Actus Purus*). Hence the
overcoming and removal of sexual tension leads to the state of
decisive pacification and rest (entrophy). If man was originally
created according to the "model of God," as a "being" originally
bisexual, then this gnostic-theosophic and false doctrine has
obtained its androgynous concept of God from a false idea of
man.

The kernel of truth which is found at the basis of even this
doctrine was shown in the ontogeny of sex differentiation as well
as in the latent presence of characteristics belonging to the opposite
sex and their stronger appearance after the "change of mental
dominance." (Cf. above, under *Psychology of sex*, references to
animus and *anima*.)

d. Sex in the plan of creation—The natural order

According to Catholic doctrine, sexuality and the sex instinct are by no means sinful. This view is in opposition to the teaching of Luther. Concerning the original plan of creation of man in paradise, it must be held that, even without the fall into sin, procreation of the human sexes, as well as the reproduction of the other sexually differentiated beings, would have followed without sin and in a sexual manner.

The fact that Christianity has not undervalued sexuality as the source of natural life arises simply from the fact that marriage, since the time of Christ, has been raised to a sacrament and established in the supernatural order. A more unequivocal affirmation of a rightly ordered sexual life cannot be given. (Cf. Matt. 19:5— *et erunt duo in una carne.*)

The question arises whether sexuality belongs perhaps only to the present order, whether after death it is a superfluous garment removed from the immortal soul. (Cf. Matt. 22:30—*neque nubent neque nubentur.*) Since the Church teaches not only the immortality of the soul, but also the resurrection of the body, the question is raised whether all sexual differentiation is completely removed at death and life in its perfection is asexual. The words of Christ, *neque nubent neque nubentur,* pertain only to the actual function of sex; there is no reference to the removal of any sexual characteristic of personality—no suggestion that sex pertains only to this present order and then disappears. It would otherwise be difficult to explain how the soul as "the form of the body" could effect the sexual differentiation in the body; what is more, the body would be the formal principle of the soul (as some modern psychologists hold today).

Finally, the honor paid to the Mother of God by the Church is inseparably united with the character of her womanhood.

e. The supernatural order

This concept is strengthened when the sacramental character of marriage is deeply comprehended, since in the sacramental consummation there is a union of the supernatural order and the natural order.

(a) *Analogia entis*

The doctrine concerning the *analogia entis* can scarcely find a clearer expression. The understanding of the depth and extent of *analogia entis* was unfortunately lost during the time of the Reformation, so that it was taught that human nature was radically corrupted through original sin. The erroneous judgment concerning concupiscence, and the consideration of sexuality as sinful, can be explained from this basic error. The hostile attitude toward sex unjustly attributed to the Church is a heretical doctrine and is anything but Catholic.

(b) *The order of life—The laws of life*

The doctrine of the Church, proceeding from such an exalted idea and concept of sexual life and marriage, has highly esteemed the preservation of purity and considers every sexual abuse a violation of the sacred order of life. Even this strictness has been greatly misunderstood. Rightly understood, it is merely the expression of human and divine love. The violation of the order of life in the sexual sphere brings disaster to both the individual and to society. Such violations are due ultimately to the incapability of attaining true love and of rising beyond one's ego. Persistence in one's egocentric tendency or behavior is the actual sin which separates one from union with God and man.

Those who do not succeed in overcoming habitual auto-eroticism complain that life seems to them completely unreal. This complaint leads one to the kernel of the ontological meaning of the nature of love. God is the highest and absolute real Being, *Actus Purus*, and at the same time, Love itself; the First Cause of all being, all love and knowledge of all created beings. The laws of being are at the same time laws of knowledge and of life. Every created being is but a participation ($\mu\epsilon\theta\acute{\epsilon}\xi\iota\varsigma$) in the absolute being of God.

Love in its deepest meaning is the complete affirmation of the existence of the being loved. From this ontological knowledge we get an idea of the identification of "knowing" and "loving" as used in the Old Testament, in which the words "to know" are used to express the physical union of love. In God, being, knowledge and love are one; truth and charity flow from one source. The greater the true ability to love, the greater the ability to know: *Quantum amabunt, tantum cognoscent*. Hence in continuous sexual abuse, there is a diminishing of the power of knowing. In this, sexuality manifests itself as the touchstone for the trying and proving of man in *statu viatoris*.

Herein is realized the effect of man's failure to go beyond pure animal sexuality. The interpretation of human nature becomes all the more tragic the more one is prone to look upon sexual weakness as "human." In the right order, sex serves not only the Eros, but transforms itself into *caritas*, in the Agape. That is the meaning of sublimation, truly understood.

f. Virginity

From the above, we can easily perceive the deep meaning to be found in the sacrificing of marriage and sexual love in the state of virginity, when this sacrifice is made out of love for God. Every true sacrifice is a surrender to God of a natural gift which is transformed and received as a supernatural gift. Hence renunciation through supernatural motivation is not a curtailment, but the highest unfolding of humanity. The free renunciation of parenthood does not imply a lack of fatherliness or motherliness, but rather a fulfillment and transformation into spiritual paternity or maternity. It implies a richer fruitfulness on a higher plane, and brings to society benefits from Him from whom all fatherhood in heaven and on earth takes its name.

g. The ends of marriage

Hence, even the physically sterile marriage, rightly formed, can become rich in spiritual benefits. If the meaning of marriage were exclusively contained in the primary marital end of *procreatio prolis*, then marriage would merely be a "breeding institution," and the specifically human *mutuus adiutorium*, the *mutuus fovendus amor*, as well as mutual sanctification, would be excluded.

It is something else when the primary end of marriage is deliberately and sinfully frustrated. In this case, sexual union does not serve life, but comes under the law of death, as does ultimately every egocentric sin against love: "He who would save his life will lose it" (Matt. 16:25).

h. Eros and Thanatos

With this expression we wish to mention briefly the deep relation between love and death ("Eros and Thanatos," Freud). It has been demonstrated that in the most primitive levels of living beings reproduction coincides with the life termination of the individual. This mysterious relation extends beyond the biological realm. Its most horrible corruption is repesented by sexual homicide, its highest consummation by the sacrifice of life for love. "Greater love than this no man has."

By a vicarious sacrificial death, the immortal God overcame the death of mortal man, so that man might have life. *Mors et vita duello conflixere mirando. Dux vitae mortuus regnat vivus!* So death becomes the gate of life (*mors ianuae vitae*). "Separation from life" becomes a "living" with God.

In this regard, there is the further interpretation of the frequently expressed relation between Eros and mysticism. Dante in his supreme beatific vision perceived: *L'amore, chi muove il sole e l'altre stelle*—"The love which moves the sun and the other stars" (Par. XXXIII, 145).

Whether and how far the transport of mystical ecstasy can express itself in physical erotic sensation—that is, whether and when there is a suspicion that there is present the transference from the religious realm into the sexual—in general cannot be said, and in concrete is difficult to judge. Yet there is the possibility that even genuine ecstasy can deeply affect the personality of man. It is permissible to allude to such relations, but it is better to remain respectfully silent about them.

In summary, we can say that the ultimate meaning of sexuality in man can never be comprehended from merely the biological view. The biological presents the basic stratum of the personality, but this rises with its highest points into the supernatural. The words of Nietzsche, that the species and degrees of sexuality extend to the highest point of the spirit, are, rightly understood, to the point. The materialistic view that man is merely, as it were, the "basic" germ-tract bearer of life, and that the individual personality is only a passing appendage, must be rejected. Moreover, sexuality with its effects belongs as an accident, but as an *accidentia inseperabilis*; and this order, in the sense of the *analogia entis*, has a relation of correspondence to the superior order of being.

B. SPECIAL QUESTIONS

1. POLLUTIONES NOCTURNAE

a. Concept

Nocturnal pollution is the occurrence, in a dream, of the spontaneous effusion of semen, with an accompanying stimulation from orgasm, by which one is generally awakened from sleep. With women, there is an analogous occurrence, which does not always reach the point of orgasm. The effusive secretion comes chiefly from the gland of the *vestibulum* (*humor vulvovaginalis*).

Moral textbooks distinguish between *pollutio involuntaria* and *pollutio voluntaria*. The latter will be treated in the following section. The ordinary and customary designation of *pollutio* refers only to the former. In general, it is considered as a purely natural occurrence of spontaneous compensation for sexual tension.

Besides these pollutions, which are physiological, there are also others of a pathological nature.

b. Distinction between pollutio, spermatorrhea and destillatio

Physiological pollutions are to be distinguished in a twofold manner: According to the physiological aspect with the notion of *destillatio*, and according to the pathological aspect, with abnormal pollution and in particular with spermatorrhea.

Pollution is abnormal when it is increased in degree and frequency or when it qualitatively deviates from normality. The latter would be the case with spermatorrhea, a frequent effusion of seed, even daily, which mostly takes place with orgasmic stimulation. With spermatorrhea, there is no feeling of relaxation but only that of exhaustion.

It would be a mistake to assume that every case, even that occurring every day, in which there is a secretion without orgasm, is a case of abnormal spermatorrhea. This can also be merely mechanically brought about through pressure (e.g., during defecation) on the filled *vesiculae seminales*.

As regards the definition of *destillatio*, there is a difference among the authors. Some authors even designate *eiaculatio* as *destillatio* when this does not constitute a *verum semen*. It seems more correct to understand by *destillatio* only the drop by drop resulting secretion, without orgasm, which, especially *ante copulam*, consists of an enormous number of sperm and which per se can be fertile (prolific).

c. Medico-pastoral view

The pastoral-medical judgment is based on the fact that the physiological nocturnal condition serves as a natural release of sexual tension (*exoneratio naturae*). Hence it presents no cause for preoccupation, neither from the standpoint of health or morality.

In regard to anxiety, compulsion neurosis, hypochondria and scrupulosity, it must be held that the origin of the neurosis is to be ascribed neither to pollution as such, nor to sexual abstinence, but above all, to a psychopathic predisposition and nervous constitution.

Frequent and daily pollution is almost always a symptom of sexual neurasthenia or excessive excitability.

Frequent and pathological pollution is likewise not the cause of the abnormal condition, but its effect and symptom.

With right has Antonelli condemned the practice of doctors who advise patients disturbed by the occurrence of pollution to give themselves to extramarital intercourse.

There is no need of special therapy in cases of nocturnal pollution which are within the normal scope. If it is an abnormal condition, then the basic malady, the neuropathy, and at times the corresponding organic malady, as such, is to be treated.

d. Theologico-moral view

Just as there might be an exaggeration in regard to the hygienic sphere, so there might also arise an exaggeration in the moral sphere. According to the general teaching of moralists, there is nothing wrong in feeling satisfaction in the alleviation and relaxation which comes from nature itself. There is no sin involved in giving consent to the process if this is based on the fact that the alleviation does not follow through one's own fault, namely, that it is free from sin.

If the sensual feeling is per se the object of consent, then the boundary of what is permitted is crossed. It is in crossing this border that dangers lie. Inner consent to the *delectatio venerea* easily leads to free co-operation and consent during the time one is awake. If this were so, then it would be a case of *pollutio voluntaria*.

There is also the danger of occupying oneself intensely with thoughts concerning venereal feelings. Herein lies a risk, not to be taken lightly, of weakening the will against illicit venereal pleasure, especially in the case of young and unmarried persons.

It is the task of sexual pedagogy to realize such dangers and to meet the same with proper means. In order to strengthen resistance of the will, the meaning and extent of sins of thought are to be rightly comprehended and evaluated.

Neither the *primi motus carnales* as such, nor even the physiological *exoneratio naturae* is sinful, but only the conscious consent to every illicit *delectatio venerea*. Hence, even in the question of *pollutio involuntaria*, there is the possibility of a rigorism causing anxiety, as well as of a laxism which does not accurately heed the prescribed limits.

2. POLLUTIO VOLUNTARIA (MASTURBATION, IPSATION)

a. Concept—Terminology

Self-abuse is many times incorrectly called onanism. This designation is to be avoided, since it confuses self-abuse with the sin committed by Onan (Gen. 38:8-10), rightly called onanism. The latter refers to *copula interrupta*. (Cf. below, *Abusus matrimonii*.)

The designation " mollities " is found in the works of theology. The term *pollutio voluntaria* is applied to the sin of the male, and masturbation (from *manu stupratio*) is applied to that of the female. In works of medicine the term " masturbation " is used without distinction of sex, but this is not completely precise or accurate. The common designation for both sexes would be found in the word " ipsation " (M. Hirschfield).

b. Intra or contra naturam

In the medical literature of the last decade, ipsation has been considered a spontaneous and natural " action of compensation." This idea was propagated by popular authors and even given place in scientific works. It must seem to some unscientific rigorism when ipsation is considered a *peccatum contra naturam* by moral theology.

Despite this, there are weighty reasons for this authoritative judgment.

In the *peccata intra naturam*, only such sexual lapses are considered in which the natural sex act, an *actus per se aptus aa generationem*, takes place. With this external criterion, there is also an interior criterion. Man is completely aware of the unnatural character of the sin. He feels it to be a degradation of the human personality. This natural feeling—a function of the conscience—can be dulled and misled, but consciousness and awareness of the inordination is definitely basic.

c. Dangers and effects

In former times the dangers of ipsation were as much exaggerated as they have in recent times been underestimated. In the literature of modern medicine it is almost without exception considered an innocent action of compensation. There is a complete denial of harmful effects, and ipsation is considered as harmless as normal *copula*: " It is neither a sickness nor a vice " (Hodann). This idea must have a more nearly disastrous effect on youth than the former notion. If the earlier opinion often led to a compulsion neurosis, anxiety and feelings of shame in certain persons, so the later view brings about an undestimation of the sexual act, causing disastrous effects both to the individual and to society.

A great number of neurotics have sought help through psychoanalysis, and this means has uncovered the continuous effect of sexual trauma in the subconscious, and advanced new ideas concerning the lasting effect of such occurrences, among which is ipsation.

The question whether there are specific " onanistic symptoms " is to be denied in regard to physical symptoms. The same symptoms are ascribed, by the same authors, to sexual abstinence. There are no specific symptoms arising from abstinence or onanism. We find at most unspecific symptoms of bodily exhaustion, or nervous eroticism. More important than the bodily symptoms is the mental behavior. This permits one to conclude more concretely against ipsation.

The more basic reason for the typically shy and depressed nature is the tendency toward solitude found in the auto-erotic fixation upon one's ego, and in the shame and reproaches of conscience.

The almost never-absent and pronounced psychopathic characteristics found in cases of excessive ipsation are to be considered as the effect of ipsation, but psychopathy can just as well be the cause of unrestrained ipsation. It would be better to consider the latter as a symptom of more serious psychopathic disturbances.

Excessive ipsation is not necessarily identical with habitual ipsation. The latter can take place without cumulated excess (many times in one day). Habitual cases are nearly always connected with psychopathic characteristics. But it would be dangerous to assume that psychopathy is always the cause and the sole cause, and never the effect, of ipsation. According to most recent knowledge, the possibility of serious danger and injury to health through ipsation can no longer be denied. In order to have a clearer grasp of the problem, exaggeration on both sides should be avoided.

It is as harmful to represent the matter pessimistically to those seeking help and thus bring on anxiety and confusion, as it is to depict the practice as harmless and trifling. Among the apparent effects, an important one is the habituation in inadequate sexual stimulation, which in many cases is the cause of potency disturbances and sensation disturbances later, in marriage.

The mental effects of ipsation are to be seriously evaluated. The habitual practice of ipsation leads to mental-behaviour problems characterized by a breakdown of self-confidence, loss of the realization of self-worth and, in place of the latter, a substitution and fixation of feelings of inferiority. With this, there arises a mental isolation which becomes worse. Seriously sought isolation leads to auto-eroticism. This fixation is accompanied by loss of genuine ability to love and of ability to transcend one's ego, and thus leads to egocentric concentration. With these, there arises a severe change of attitude toward religious obligations and even conscious obstinacy and hatred.

d. Pedagogical evaluation and view

Of great concern is the physical and mental harm caused by the extensive spread of evil among both sexes and also the evil in regard to national health and morality. It is not a matter of unconcern whether the rising generation of youth allow themselves to be overrun by the first impulse of the sex instinct without resisting. Ipsation in puberty presents a dangerous inroad for moral weakness (L. Bopp). It is the task and purpose of sex pedagogy to strengthen, at the right time, the power of resistance. From this fact arises the responsibility of teachers, leaders of institutions, homes, etc.

e. Therapy—Prophylaxis

(a) *Possibilities of physical therapy*

It is not possible to cite the countless means suggested for the treatment of ipsation. The limits of physical treatment are relatively narrow. The possible means can be divided into medicamental, surgical and physico-dietetic. The use of these means alone, though having a sustaining value, would be insufficient.

(1) *Medicamental therapy (Therapy with drugs)*

Among the most important drugs, we have, first of all, camphor; best in the form of monobromated camphor (*camphora mono-bromata*); then follows calcium, especially when mixed with bromide; then the homopathic remedies: nymphaea, preferable for women, and lupulin for men. Attention, especially in women, should be paid to the cause of excessive itching (pruritus), e.g., pinworm or seat worm infection (oxyuriasis). In cases of symptomatic pruritus, the basic organic disturbances should be treated as causal. Diabetes is also to be taken into consideration. Starting with the consideration that the hypophysis functions as a motor of sexuality and the epiphysis as a check on sexuality, authors have recommended epiphysis extract with success in many cases.

(2) *Surgical therapy*

The possibilities of surgical therapy are more limited than those of medicamental treatment. Yet, when an indication is present, they should not be neglected. In older works, the question of castration in connection with habitual ipsation was discussed. This is to be rejected both on medical and moral grounds.

The incision of the *frenulum praeputii*, which makes erection painful, is to be rejected. This can, later in marriage, disturb the end of marriage, that is, give cause to the origin of impotency. As regards women, the *excisio clitoridis* has sometimes been recommended; this is, on similar grounds, also to be rejected. In many cases of *pruritus vulvae*, multiple cauterization of the labia can be successful. All the recommended surgical means are always only peripheral possibilities of therapy. The main therapy is basically psychotherapy, effectively supported by physico-dietetic means.

(3) *Radiation therapy: Hygienic regimen*

In many cases, the use of radiotherapy, qualitatively and quantatively given according to the individual, can be very valuable. Physical means have for a long time played an important part in the treatment of ipsation. This would consist of: a hardening of the body, exercise, work and travel, bodily exercise to the point of fatigue, provision for healthy sleep, hard bed, bathing with cold water, well-arranged division of the day; greatest possible order in the morning and going to bed early; cleanliness and care of the body without a too intensive occupation with self. Of importance is simple, non-stimulating food, avoidance of alcohol, nicotine, spices and avoidance of sexual stimulations caused by environment. Of importance likewise is the avoidance of thoughts of an erotic nature, a curbing of phantasms, etc. Under certain circumstances, a temporary strict fast can be very effective as a therapeutic means.

(b) *Psychotherapy*

The possibilities of physical therapy are numerous, and with proper use can be effective. But psychotherapy remains the most important and most decisive medical therapy. It often uncovers the deeper causes of faulty behavior. Without going into the details of psychotherapy, let it merely be remarked that it is important to uncover the causal factors of psychic misbehavior which go as far back as childhood and those of a narcissistic-autoerotic inclination. This must begin with a consideration of the environment of home life, whether the parents lived a happy married life, etc.; the behavior of the person during school years and puberty, his adjustment to society, isolation, resentment, etc. Of great importance is the question of religious education, of the development of the capacity to love, and the removal of egocentricity. If there is no success in removing this unhealthy fixation, then even psychotherapy has scarcely a chance of being successful.

So important is it to unite psychotherapy with a correctly formed sex pedagogy and, in cases of necessity, with healing pedagogical means, that every therapy remains incomplete when a reconstruction of personality from within does not take place. Here the religious powers are the decisive factors.

(c) *Prophylaxis (Preventive treatment)*

Therapy and prophylaxis must go hand in hand. Of greatest importance is the creation of an atmosphere and environment free from harmful influences. Even social conditions can affect the entire sphere of the sex question in an unfavorable manner. The task of prophylaxis lies not only in the hygienic and biological, but also in the social and pedagogical, fields.

As important as opportune and correct sex knowledge is, yet no purely rational instruction can suffice alone. In the first place, there is need of strengthening the moral power. Here, rightly understood, asceticism can contribute, even in a purely natural manner, to the strengthening of the will.

(d) *Natural and supernatural remedies*

As important as it is to exhaust all the natural means, it is even more important to realize that these alone do not suffice. Only through the uniting of natural and supernatural means can an evil extending beyond the physical be overcome, and can one represent to man, even from the metaphysical viewpoint, the problem of existence. This cannot come about without the help and means of grace.

In practice this means the united efforts of spiritual adviser and doctor. The doctor alone cannot solve the problem, and the spiritual adviser can scarcely do without the assistance of the doctor.

f. Evaluation according to moral theology

That "mollities" is per se a grave sin in which the principle of *parvitas materiae* (which would exclude a serious sin) does not apply, is evident from the nature of the action. But there are circumstances, especially in regard to habitual ipsation, that must be considered. These circumstances diminish imputability, since they include neuropathic or psychopathic symptoms. In order to ascertain such cases, the assistance of the doctor is necessary.

Under the *status plus minusve*, pathological, even organic causes, come into play. In moral textbooks, even the question of pruritus is fully treated, especially the question of whether it is permitted to counteract pruritus by rubbing (*Num liceat pruritum, quem quis patitur in verendis, tactu vel fricatione abigere, quantumvis pollutio sequator*).

Regarding this point, the confessor is urged to be cautious and to make sure that the penitent does not use pruritus as a pretense, especially if the penitent shows himself to be informed concerning the matter.

It would be basically wrong to designate, in this matter, everything as a "deviation" and thus seek to remove all fault. In this way, no one, not even the person afflicted, is helped. Momentarily he may be assuaged, but he will persistently be of the thought that his defeat or suffering is based merely on a pathological predisposition, and this hinders every hope of betterment and cure and likewise diminishes the power of moral reconstruction.

g. Pastoral points

As necessary as the regular use of the means of grace, especially the sacraments of Penance and Eucharist, are for this form of suffering, yet it would not be right to allow in general the reception of Communion without confession, by assuming that every individual case is pathological and hence devoid of serious guilt. Neither laxism and underestimation of the case nor rigorism will attain the proper end. There is no doubt that the task of the confessor is a difficult one. He must have endless patience in order to help the penitent who relapses into sin, not to lose courage; yet he must not completely exonerate the penitent, lest the moral will of the latter become paralysed.

He must bring to the attention of the penitent the possibility of relapse and prepare and strengthen him so that he will not lose confidence, and will avoid feelings of despair, since there is no reason for these. He must encourage the penitent to rise after every relapse into sin and, when possible, to receive sacramental absolution as soon as possible, yet help the penitent to avoid making confession something commonplace. The seriousness of the matter would, without doubt, not be truly calculated if the entire thing were considered as something merely pathological and the obligation of going to confession removed.

It is the case of a sin which more than any other gives way to the forces which drag man into the depths of distraction—if for no other reason than that it is near at hand. Yet it is exactly because of this fact that it is very important to overcome it.

h. Supernatural viewpoint

Pastoral Medicine in its mode of treating problems in a universalistic or complete manner cannot pass over or overlook the problems which no longer belong to the realm of medicine. If these are no longer topics of medical consideration, they should at least be known and given recognition.

The problem under consideration entails a viewpoint that is extra-natural, outside the natural order, and one that is supernatural: The former involves the co-operation and workings of demonology and the latter has to do with the workings of grace.

It is as sure and definite that the corrupting forces of demonology play an important part in habitual ipsation as it is definite that the ultimate basis for a cure of ipsation lies in grace.

The renewal of genuine and supernaturally founded love in the soul is of basic importance. The love of God is the foundation of all morality and of every true love for men. When this becomes the decisive power in one's life to which all else is orientated, then the human will conforms to the will of God. If the afflicted person progresses to the point where he says from the depth of his soul: "I do not want what God does not want," then the purpose of soul-direction has been attained; then may one say: *ama et fac quod vis* (St. Augustine).

In the manner that man has learned to obey God, will the flesh learn to obey him: *Tu Deo et tibi caro!*

3. SPERM EXAMINATION

a. Concept: Verum semen

The sperm (*semen virile*) is produced in the testes; hence the basic criterion for the establishment of genuine sperm (*verum semen*) is its extraction from the male germinative glands (*a testiculis elaboratum*). Besides this external secretion, the germinative glands, as endocrine glands within the complete endocrine system, have another function, that of internal secretion.

Besides the genuine germinative substance prepared by the genital glands and containing the sperm, there are different "accessory" glands producing secretions, viz., the prostate. Cowper and Littre glands, whose function is to activate and conserve. Whenever the connection between the sperm-preparing glands and the external world is broken, a true semen cannot be outwardly secreted; what is then secreted is only a product of the accessory glands, a *humor prostaticus* and not *semen virile verum*.

This distinction has become of great importance for the establishing of impotency in the canonical marriage process.

b. Importance of sperm examination

The development of the modern biology of generation dates back to the discovery of human sperm by Hamm and Swammerdam (1677-1680). The more recent doctrine concerning generation and fertilization is based, for the most part, on these researches, which were made possible through the use of the microscope introduced by Leuwenhoeks. The practical use of the discoveries led to attempts at artificial insemination, which has acquired importance in animal breeding (cf. below, *Artificial insemination*).

Moreover, microscopic examination of the sperm has been of great importance in the following cases:

(1) Encyclical "Casti Connubii," N. 102.

(2) For the treatment of sterility, sperm examination has become a basic factor and cannot be eliminated in a proper sterility therapy: it would be a grave mistake to prescribe more or less efficacious measures for the wife before finding out definitely the generative capacity of the husband by proof of the existence of living sperm.

(3) This is of greatest importance in Forensic Medicine, especially in the marriage process, paternity cases, etc.

Even in canonical marriage processes, the outcome of the process can, in certain circumstances, be established by means of examination of sperm and its composition; and the determining of the nullity of a marriage can eventually depend on whether a *verum semen* or merely a *humor prostaticus* is elaborated or extracted.

In canonical-medical investigations the situation becomes complicated by the fact that the "identity" of the extraction must be assured by avoidance of error brought on with intention to deceive. Hence the doctors in juridical cases are at present almost unanimous in the opinion that this can be the case only if the sperm is obtained *per modum pollutionis voluntariae (seu masturbationis)*.

Opposed to this is the doctrine that, even for a good end or purpose, as, for example, in the treatment of sterility and other cases, no means can be used which of itself is evil or morally illicit. *Pollutio voluntaria* is in se such an illicit means. There arises an apparently difficult dilemma, but this can be solved if good will is shown in the matter.

c. Diagnostic value

The diagnostic value of sperm examination is undisputed. This is so if for no other reason than that it answers the following questions:

(1) Can the existence of sperm be proved?
(2) Are these normally mature or not?
(3) Do they possess normal mobility?
(4) Are they present in a normal amount?
(5) Are there pathological forms of sperm present?
(6) Are there pathological admixtures of cells together with the sperm?

Concerning these questions, the following is to be noticed:

ad (1) The absence of sperm (azoospermia) is due either to the primary disfunction of the glands (aspermatism) or secondarily, to the occlusion of the different paths (azoospermia through obliteration). The latter is of greater practical importance.

ad (2) It is important to distinguish whether the presence of immature forms is due to too frequent discharge of the sperm or insufficient capacity to attain maturity (immaturospermia from hyperfunction or hypofunction).

ad (3) Immobility does not of itself prove that the sperm are dead (necrospermia). Proof of the latter is had when even fresh sperm does not react to activating substances and present a hypernormal receptivity for the hemoglobin content (hyperchromia). A real necrospermia denotes incapacity to generate.

ad (4) A notable scarcity of sperm (oligospermia) is practically equivalent to azoospermia. It denotes not only quantitative but also qualitative inferiority of the sperm and consequently the incapacity to generate. A small degree of scarcity is irrelevant.

ad (5) The frequent presence of abnormal forms is likewise pathological (Moench). Anisospermia and poikilospermia can be distinguished according as the sperm are different merely in size or also in form.

ad (6) The presence of pathological cellular elements indicates the existence of inflammatory ailments. In practice, the most important of these is gonorrhea.

The above demonstrates the importance of the conclusions arising from examination of the sperm. On the other hand, there arises the difficult question of whether these examinations can be made by a method which is not objectionable.

d. Methods

Among the methods used for the obtaining of sperm for examination, we distinguish two principal groups:

(1) Methods *cum copula*, which are connected with a sexual act;
(2) Methods *absque copula*, without the sexual act.

ad (1) Among the methods *cum copula*, the following are indicated:

(a) *Per modum pollutionis voluntariae;*[1]
(b) *Per modum copulae imperfectae—sive condomisticae sive onanisticae* (*coitus interruptus*);
(c) *Per modum copulae perfectae.*

Among the methods mentioned, only the last is not objectionable from the moral standpoint, but in practical application several difficulties present themselves.

In forensic cases, it is scarcely applicable, since the married couple are opposed to each other in the capacity of litigants.

ad (2) Methods *absque copula*:

(a) The squeezing or pressing out of the *vesiculae seminales;*
(b) Paracentesis of the *cauda epididymis*;
(c) Paracentesis of the testicles.

---

[1] In this case, a sexual act, but not *copula*, is implied.

None of these methods fully satisfies the designated requirements. In cattle breeding, an electrophysical method of obtaining sperm for the purpose of artificial fecundation has been applied very successfully. It has not yet been applied to man, but in theory seems applicable. The question is whether this can constitute the basis for a method that is morally unobjectionable.

Without doubt, masturbation (ipsation), considered by authors as the most secure and positive method, is absolutely inadmissible from the medico-pastoral standpoint. It is incompatible with human dignity. But even from the scientific standpoint, this method, as also that of *copula imperfecta*, raises very serious pertinent objections. Even for forensic purposes, such methods do not furnish the surety that authors attribute, for example, to masturbation.

The diagnostic value of the methods of paracentesis is much less than that claimed by those upholding the same.

The method of *copula perfecta* still seems to be the most appropriate for extra-forensic purposes (for example, the treatment of sterility and counsel concerning the same).

For forensic purposes, an electrophysical method could satisfy all the requirements as long as it could be applied to man and provided it were considered morally unobjectionable.

e. Moral judgment

Following are methods of obtaining semen for examination, together with moral judgment concerning their licitness:

(a) masturbation; (b) contraceptive device, i.e., unperforated condom or a vaginal sheath; (c) withdrawal before orgasm with ejaculation *extra vaginam*.

(a) (b) and (c) are *certainly illicit*.

(d) use of perforated condom during intercourse; (e) removal of semen immediately or soon after intercourse from the genital tract of wife; (f) direct removal of semen by aspiration from the testicles or epididymes; (g) expression of seminal fluid, by massage, from seminal vesicles.

(d) (f) and (g) are *probably licit*.

(h) semen is obtained from an involuntary emission; (i) removal of semen, about hour after intercourse, from the genital tract of wife as by a cervical spoon or vaginal cup; (j) expression from the male urethra of seed remaining after normal intercourse; (k) testicular biopsy.

(h) (i) (j) and (k) are *certainly licit*.

No judgment is here made on scientific value of methods.

f. Doctrinal decision of the Church

Such a decision by the Holy Office exists in reference to the use of *pollutio voluntaria* for the purpose of microscopic examination of the sperm, and this is negative.

With this decision of June 24, 1929, and with the position taken by the moralists, the judgment was pronounced primarily concerning the obtaining of sperm *per modum pollutionis voluntariae—absque copula*—and implicitly concerning methods *per modum copulae imperfectae seu onanisticae seu condomisticae*. Even for judiciary ends, the Catholic doctor can only make use of a method which is completely free from any moral objection.[1]

4. ARTIFICIAL INSEMINATION

a. Concept

By artificial insemination (*fecundatio artificialis*) is understood:

(1) The introduction of the sperm in the vagina or the uterus or the *organa postvaginalia absque copula naturali*;

(2) The introduction of the sperm in the *cavum uteri post copulam naturalem*.

In this latter case, it is better to speak of help toward fecundation rather than artificial insemination.

b. Historical view

Artificial insemination has a close relation to the discovery of the sperm cells.

In 1680, Swammerdam made the first attempt at artificial fecundation with fish; this has led to systematic artificial fish breeding. In 1789, Spallanzani succeeded in bringing about the artificial

[1] For other methods, cf. McFadden, Charles, O.S.A., *Medical Ethics* (Westminster, Md.: Newman Press, 1956).

fecundation of a female dog. In 1799, Hunter made the first attempt at innoculation of the human species with sperm deposited *extra vaginam* (in a case of hypospadias). About 1860, Sims succeeded in effecting, for the first time, the innoculation of sperm, with consequent pregnancy, which, however, terminated in abortion in the fourth month. From that time on, artificial insemination was often used. A lively controversy arose concerning its legal and moral liceity. The faculty of Paris, in 1885, rejected a thesis of Gerard " craint en sanctionnent ce travail de fournir à une certaine catégorie de médecins per scrupuleux, l'occasion de se livrer à des opérations luches, dangereuses pour la familie et pour l'état, et qui seraient bientôt du domaine des charlatans." Shortly before this time, the tribunal of Bordeaux had condemned a doctor and declared artificial fecundation indecorous, " qui porrait même, en cas d'abus, créer un véritable danger social."

The legal society of medicine of France in 1883 had, however, declared artificial fecundation " une opération correcte . . . comme dernière chance pour arriver la procréation." In recent times, active propaganda in favor of artificial fecundation has been renewed.

In the early months of 1943, an inquiry was made in Berlin regarding this theme, in which practically all the authorities on gynecology participated. Only Stoeckel of Berlin rejected artificial fecundation as a brutal mechanization of the reproductive process and as incompatible with the sanctity of marriage, inasmuch as a third party was introduced as a donor of sperm. Knaus enthusiastically favored artificial fecundation, even artificial fecundation *cum semine alieni viri*. He reported the case of a sterile couple (the husband was sterile) in which he used as a donor (*per modum pollutionis*, cf. above, concerning what has been said in regard to examination of the sperm), one of his alumni, and this resulted in pregnancy.

He ascribed this success to the observance of his theory of ovulation (cf. *Facultative sterility*) and called the method " directed insemination."

From the statistics obtained in the U.S., it has been known that this method has been widely used, and with a relatively high percentage of success.

The critique of artificial fecundation has to evaluate the problem from the medico-biological, the juridico-social, and the moral standpoint.

E

c. Medico-biological problems

(a) *Physiological postulates*

The physiological postulates of artificial insemination are based upon a theoretical and most exact research concerning the natural process of fecundation.

For this purpose, the ovarian cycle of the female (concerning the related theories of Knaus and Ogino, cf. below, *Facultative sterility*). Further, an exact examination of the sperm is required in order to establish the capacity for fecundation. Many authors hold that the orgasm of the female is of importance for conception. Moreover, the hormonal factors as well as the importance of the influence of vitamins (especially of Vitamin E) are to be taken into consideration. Finally, the chemico-physical conditions (acidity of vaginal secretion) and the thermic factors which can have an injurious effect upon the sperm must be considered.

(b) *Indications*

If we take into account these presuppositions, artificial insemination comes into consideration in the following "indications":

(1) *On the part of the male*

Authors adduce the following as motives of indication: relative or absolute impotency, functional disturbances of potency; organic deficiencies, formation defects (hypospadias, epispadias); deviations of the *membrum virile*; adipositis, enormous hernias and hydrocele, elephantiasis, etc. A special role is played by those diseases in which, through an obliteration of the deferent seminal paths, azoospermia has resulted. The most frequent cause of these conditions is inflammation, mostly from gonorrhea of the epididymis (epididymitis).

(2) *On the part of the female*

Artificial fecundation is indicated when organic disturbances which impede the entrance of the sperm into the uterus are present; moreover, with defluxion of sperm or incapacity for receiving or retaining the semen, stenosis of the mouth of the womb; atresia and conglutination of the *orificium externum*.

In definite circumstances, certain anomalies of the position of the uterus can represent an obstacle to conception. Finally, artificial fecundation is motivated because of the laceration of the mouth of the uterus, ectropion through laceration, erosions, cervical polyps.

(c) *Contraindications*

The following are designated as contraindications: pathological nature of the sperm, constitutional diseases, tuberculosis, syphilis, diabetes, carcinoma, hereditary diseases, alcoholism, toxicomania; serious hypoplasia of the genital organs; neoplasm, infantilism of a high degree. Certain authors also include old age.

(d) *Critique of the indications*

The following is to be said concerning the critique of the indications: on the part of the male, many of the mentioned indications are the basis of impotency in the strict canonical sense and are almost always *impotentia antecedens et perpetua*. Hence in this case the declaration of nullity is to be considered rather than artificial insemination, which, in this case, is possible only *ab alieno viro*.

In light cases of malformation, surgical therapy is indicated. This is so especially and, almost without exception, in all cases which are considered as indications on the part of the female. In more serious cases of malformation of the genital organs, the operation appears naturally contraindicated in view of justified eugenic considerations. But otherwise, the greater part of the mechanical hindrances of conception which are found in women can be surgically treated with a certain surety. *Vaginismus*, when it is irremediable, determines impotency but does not justify artificial insemination.

(e) *Methods*

In conformity with the concept of artificial insemination, the following are to be distinguished:

(1) Methods *cum copula perfecta*;
(2) Methods *absque copula perfecta*.

In practice, only the vaginal and uterine methods are considered. The intraperitoneal method is no longer in use. The methods are, for the most part, based upon the introduction of the sperm *intra vaginam* or of the application of the same in front of the *orificium uteri* or even the direct introduction of the same into the cervical canal or into the *cavum uteri*. This cannot be effected without the aid of instruments (syringe, canals and probe).

The real problem consists in the method of obtaining the sperm (cf. above, *sperm examination*). The obtaining of the sperm by means of a method which is not unobjectionable is the point in which the moral liceity of artificial fecundation is shattered, inasmuch as this is connected with the cited methods. There is reference here especially to the obtaining of sperm *per modum pollutionis voluntariae, per modum coitus onanistici seu condomistici* (*copulae imperfectae*).

Only a method by which the sperm is brought *intra vaginam* exclusively by a perfect and normal conjugal *copula*—and, in order to remove any mechanical hindrance toward conception, by the aid of an instrument (probe) is led over the narrowness of the cervical canal into the *cavum uteri*—can be seriously considered.

Such a method can be considered an aid toward conception (*adiuvatio naturae*). All the other methods are to be rejected. Moreover, they bring a certain percentage of danger not to be overlooked. As a result of inflammatory reactions, they can provoke an irreparable secondary sterility. In other words, they can transform a sterility which can be healed, into a permanent and incurable sterility.

Despite the above-mentioned favorable statistics of the U.S., the probability of success must be considered as relatively modest. A critique of the indications, the methods and the possibility of success clearly shows that artificial insemination does not have the importance attributed to it by its patrons.

There are only relatively few cases in which it, after all the other methods have proved themselves inefficacious, can be taken into consideration, and the method *cum copula perfecta* which we have called above *adiuvatio naturae* suffices for these cases. In all the other cases, the importance of artificial fecundations is either artificially exaggerated, or exaggerated through propaganda; or it is a matter (as in artificial fecundation *ab alieno viro*) of a process which, a priori and basically, must be rejected.

d. Legal and social problems

From the legal standpoint, there is reference principally to two complex problems:

(1) The question of the legal liceity of intervention;
(2) The question of the legitimacy of a child born by means of artificial insemination.

In artificial insemination *ab alieno viro,* these questions are further complicated because of the unforeseen entanglement of serious difficulties regarding the family, public and penal right. At the assemblage in Berlin, already mentioned, Schlaeger upheld the standpoint of positive law, according to which the end of the state (in this case, racial selection, population policy) constitutes the legal basis for the action of the doctor and hence even for artificial insemination.

Basically, artificial insemination would be a licit means for the attainment of this end. Artificial insemination effected by the sperm of the husband can never impugn against proper customs. The collaboration of the doctor is unobjectionable; regarding doubt of paternity, it could possibly be avoided.

Schlaeger also declared that artificial insemination, by the sperm of a stranger, is legally licit if both spouses consent to it. In this case, serious legal problems can arise from the eventual contesting of the legitimacy of the child—for example, if later the donor who claims the child as his becomes incapable of generating.

In view of the fact that, in artificial insemination *ab alieno*, there can be present the penal circumstances of adultery, of pandering and of change of personal state (cf. Bardenheuer), it is also to be noted that adultery and pandering, in order to be effected, require true *copula* (Loenne). The change of the personal state by the doctor could, according to Loenne, be brought about by modifying the birth certificate so that, beside the name of the mother is placed, not the name of the " father," but that of the " mother's husband."

We can only briefly mention here the complicated legal problems that can arise. These few examples will, however, be sufficient to demonstrate the enormous import of the problem. The recent propaganda for artificial insemination, especially *ab alieno*, affects the solidity of marriage as such and as the foundation of the entire social order.

The dangers which arise from the uncertainty of parentage are not to be overlooked. If artificial insemination with the sperm of a donor were used to a great extent, then marriage between persons who are *de facto* half brothers and sisters, without their knowing it, would not be prevented.

Even the proposal, apparently without import, of changing the birth register, has enormous effects: there lies in this nothing less than the anchoring of matriarchates *via facti*, that is, of a sociological structure whose roots are those of the naturalistic-evolutionary ideology. It is only a step from artificial fecundatio *ab alieno* to open adultery and to the dissolution of matrimony as a firm legal union.

In the abandoning of matrimony in favor of a simple selective idea, monogamy, as the intangible basis of order, ceases to exist. In this way, tendencies inimical to marriage, as held by C. von Ehrenberg in 1907, will be realized.

Because of the seriousness of the situation, one can no longer smile at the old utopias. It is very clear how right was the decision of the Bordeaux tribunal of 1883, which recognized artificial insemination as *un véritable danger social*.

e. Moral judgment

Since early times, the Church has considered the *procreatio prolis* as the *finis primarius matrimonii*. The *finis secundarii* justifies the *usus matrimonii* only insofar as the *finis primarius* is not culpably excluded.

In the face of attempts to divest the *finis secundarii* of its subsidiary nature and to do so at the cost of destroying the primacy of the *finis primarius*, the Church necessarily had to issue a warning (cf. *Facultative sterility*).

Admonition also had to be made against all tendencies to transform the *finis primarius* into the only and exclusive purpose justifying matrimony, and possibly to elevate it to the *finis substantialis* or *essentialis matrimonii* (cf. below, *Theory of impotency*). The attempt to consider matrimony an "institute of reproduction" necessarily leads to the idea of a mere institute for breeding.

It remains incomprehensible how the fundamental moral concepts are so confused that learned and illustrious doctors and educators of the present academic generation no longer see illiceity and unworthiness in this action and even demand the co-operation of the doctor as a duty, appealing to legal institutes of the pre-Christian era (as in the case of *adiutor generationis*)—as if two thousand years of Christian civilization has passed without making an impression. One of the effects of this tendency can be found in the view of technical science which does not wish to recognize any obligation of the superior order.

As has been so well observed, the persons who propagate birth control are in great part the same persons who propagate *fecundatio artificialis*.

Prescinding from the general considerations of the essence of marriage, which are particularly based on the clear definition of the encyclical "Casti Connubii," we find elements in *fecundatio artificialis*, in its execution and methods, which of their nature are illicit.

We can here prescind from the only method concerning which we have already expressed our judgment, a method which is simply an *adiuvatio naturae* and therefore not objectionable.

Within the restricted limits in which it can be considered, it can be of great utility.

Moreover, even here, the principle *Non sunt facienda mala ut eveniant bona,* must prevail.

The methods, in se illicit, of obtaining the sperm *per modum pollutionis sive copulae imperfectae* must, from the Catholic moral standpoint, be rejected.

The *fecundatio artificialis ab alieno viro*—no matter what method is used to accomplish it—is to be completely rejected inasmuch as it is absolutely and, in se, incompatible with the essence of Christian matrimony, and even with natural matrimony.

f. Doctrinal decision of the Church

A decision of the Holy Office of March 24, 1897, has answered with the formula *Non licere* to the question: *an adhiberi possit artificialis fecundatio.*

With this answer, the question concerning the liceity of *fecundatio artificialis* is clearly and unequivocally decided on the part of the supreme ecclesiastical doctrinal office. It is a *res iudicata* and there can no longer be any doubt about the matter.

In recent times, Pope Pius XII directed an allocution to the participants of the Fourth International Congress of Catholic Doctors, held in Rome in 1949, the importance of which is on the same level as a doctrinal decision.

In regard to the question of artificial insemination, the following has been stated:

(1) The practice of artificial insemination, when it is applied to man, cannot be considered exclusively, nor even principally, from a biological and medical viewpoint, while leaving aside the viewpoint of morality and law.

(2) Artificial insemination outside marriage is to be considered purely and simply as immoral.

In fact, the natural law and positive Divine law are such that the procreation of a new life may only be the fruit of marriage. Marriage alone safeguards the dignity of husband and wife—in the present case, particularly that of the wife—and their personal well-being. Marriage alone provides for the good and for the education of the child.

Consequently, there is no possibility of any divergence of opinion among Catholics regarding the condemnation of artificial insemination outside marriage. A child conceived in such conditions is, by this fact alone, illegitimate.

(3) Artificial insemination in marriage, with the use of an active element from a third person, is equally immoral and as such is to be rejected summarily. Only marriage partners have mutual rights over their bodies for the procreation of a new life, and these rights are exclusive, non-transferable and inalienable. So it must be, out of consideration for the child. By virtue of this same bond, nature imposes on those who give life to a small creature the task of its preservation and education. Between marriage partners, however, and a child that is the fruit of the active element furnished by a third person—even though the husband consents—there is no bond of origin, no moral or juridical bond of conjugal procreation.

(4) With regard to the lawfulness of artificial insemination in marriage, it is sufficient for us at present to recall the principles of the natural law. The simple fact that the desired result is obtained by this means does not justify the employment of that method; nor does the desire of marriage partners—most legitimate in itself—to have a child, suffice to prove the lawfulness of recourse to artificial insemination for the fulfillment of that desire.

It would be false to believe that the possibility of a recourse to that method would render a marriage valid between two persons who are unfitted to contract marriage because of the impediment of impotency. Moreover, it is superfluous to indicate that the active element can ever be lawfully obtained by acts that are contrary to nature.

In conclusion it is stated: Although one may not exclude a priori the use of new methods simply on the grounds that they are new, nevertheless, with regard to artificial insemination it is not only a case of being extremely reserved, but the idea must be rejected entirely. With such a pronouncement, one does not necessarily prohibit the use of certain artificial methods intended simply either to facilitate the natural act or to enable the natural act, effected in a normal manner, to attain its end.

5. STERILITY

a. Concept

The definition of sterility is much more difficult than appears at first sight. Ordinarily by sterility is meant the infecundity of the woman, for the cause of infecundity is sought only in her. In many cases, however, the cause is found in the man. Then it is a matter of finding out whether it is a case of sterility or impotence.

The delimitation of these two concepts is, on certain points, established by medicine and civil law in a way different from Canon Law. (Cf. below, *Theory of impotency*.) It is preferable to convert the idea of sterility to the "sterile marriage."

Actually it is in the marriage partnership that the part played by sterility is preponderant. Although the physiological elements are the same, there is a great difference between matrimonial and extramatrimonial sterility.

Further difficulty is presented in determining after how long a time a marriage is to be considered sterile. The extent of two years is considered the minimum term. However, if sufficient organic deficiencies are not encountered, in certain circumstances it must be held that conception even after a notably long time is possible.

b. Classification

Besides matrimonial and extramatrimonial sterility, we distinguish

E*

sterility *ex parte viri* (*impotentia generandi*), *ex parte mulieris* (*impotentia concipiendi*), and sterility *inter partes*. In this latter, we must distinguish a sterility *ex utraque* and one *ex neutra parte* (so-called incompatibility), and finally, physiological and pathological sterility.

Examples of physiological sterility are:

(1) *Sterilitas tempore praegnationis* (exceptions: superfecundation and superfetation)
(2) *Sterilitas tempore lactationis*
(3) *Sterilitas tempore ageneseos* (cf. *Facultative sterility*).

The following forms of sterility must also be distinguished:

(1) Temporary and permanent
(2) Absolute and relative
(3) Primary and secondary
(4) Voluntary (facultative) and involuntary (obligatory)
(5) Natural and artificial sterility.

Some authors even distinguish between sterility and infertility. In this latter, there is no capacity to conceive (*impotentia concipiendi*), but effective lack of children resulting from the incapacity to bring pregnancy to termination (*impotentia parturiendi*).

c. Historical view

Importance was attributed to sterility already in Holy Scripture (cf. Rachel, Elizabeth, *quae vocatur sterilis*, etc.). Not only to the Jews, but also to numerous other ancient peoples, a sterile marriage gave the husband the right to repudiate the wife (*libellus repudi*). Christianity definitely broke with this tradition.

Among the doctors of antiquity, Hippocrates, Celsus and especially Soranus and Dioscurides showed a great interest in sterility. In the Middle Ages, both St. Hildegarde and St. Albert the Great clarified many questions.

In more recent times, the following are to be especially mentioned: Van Swieten, Sims, and more recently, Doederlein, Sellheim and others. Great importance was attached to the discovery of "perturbation," computed by Rubin in 1914 and its radiological evaluation in hysterosalpingography. (Cf. below.)

d. Statistical data—Diffusion

According to statistical computations, among civilized people five to ten per cent of all marriages are practically sterile. In the last ten years, this percentage has increased in the large cities and reached ten to twelve per cent (Doederlein). In certain dynasties, with accentuated consanguinity, it seems to have reached thirty-two per cent. The numerical proportion of artificial sterility is on the increase, especially where sterilization is legal.

Even the proportion of male sterility may be on the increase as well as that of secondary sterility, as a result of venereal and puerperal infections, abortion and birth control, and all types of *abusus sexualis*.

The probability of conception in sterile marriages is ten per cent after two or three years of marriage, and from five to seven per cent after three to six years; and after the seventh year of marriage, it falls suddenly to almost zero.

e. Causes and forms (Etiology and symptomatology)

We must, first of all, distinguish the causal factors as endogenous and exogenous.

(a) *Endogenous causes*

Among the endogenous causes, the following are to be mentioned: congenital deformities, aplasia, hypoplasia, infantilism, constitutional anomalies, especially intersexualism; hormonal disturbances such as *dystrophia adiposogenitalis*, obesity, leanness, *diabetes mellitus*; disturbance of the hypophysis, thyroid, adrenal and ovaries. Of importance is the sterility arising from the removal of the thyroid (*cachexia strumipriva*).

Besides the hormones, the vitamins, as active substances, play a similar but predominantly exogenous role. Even hereditary factors—and in certain circumstances, race—also concur in sterility. In the last case, it seems to be a matter more of psychological and social elements—that is, of a rather exogenous nature—which more than sterility determine practical infertility. In certain circumstances, even the diversity of blood groups can contribute to incompatability of the germ cells, a phenomena which up to now has found no other explanation. Thus, in those cases marriage remains infertile, inasmuch as the findings are absolutely negative in both partners, while both can be fertile with other partners. In many cases of incompatibility, the possibility of concurring extraphysical factors must be taken into consideration.

(b) *Exogenous factors*

The exogenous factors exercise a predominant action in the following cases: anomalies of conception conditions which in turn have their origin in the conditions of *copula* itself. Dyspareunia on the part of the woman, frigidity, *vaginismus* and certain sexual neuroses, as well as unfavorable mental conditions of all kinds, can make conception difficult.

In se, orgasm is not unconditionally necessary for conception, as is proved from cases of women who have become pregnant while unconscious, but it is certain that orgasm favors conception. It would be false to have too mechanistic ideas concerning the act of copulation and the conditions of conception.

Even the question of *situs in copula* can, in certain circumstances, be of importance.

There are also disturbances of a predominantly organic nature—for example, the complete spilling of sperm in the case of hiatus vulvae; the prevention of conception due to stenosis of the mouth of the uterus, *conglutinatio orificii* through anomalies of position (*retroflexio, descensus,* prolapse); traumatic effects such as laceration of the cervix and ectropion. Especially frequent is sterility caused by infectious diseases; such as the secondary sterility caused by venereal infection (gonorrhea)—not seldom acquired by the husband during marriage—often accompanied by serious complications (salpingitis or pyosalpingitis, parametritis and perimetritis, etc.).

Occasionally secondary sterility appears in the form of " one-child sterility." Very serious are the effects of *abortus artificialis,* especially when repeated often. Even chronic *fluor albus*, apparently harmless, is not without importance.

Among the chemico-physical factors are the vitamins already mentioned. Of special importance is Vitamin E (known as the antisterility vitamin).

Significant is the acidity of the vaginal secretion. In recent times the question of so-called sperm absorption has been the object of particular study. An excess of sperm absorption can, through the formation of antibodies, lead to "sperm immunity" and hence to a sterility of hormonal origin.

Nymphomania can act in an analogous or identical manner to excessive masturbation. This latter as an inadequate sexual stimulus can lead to dyspareunia and to nervous and ovarian disturbances.

Lues and tuberculosis can condition sterility, and in the form of blastophthoria (Forel) can lead to infertility through habitual abortion.

Local, genital tuberculosis (oopharitis, salpingitis) can cause sterility. These forms are mostly irreparable. Tumors and gynecological diseases of every other kind, especially myoma and ovarian tumors, play an important role as causes of sterility.

Finally, inadequate or excessive therapy can produce a "iatrogenic" sterility. To this type artificial sterility also belongs, inasmuch as it is provoked by inopportune surgical interventions (ovariotomy, total extirpation).

When sterility is due to the man, it is well to refer to the chapter on impotence. Here it is necessary only to mention the importance of sperm anomalies studied by Moench (cf. above, *Sperm examination*).

(c) *Social influence of environment*

Among the exogenous factors, the social influences arising from the environment must be considered.

With regard to nutrition, both undernourishment and excessive eating, or "fattening" (Stieve), can lead to sterility.

Most instructive for the effect of environmental factors are the phenomena of war and imprisonment (amenorrhea).

Stieve studied, in particular, imprisonment amenorrhea and demonstrated that it stands in essential relation to physico-nervous influences.

Climatic influences also have effect. Eskimo women do not menstruate or conceive during the long polar night.

Life in the large cities, urbanism and the "damages of civilization" (Zeiss, Pintschovius) are of the greatest importance as social causal factors: the intensified tempo of life, the harmful erotization of the atmosphere, the impurity of the air, the remoteness from nature, the conditions of habitation, nutrition and occupation—all contribute to increasing the effect of harmful elements of different kinds.

Even in this sphere, an important part is played by the increase of *abusus sexualis*. Typical of the large city is the damage to reproduction caused in the woman who is active in industry. In many occupations, the direct " professional intoxications " (lead, mercury, arsenic, carbon of sulphur) play a damaging role. In this respect, it is necessary to point out the part of the germicidal toxins. Among these, nicotine has a specific damaging effect upon the female genital organs (Hofstaetter). The same can be said of alcohol and stupefacients of every kind (opium and other narcotics). Grave damage to the function of the germinative glands can be effected by roentgen X rays, radioactive substances, etc.

From the standpoint of fertility, even excessive participation in sports and excessive study on the part of women have proved to be harmful. In regard to spending very many early years in educational institutions, late marriage too has become a dangerous factor from the social viewpoint. On the other hand, precocious marriage, an abnormal phenomenon characteristic of post-war times, has produced more damage than advantage.

What gives particular cause for concern is the fact that certain of these phenomena now occur on a mass scale, as the center of gravity of the population tends more and more toward the large cities.

Many researches have studied the question whether, in these cases, there are not already the irreparable phenomena of degeneration.

f. Therapy

The therapy of sterility is one of the most difficult and subtile tasks of gynecology. It requires the most precise research of the causal factors in each case and psychological comprehension: research that makes use of all possible useful means and exercises the greatest care in avoiding every form of pernicious polypragmatism. An exact diagnosis is indispensable and, in every case, a previous examination of the sperm.

Therapy begins with the most simple measures, and only when these are insufficient should there be recourse to more effective methods. Of great importance is the establishing of an exact " meno-gramm " for the purpose of exercising a continuous control of the cycle (cf. *Facultative sterility*).

All the modalities of conjugal life are to be taken into account and are to be evaluated in order to establish the therapeutic plan. *Congressus* must be adapted to the conditions most suitable for conception. In certain cases it can be advisable to change the *situs* (lateral position) in order to favor conception.

The hormonal therapy must not be systematic but must be adapted to the individual cycle.

Physical therapy, especially diathermy and the application of short waves, represents one of the major advances in the treatment of sterility.

Balneotherapy, especially in the so-called baths of women (mostly mud-baths), has shown itself effective in eliminating the residue of adnexitis, parametritis and of the exudate.

A temporary complete abstinence from marital intercourse is important in order to obtain a curative effect. In states of exhaustion, trips are to be recommended. Psychotherapy is most important, especially in sexual neurosis.

Surgical therapy has been at times overestimated. Within certain limits it can be very helpful. Often, very simple intervention, such as sounding and dilation can be of aid. Before resorting to grave interventions one must form clear ideas concerning the probability of their success.

In these cases "perturbation" according to Rubin has become very valuable: examination of the condition of the tubes through insufflation of air; and also hysterosalpingography (the filling of the *cavum uteri* and tubes with contrast oil for radiological representation). These interventions are not completely free of danger; hence an accurate mode of realizing them is required, and further, they are not to be used indiscriminately.

The choice of surgical methods is to be directed according to the fundamental disease. Occasionally a chronic inflammation of the appendix (appendicitis) is the cause of sterility.

Surgical procedures having unnatural and artificial effects should be avoided as much as possible. With cases of congenital deformities, one must be especially prudent with surgical intervention. Artificial fecundation is recommended as a *ultima ratio*. This calls for added reservation. In every circumstance, methods which are in se immoral, especially *fecundatio artificialis a viro alieno*, are to be avoided.

Only those methods are allowed which imply an *adiuvatio naturae* as, for example, in the case of stenosis of the mouth of the uterus, the elevation, by means of a probe or other means, of the sperm normally deposited *intra vaginam*.

Ovarian transplantation by using the healthy organ of another woman is very doubtful.

Biological and complicated legal problems which are difficult to solve can arise from such operations.

g. Social and legal viewpoints

(a) *Social questions*

The social importance of sterility arises from the fact of its being socially conditioned and from its diffusion among the masses. Its evaluation varies according to the importance it assumes in respect to the birth problem. It is always unsatisfactory when the evaluation is made exclusively from the demographic-political standpoint. The diffusion among the masses of *abusus matrimonii* has notably contributed to the diffusion of secondary sterility. Occasionally, voluntary sterility at the beginning of marriage has been transformed, in a secondary way, into an involuntary (obligated) sterility.

Sterility is also one of the most important causes for the spread of divorce.

Its social importance has given occasion to the institution of public clinics to assist the sterile. Such an institution can be approved provided that it remains immune to spreading erroneous teachings. Its association with properly orientated marriage counseling which is directed, not merely to eugenic ends but also to universalistic ends, can be most useful. Also valuable would be the participation of representatives of social justice.

(b) *Legal questions*

A series of legal questions arises in respect to the juridical institution of adoption. Basically, this is to be recommended. The minimum age for adoptive parents prescribed by law can be lowered by appeal in a case of medically ascertained sterility. Further questions arise concerning the civil and penal responsibility of the doctor because of technical errors in the treatment of sterility or errors which have caused sterility. Special, complicated legal questions arise in a case of artificial insemination, especially when the doctor accomplishes this with sperm outside marriage.

Today, the most important question is that of deciding whether sterility can be a valid reason for divorce. Certain recent legislation has ceded to this view. In this, the possibility of most serious legal damage is present, especially for the woman who will remain abandoned and without protection, and whose security rests solely upon the stability of the marriage bond guaranteed by the legal order.

Canon Law, differing from the civil laws mentioned, has always refused to acknowledge sterility as a matrimonial impediment or as a reason for invalidity (*sterilitas matrimonium nec impedit nec dirimit*, canon 1068, #3). This is so, according to canonical and traditional jurisprudence, even for the mulier excisa. A new current tends to recognize impotence in this (cf. *Theory of impotency*). Such an acknowledgment would inevitably lead to a recognition of the viewpoint of certain civil laws which have considered marriage exclusively as an institution for reproduction. If this concept should prevail even in Canon Law, then the *procreatio prolis* would no longer be considered the *finis primarius matrimonii*, but the *finis essentialis seu substantialis*, i.e., the basis of matrimony.

h. Metaphysical and theological viewpoint

These legal considerations extend to ultimate problems of legal philosophy and metaphysics. The appeal to the natural law has been made, in favor of divorce, because of sterility, since such a marriage would not fulfill the purpose intended by nature.

Natural law, rightly understood, is based on a just insight into the essence and nature of things; in this case, the essence of matrimony is the essence of man. The real nature of the human being is that he is a *creature*, created and surrounded by limitations. In the last analysis, it does not depend on his will whether a marriage shall have or not have the blessing of fecundity. The phenomenon of incompatibility clearly shows that, beyond the question of human reproduction there is also an unexplored metaphysical basis.

It is not man himself who "arouses" a new life. The power is solely loaned to him by the Creator in the sense of a *subministratio naturae*.

The human soul and, with it, the specifically human life, is called into existence directly by God Himself. Contrary to the heresies of "generationism" and "traducianism," which tend to arise in a biological raiment, the Church has unequivocally held to the doctrine of "creationism." When man seeks to dominate life, he repeats the *non serviam* of rebellion.

i. Pastoral problems

Knowledge of sterility, of its causes and its disastrous effects on matrimony, and of all its other psychological effects, is of great importance for practical pastoral activity.

Experience teaches that sterile marriages are exposed to dangers of greater intensity than fertile marriages; above all, when they have begun with voluntary sterility and have become sterile in a secondary manner because of *abusus sexualis*; when only one child was desired who later was lost to the parents; when the guilt feelings and reciprocal reproach lead to desperation.

The effects of sterility in the field of criminal psychology have shown how in this realm one cannot imagine the aberrations into which man can fall. "A woman is prepared to go through hell for two things: not to have a child when she does not want one, and to have a child when she cannot have one" (Godell).

When desperation leads to any means, no matter how immoral, in order to have a child at any cost, it is a matter almost without exception of a marriage which lacks the firm basis of religious conviction or has lost the same.

On the other hand, even a sterile marriage can become a source of abundant blessings if a spouse bears with resignation an inculpable sterility and accepts it as a cross or repents of a culpable sterility and abstains from reproaching the partner in marriage; if the couple can carry on their solitary way of life traversed in common and make it a way of sanctification. Then, even the physically infertile marriage can bring abundant fruits of spirituality, love and grace, and thus realize its most profound nature as a great sacrament.

6. IMPOTENCY

a. Concept

By impotency, in the strict sense, we mean the incapacity for *consummatio matrimonii*, in the sense in which Canon Law uses the term; that is, incapacity for *penetratio vasis debita* and the *effusio (veri) seminis intra vaginam*.

This definition serves as a norm for Pastoral Medicine.

The medico-pastoral significance of impotency has its basis principally in this: that impotency, according to canon 1068 (CIC), represents a matrimonial impediment or cause for nullity. In the canonical marriage process there arise for the medical expert serious problems which require an accurate knowledge of the matter.

The following exposition considers in a special manner this necessity. In a wider sense, the concept of impotency includes the incapacity for *coitus (impotentia coeundi)* as well as the incapacity to generate *(impotentia generandi)*. The concept of *impotentia generandi* coincides substantially with the canonical concept of *sterilitas*.

In general, by impotency is meant incapacity for marital intercourse, the *impotentia coeundi*.

But since the concept of *impotentia coeundi* is taken in a wider sense by Canon Law than by present-day legal medicine, the distinction in use by this latter between *impotentia coeundi* and *impotentia generandi* does not have the same meaning as the canonical distinction between *impotentia* and *sterilitas*.

Today, in legal medicine, by impotency is meant the incapacity for *erectio sufficiens* and *immissio membri virilis*. For the *consummatio matrimonii*, for the *fieri unam carnem*, Canon Law requires something more than capacity for a mechanical *immissio* and precisely requires a *penetratio vasis debita et effusio veri seminis intra vas mulieris*.

Hence numerous cases fall under impotency (namely, *impotentia coeundi*) which, according to present-day legal medicine, are taken simply as *impotentia generandi*, as, for example, cases of vasectomy in men.

b. Classification

According to the letter of canon 1068, the following species of impotency are to be distinguished:

(1) *Impotentia absoluta vel relativa*, according as the impossibility is manifested toward every person or only a certain person;

(2) *Impotentia antecedens vel subsequens* (to matrimony); only antecedent impotency determines nullity;

(3) *Impotentia perpetua vel temporanea*, according to whether it is curable or not;

(4) *Impotentia ex parte viri vel ex parte feminae vel inter partes;*

(5) *Impotentia naturalis vel accidentalis*, according as the impotency is based on a congenital basis or acquired in a secondary manner;

(6) *Impotentia organica (instrumentalis) vel functionalis*, according as the impotency is of organic nature or merely functional;

(7) *Impotentia physica vel psychica*, according as the impotency has a predominantly physical or psychic origin.

c. Causes and forms (Etiology and symptomatology)

(a) *Organic causes*

Among the anatomo-organic causes of impotency, the following are to be mentioned:

(1) Congenital deformities. On the part of the male, the following are to be mentioned: genital aplasia; hypospadias and epispadias, cryptorchidism, pseudohermaphrodism (genuine hermaphrodism is in practice scarcely ever proved). On the part of the female: *aplasia vaginae*, atresia of the hymen and of the vagina, diplogenesis, etc.

(2) Constitutional anomalies, especially infantilism, intersexualism, hypoplastic constitution; so-called eunuchism, dystrophia adiposogenitalis; disturbances of the endocrine glandular system (myxedema), interrenalism, metabolic disturbance with an endocrine basis—for example, diabetes.

(3) Defects acquired in a secondary manner, whether as a result of trauma or as a result of operations: castration, vasectomy, implement lesions, war injuries, cauterizations, burns, scars from inflammations, adhesions, etc., atrophy of the testicles; axial deviations—for example, *recurvatio membri, induratio plastica penis—*

also adipositis of high degree, immense hernias and hydroceles can become an impediment to the consummation of marriage.

(4) The so-called disproportion of the organs. Ordinarily, it is a matter, in these cases, of the abnormal size of *membrum virile* in respect to a narrow vagina. According to the predominant opinion, the disproportion can be the cause of an *impotentia inter partes* and eventually also *ex una parte*.

It must, however, be remembered that in these cases the purely arithmetic disproportion of the organs does not of itself alone constitute an absolute impediment toward the consummation of marriage, since, normally, the elasticity of the vagina—adequate for the act of birth—is sufficiently large to overcome it.

But when, to this arithmetic disproportion constitutional defects (infantilism) or abnormal conditions of the organs (rigidity) are added or even psychic causes (subconscious refusal of the partner), mental fixation upon a premarital bond, the habit of inadequate sexual stimulation, inaptitude, impatience, indelicateness at the time of first advance—then the disproportion is often transformed into an inseparable impediment toward consummation, not of itself, but in concommitance with other external circumstances. For the skilled in the process of impotency, these things are of basic importance.

(b) *Functional forms*

The purely functional forms coincide by and large with the "psychogenic" forms. They are manifested in various ways. In the female, the most important form of functional impotency in practice is *vaginismus*, which is a neurosis of spasmodic defense, of quasi-exclusive psychic origin. The distinction between "genuine" *vaginismus* (of purely psychic origin) and *pseudo-vaginismus* (in which organic factors prevail), must not be taken in a strict sense.

Among the disturbances of feeling in the female the following are to be mentioned: dyspareunia, frigidity and absolute sexual anesthesia.

(c) *Differences of degree*

Even in regard to degree, there are multiple degrees of transition from forms consisting of slight disturbances of potency or potency debility up to complete impotency.

Besides *erectio deficiens, erectio imperfecta, insufficiens, non persistens,* there is to be considered *eiaculatio praecox,* in which the fact that it constitutes a form of potency debility seems paradoxical.

Occasionally, neuro-obsessive mechanisms play a role in " conditioned " impotency. A particular case of this form is the so-called " impotency caused by defloration."

(d) *Causal factors*

As in the field of psychopathy, so also with impotency, we must distinguish the causal factors as exogenous and endogenous.

(1) *Exogenous factors*

The following are the most important exogenous factors:

(aa) Traumatic causes.

(bb) Inflammatory diseases. In this sphere, gonorrhea, with its complications, and also lues and tuberculosis, play an important role.

(cc) Intoxications. The most important are the chronic intoxications of alcohol, cocaine, morphine, opium, hashish, marijuana, of nicotine, and, in short, all narcotics. And further industrial poisons: lead, phosphorus, mercury, arsenic, carbon of sulphur.

(dd) Radiant energy, especially the roentgen rays.

(ee) Organic nervous diseases: tabes, myelitis, syringomyelia, multiple sclerosis, apoplexy, encephalitis, etc.

(ff) General illnesses, both of an acute and chronic nature.

(gg) Hormonal disturbances.

The last three groups also belong partly in the sphere of the endogenous factors.

(2) *Endogenous factors*

(aa) Habituation toward inadequate sexual stimulation: fixation on masturbation, homosexuality and all kinds of perversion.

(bb) Neuroses. In the origin of sexual neuroses, partly hysterical and partly neuro-obsessive reaction mechanisms have a part.

(cc) Premarital mental associations. These are not to be underestimated in their significance and retarded effect.

d. Therapy

The therapy of impotency is very important for Pastoral Medicine, because in the canonical process the question of curability is often of decisive importance.

(1) Surgical therapy can be indicated in forms that are of organic-physical origin: phimosis, hymenal atresia, hernia, less serious forms of hypospadias, etc.

(2) Medicamental therapy is most efficacious in the form of hormonal therapy; this, however, must never be schematic.

(3) Physical therapy has acquired importance in recent times, especially in the form of diathermy, short-wave treatment and high frequency (D'Arsonval). This can eventually be combined with hormonal therapy and psychotherapy.

(4) Psychotherapy. In all cases in which a psychic factor intervenes etiologically, it is opportune to use psychotherapy in its various forms. Its importance is still on the increase. Even here, as always, the will imposes limitations.

e. Psychological evaluation

In order to accurately decide on cases of impotency in the matrimonial process, a psychological evaluation is important, especially where a matter of psychogenic origin is concerned.

Depth psychology, with the discovery of subconscious correlations and mechanisms, has without doubt opened fields which formerly were inaccessible.

Besides these subconscious correlations, discovered for the first time by psychoanalysis, which, in the individual case, are almost always found hidden in the form of impotency, modern psychology has directed its view even toward metaphysical correlations which can be encountered in disturbances of the " capacity for loving."

The capacity for true contact or relatedness to fellow beings, by going out of one's ego, is frequently disturbed.

Occasionally a very strong mother fixation conditions impotency in man later on. Egocentric fixation is always an obstacle to a full psychic relaxation or surrender, without which even a physical consummation of matrimony often fails or at least meets with difficulty.

Subconscious guilt feelings, as well as feelings of inferiority, mental inhibitions, etc., can play a role that must not be overlooked. In the individual case, a subconscious repulsion of the marriage partner can make the delimitation between impotency and lack of consent difficult to determine.

In these cases, the general norm can be this: that all the factors derived from an unconscious opposition affect potency, while consent comes exclusively from the conscious psychic strata.

f. Social and legal problems

The social importance of potency disturbances can never be too highly appreciated with regard to their effect in marriage. Marriage as the basis of human life in common is affected essentially and substantially by potency disturbances. These can lead to serious conjugal conflicts which produce tragic effects, especially in cases in which a declaration of nullity is not legally possible.

Modern propaganda in favor of artificial insemination *cum semine alieni viri* shows what aberrations, incompatible with the essence of marriage, can be occasioned by impotency.

We mention here only the varied eugenic, social and legal questions which arise in this matter.

Even with regard to sterilization (vasectomy) and gynecological operations, serious legal questions and especially questions pertaining to Canon Law arise. The question of whether a vasectomized man or a *mulier excisa* has the capacity for contracting marriage comes up. This great controversy among the canonists is a matter of deciding whether, in these cases, there is present the canonical impediment of impotency, in the sense of canon 1068 or simply that of sterility, which latter *matrimonium nec impedit, nec dirimit*. On this important controversy, see the following section.

g. Metaphysical problems

The consideration of the causes on the part of depth psychology and, above all, the extension of the viewpoint of potency incapacity from the "incapacity regarding the act" to the incapacity to "love," have brought to light important metaphysical problems.

Speer has rightly realized that in a man incapable of love and not knowing how to go beyond his ego, the mystery of "separation from God" and neighbor is effected. Even in the case of impotency, behind the physico-pathological phenomena, we see the workings of a metaphysico-pathological phenomenon. The doctrine of Scholastic philosophy on the relation between "potency and act" also has a deep significance for the interpretation of impotency. The relationship of potency-act subsists in the sense of *analogia entis*, even behind these external forms of being. God, the infinite creative power, is *Actus Purus*; the human generative power is, in a certain manner, a participation in the creative power of God, under the species of an entrusted life. This fact shows the serious offense that is committed against the law of life in *abusus sexualis*, an offense which indicates itself at times by the loss of potency or the loss of the capacity to love. The desperation that can lead the impotent person to extreme resolutions, including suicide, takes on at times an absolute diabolical character.

In regard to the importance of sexual life for the individual and society and its position as a test for man, as a landmark from which "part two ways of life," it is clear that the *mysterium iniquitatis* makes its effects felt in this realm, often fatally in those who are human "sexual disasters."

It is possible that a conjecture concerning these relations is also the basis of the doctrine of the *impotentia ex maleficio*, such as was particularly formulated by Sanchez. That, together with natural causal factors, even supernatural or extranatural factors can be operating, needs no demonstration for one who believes in the real existence of the supernatural and its opposite.

Gasparri quotes Feije on this point: *ex maleficio impotentiam oriri posse absque temeritate negari nequit.*

According to Gasparri, the criteria mentioned by Sanchez do not per se necessarily prove an extranatural causation, nor are they sufficient of themselves to require exorcism. This can never be exercised *inconsulto Episcopo* (cf. Tonquédec).

In certain cases, especially when it is a matter of attempting adulterous relations, a "function of conscience" can directly be seen in impotency that takes place in a sudden manner. The lack of such a reaction can also be a sign of dulled conscience. In all these cases there remains the question: At what point does the purely natural and physiological phenomenon cease and extranatural participation begin?

Catholic science can study this question only with the most rigorous critique and with the greatest circumspection. Nothing can

be of worse service to the Church than a naïve and uncritical supernaturalism. Hence we must be especially grateful to Cardinal
Gasparri for having treated such questions with great prudence.

But we must basically hold the possibility of extranatural intervention, at least, as a concomitant factor, and should not a priori
deny and relegate it to the realm of superstition.

It was the modern research of depth psychology which again
brought to light these facts, belief in which was seriously shaken
during the era of materialism. It is the exclusive task of Catholic
science to give these facts the proper interpretation.

7. THE THEORY OF IMPOTENCY (IMPOTENCY OR STERILITY?)

a. Concept

One of the most difficult and important controversial questions of
Canon Law is that of the "capacity to contract marriage" on the
part of a *mulier excisa*, i.e., a woman from whom the internal
reproductive organs (ovaries, uterus and tubes) have been removed
by surgical operation.

Although there is no controversy among the canonists concerning
the castrated or vasectomized male, since the question was definitely
decided by Sixtus V (Constitution "Cum frequenter," 1587) in the
sense of canonical impotency—yet concerning the female the
question has not yet been resolved. It has not been definitively
decided whether, in the case of *excisio mulieris*, there is present
impotency in the canonical sense, with the legal effect of the *impedimentum dirimens* and of the nullity of a marriage already contracted, or whether it is simply a case of *sterilitas*, which, according
to the meaning of canon 1068, #3, *matrimonium nec impedit, nec
dirimit*.

The first opinion, according to which it is a case of impotency in
the sense of canon 1068, #1, is designated as the "theory of
impotency," the latter as the "theory of sterility."

b. Historical aspect

The development of the problem has its historical origin in the
question of the capacity of the castrated for marriage.

In the era of decadence of the Roman empire, marriages of the castrated became a social danger, since they were contracted with the intention of *frustratio prolis*.

Hence, they were forbidden by the Lex Iulia and Papia Poppaea (A.D. 4—9). Similar phenomena were verified at the beginning of medieval times, especially in Roman lands. Hence, the cited Constitution " Cum frequenter " prohibited these marriages on the basis that the castrated a *verum semen effundere non possint*; that is, that in such marriages neither the primary purpose, the *procreatio prolis*, nor even the secondary end, the *sedatio concupiscentiae*, could be realized and that from such a union, true satisfaction could not result, but rather an increase of desire *nova incentiva libidinis oriuntur*.

With reason did the authors of a later day distinguish between a *verum semen*, i.e., a *testiculis elaboratum* and a pure *humor prostaticus seu Cowperianus*, a simple secretion of the accessory glands.

The matrimonial capacity of man requires, according to this opinion, not only the capacity of *erectio et immissio membri*, but also the *effusio veri seminis*.

Hence in the canonical sense there is in man impotency even in those cases in which modern legal medicine supposes purely *impotentia generandi* but not the *impotentia coeundi*. On the other hand, Canon Law does not require for the capacity of marriage and for the *consummatio matrimonii*, proof of the existence of living spermatozoa in the sperm—in other words a *semen prolificum*. The sure proof that this is a *testiculis elaboratum*, even if *non prolificum*, suffices. For this reason, the Church has always permitted the marriage of elderly people.

On the contrary, the same matrimonial impediment of impotency is present in the cases in which, as a result of vasectomy or organic diseases (for example, epididymitis duplex) there is a so-called azoospermia from obliteration—in other words, the impossibility of the passage of the sperm (*impossibilitas transitus*) through the deferent paths, the *vasa deferentia*.

While the question of the matrimonial capacity of the vasectomized male has a long historical development, during which time the criteria of judgment have always remained the same, the question of the capacity of the *mulier excisa* is of recent times and has become a more practical question with the development of modern abdominal surgery. As beneficial as this has been, on the other hand it must be acknowledged that there have been abuses.

Many operations have been performed not so much to heal disease as to effect the sterility that followed.

Surblèd (1895) has described these abuses most effectively. But because of the fact that abuses exist, a principle which has been acknowledged to be just cannot be abandoned. (*Abusus non tollit usum.*)

The tradition and canonical doctrine of applying, in the sphere of the matrimonial capacity of the woman, a less rigorous criterion than for the man and of admitting for her simple sterility and not impotency ("theory of sterility") is based upon principles held firm for centuries and especially upon the distinction between the *principium activum seu passivum generationis*, which goes back to St. Thomas and Aristotle.

Since man is the bearer of the *principium activum*, there is required of him for the *consummatio matrimonii*, for the *fieri unam carnem*, the production of a *verum semen*. Now, what, on the part of the woman, would be considered as the correlative of the masculine *seminatio* for the *fieri unam carnem*—that is, the question of *seminatio mulieris*—remained unexplained.

Some held that this *seminatio* is formed by the secretion of the external glands; but, since it was shown that conception could take place even without this secretion, it was held, along with Aristotle, that the woman could *sine ulla propria seminatione et solo mariti semine concipere*.

On the other hand, Hippocrates and Galenus taught that the contribution of the woman toward generation consisted of the flow of menstrual blood, a view which more closely approximated the reality. Galenus directly understood the ovaries and recognized their homology with the testicles.

On the basis of these opinions, the consummation of marriage, the *fieri unam carnem* was seen in the *commixtio seminum seu sanguinum* of both partners.

From the circumstance that the ovum of the woman was not recognized and consequently its contribution to generation was not clear, arose the milder judgment concerning the matrimonial capacity of the woman; and thus the traditional "theory of sterility" limited itself, in requiring of the woman that she be capable of experiencing a *penetratio vasis debita* by the *membrum virile* and of receiving and holding the male *semen* (*semen virile recipere et retinere*).

If these requisites were lacking, then the woman was definitely impotent: in fact, in such a case, it would be a matter of *potentia coeundi* and not of *potentia generandi*.

The discovery of the follicle by Regnier de Graaff (1687) and especially of the female ovum by K..E. von Baer (1827), gave certain authors occasion to go contrary to the traditional theory of sterility by holding that this was incompatible with the new biological and physiological discoveries, and that consequently even the practice of the Holy Roman Rota (whose jurisprudence corresponded substantially with the traditional doctrine) should be changed.

The new doctrine objected to the traditional disparity of judgment regarding the matrimonial capacity of the male and female, holding that, with the discovery of the ovum of the female, the opinion holding a basic imparity (differentiation) had lost ground.

Moreover, further results favoring full parity seemed to arise from more precise research concerning the processes of fecundation. Especially important for consideration was the process arising in the cellular fusion of the nucleus of the ovum and sperm cell and the contribution of chromosome substance on the part of both sexes, in which an equal contribution by both sexes toward the "hereditary mass" was thought to be present. It thus appeared that the traditional "theory of sterility" had received its death blow.

The "theory of impotency" announced, as the new biological doctrines required, moreover, equal capacity in the proportion of germinative cells—that is, equal fecundity—on the part of the two sexes.

With the greatest consequence, Triebs—partly basing his views on pre-Scholastic Patristic doctrine—perceived the essence of matrimony in generation and declared that *procreatio prolis* constitutes the *finis substantialis matrimonii*; thus, by going far beyond the doctrine of the *finis primarius*, he considered marriage essentially an "institution of reproduction."

The following are the most famous representatives of the theory of impotency: Antonelli, Bucceroni, and in recent times, Triebs. On the other hand, the theory of sterility is held by Gasparri, Vermeersch, Oietti, Gemelli, etc.

c. Arguments for the theory of impotency

Antonelli insists upon the fact that, from the early days of the Church, or at least from the time of St. Augustine, it was unanimously taught that for the *fieri unam carnem* there was necessary, for the essence of marriage, a union from which progeny could arise (*copula ex qua possit generatio,* or *coniuges aptos esse ad generandum*).

The question of matrimonial capacity is not to be treated solely from the theological and canonical standpoint, but should be also considered from that of physiology, the facts of which must be taken into account.

The opinions held by earlier authors were based upon insufficient and erroneous knowledge, and hence upon varied and erroneous requisites.

The *capacitas generandi seu conficiendi unam carnem,* is *de essentia seu de natura matrimonii.* Hence in the *mulier excisa* there is lacking the *obiectum essentiale* of the *contractus matrimonii,* the *traditio muta* of a *corpus physice aptum ad generandum.* There is reference also to canon 1081, #2, CIC (*in ordine ad actus per se aptos ad prolis generationem*).

Hence the *mulier excisa* should be unconditionally considered impotent. Purely accidental defects (for example, position anomalies of the uterus, anomalies concerning the biochemical reaction of the vaginal secretion, etc.) simply determine sterility.

Substantial defects (loss of uterus, ovaries or tubes) determine impotency.

Triebs adds to these arguments the fact that there is only one principal end of marriage: namely, reproduction. If this end is not attainable, one cannot speak of a marriage. That which we call matrimony is an institution for reproduction. The secondary ends of marriage, in relation to the *finis substantialis,* are merely of an accessory and not subsidiary nature. In this realm, full parity between the woman and man reigns supreme (cf. also Bucceroni).

Triebs believes that he can establish a twofold error in the theory of sterility:

(1) The distinction between the *principium activum* and the *principium passivum generationis* is false. The ovum is as much an active element of generation as the sperm.

(2) The delimitation of the confines between *actio humana* and *actio naturae* in generation is likewise false, since the *effusio seminis* is independent of the will and purely reflexive.

The Code of Canon Law had formerly avoided giving a legal definition of impotency and of intervening in the controversy. But the " theory of impotency," based on modern physiology, is on the march. To Oietti's objection that physiology has not yet spoken the last word, it is answered that the discovery of the female ovum is one of the irrefutable accomplishments of research.

d. Arguments for the theory of sterility

Gasparri starts with the Scholastic distinction between *principium activum vel passivum generationis*. He recognizes in the sperm the active principle of generation and in the ovum the passive principle of generation.

Moreover, in the biological development of the human species, the beginning and end of *potentia coeundi* do not coincide with the beginning and end of the *potentia generandi*. In old people, this latter can be extinct, while the first is still present. The *potentia coeundi* is therefore presumed without limitation of age by virtue of a *praesumptio iuris*.

On the other hand, a *verum semen* is lacking in eunuchs. In the *mulier excisa*, it is not certain whether, even in the case of bilateral ovariectomy, remains of ovarian substances are not still present. In fact, pregnancies have taken place after a bilateral ovariectomy.

In the case of removal of the uterus, ectopic pregnancies are always possible, since there is no absolute *seclusio* or *occlusio vaginae*. After the discovery of the ovum, it no longer seems admissible to apply the ancient concept of *commixtio sanguinum* to the fusion of ovum and sperm.

In generation, the distinction between *actio humana* and *actio naturae* is fundamental. The *actio humana* is fulfilled with the *penetratio vaginae et effusio seminis intra vaginam*. At this point begins the *actio naturae*. Man is the active principle of the *actio humana* and the woman is the passive principle. Hence, on the part of man, the preparation of the *verum semen* is required; and on the part of the woman, merely the existence of the vagina as a *pars recipiens*. The *actio naturae* begins and is perfected in the internal organs of the woman, in the *organa postvaginalia*.

Hence impotency is present in the woman when there is present an incapacity for *penetratio vaginae*, as, for example, in *vaginismus*, in the occlusion or high degree of cicatricial restriction—even when the impediment can be eliminated without danger to life, as, for example, in case of *discissio hymenis*.

On the contrary, it is not a case of impotency but of sterility when the internal organs have incurable defects, since these conditions have no influence whatsoever upon the completion and conclusion of the *actio humana*. Only the *fieri unam carnem* and not a *conficere unam carnem* (cf. above) is required for the *consummatio matrimonii*. The first is fulfilled by the *copula carnalis* as such, even if children do not follow. A *fecundatio artificialis* never therefore effects a *fieri unam carnem*, a *matrimonium consummatum*, even if children follow.

Children born from such impotent parents are not legitimate: *Extraordinarium quidem, sed non absurdum* (Gasparri). Where the *actio humana* is possible, there is no impotency, but only sterility, even if the *actio naturae* is impeded by the condition of the post-vaginal organs.

In the concept *actus per se aptus ad prolis generationem* what has the greatest force is the words " per se ": the *actio humana* must be *in se integra*, and can never be frustrated by the will.

The matrimonial contract, which is a human contract, is perfected by a human action. Even in the case of incapacity for reproduction, God concedes the partners the *mutuum adiutorium* and the *remedium concupiscentiae*.

The practice of the Church and the jurisprudence of the Holy Roman Rota have always held fast to these accredited principles. The Church has always required only a *copula cum effusione veri seminis* and nothing more.

Even with the accomplishments of new physiological research, she has no reason to modify her tenets.

The contrary viewpoint will produce harmful consequences of incalculable import for moral and pastoral theology, for example, with regard to the matrimonial capacity of old people, the *copula tempore praegnationis*; and finally every use of marriage which does not serve for generation will have to be considered illicit.

In opposition to this, we must recall the clear and definite position taken in the encyclical " Casti Connubii " (N. 60), which declares the use of marriage licit even when, because of defects of nature and so forth, children cannot follow.

On the other hand, if marriage is undertaken with the intention of avoiding children, or if the *frustratio prolis* is the decisive motive for surgical intervention, then the marriage is definitely null, but not because of the legal reason of impotency, but rather because of lack of consent, of the consent of a will intent on contracting marriage (Arendt).

The fundamental difference between man and woman in the legal judgment of matrimonial capacity has been expounded among others, by Génicot: *ex quo patet discrimen inter feminam et virum utroque testiculo carentem.* In this way, the "parity" between woman and man is rejected. Even Scherer holds the difference regarding the declaration of impotency in favor of the woman.

Gemelli warns that the *finis primarius* of marriage is not the *finis essentialis.* He likewise warns against hastily transferring biological concepts into canonical legal science and exhorts theologians to beware of the opinion which can lead to error, that the consummation of marriage consists in the union of the ovum and sperm.

The content of the matrimonial contract is determined by natural law and not by the state of biological research. Even Oietti warns against the exaggerated evaluation of physiology.

It would not be understandable that the Church could be led astray by false opinions for such a long time and that Divine Providence would permit uncertainty concerning the validity of marriage over the centuries.

e. Practice and teaching of the Church—Earlier decisions

(a) *Jurisprudence of the Holy Roman Rota*

The jurisprudence of the Holy Roman Rota has in its decisions basically held the theory of sterility. Even if these "decisions" do not have a binding doctrinal force, the argumentation, in all its details, of these decisions of the supreme legal organs cannot be overlooked.

(b) *Doctrinal decisions of the Church*

With regard to the matrimonial incapacity of the castrated man,

F

there are doctrinal decisions. Even the Constitution of Sixtus V, "Cum frequenter" (1587) is to be considered as such.

In more recent times, the question concerning the matrimonial capacity of the vasectomized man was made the object of a decision of November 16, 1935, which concerns legal (obligatory) sterilization. In this case, it was decided that *matrimonium non esse impediendum*, inasmuch as it is a case of sterilization *iniqua lege imposita*.

With regard to the *mulier excisa*, there are some decisions of the Holy Office which speak in favor of the theory of sterility. As decisions of particular cases, they have no general validity. Rather, for the time being, for every case, recourse to the Holy See must be made since, with women, it cannot always be a priori established how great the defect is. From this it is not possible to deduce any objection against the theory of sterility. In cases of this kind, it is often a matter of *dubium facti* and not a *dubium iuris*.

From ancient times, the practice of the Church was to be satisfied with the simple capacity of the woman for the *actio humana*, and nothing else was required. The Church is aware of the recent controversies. She remains silent concerning the argument and does not wish to anticipate the explanation of science. In the corresponding cases, she declares: *Matrimonium non esse impediendum*; or, when matrimony has already been contracted: *Coniuges non esse inquietandas*. In the meantime, she prescinds from the discrepancy between the doctrine of physiology and that of Canon Law.

The principles expounded by Gasparri are a clear example of the wisdom with which the Church treats controversies of such importance and of the patience manifested in awaiting a complete clarification on the part of science.

f. An attempt toward clarification of the problem

In the controversy between the theory of impotency and the theory of sterility, the question is whether, with regard to the matrimonial capacity of the *mulier excisa*, the same rigorous criterion is to be applied to the "ectomized" man (a term used to cover not only a case of castration but also one of simple sterilization); or whether the natural differences between the sexes justify a different consideration in the case of the woman. Hence, in formulating the question of impotency or sterility, it seems more exact to consider the question of parity or difference.

(a) *The theory of parity*

The theory of parity is, according to Antonelli and Triebs, based upon these incontrovertible biological facts: the discovery of the ovum in the woman; the fundamental equality of the nuclei of the ovum and sperm in fecundation and the bilateral contribution of chromosomes to the hereditary mass.

(b) *The theory of difference*

On the other hand, important biological arguments are posited in favor of the theory of difference. A simple comparison between the ovum and sperm cell, from the morphological and functional standpoint, reveals important differences. On the one hand, the greatest cell of the body in the "repose of waiting," and on the other, the smallest cell, endowed with enormous active energy of movement.

In the same structure plan of the external reproductive organs (extroverted or introverted structure), the difference between the active principle and the passive principle of generation is evident, and this much more in the same germinative cells.

This is especially manifested by the most minute intercellular processes in which the difference between the active and passive principle is directly and most clearly seen. It is manifested especially in the importance of the centrosome, which is exclusively furnished with sperm, from which are derived the centrioles of all the somatic cells in both sexes.

The centrosome is recognized more and more as the activating dynamic center of the fecundated cell, from which the so-called polar radiation issues. A profound penetration of the biological facts as delineated by modern biology leads to full confirmation of the differentiation in nature between the active and passive principle.

This differentiation is by no means the product of the metaphysical speculation of Scholasticism, but is an evident fact.

Thus the fundamental principle upon which the doctrine of parity is based, and which appeals to modern biology, is shattered.

And even the differentiation on the part of biology between *actio humana* and *actio naturae* falls.

The sperm is the active element which penetrates the ovum. The *actio humana* is fulfilled by the furnishing of *verum semen*. This does not occur merely "in a purely reflexive manner"; it can be culpably impeded by the will. On the other hand, the woman can do nothing, by her will, to favor the production of an ovum, nor can she impede its production.

The differentiation (opposed by the theory of parity) between *actio humana* and *actio naturae* is deeply based upon the difference between the sexes.

Moreover, the ancient theory of *commixtio sanguinum* receives new light from the modern facts concerning the importance of sperm absorption. This has brought about interesting conclusions which help in the greater comprehension of the *fieri unam carnem* and which are based on physiological and biological facts. Even from this viewpoint it can be shown how justified is the differentiation between *verum semen* and simple *humor prostaticus*.

From this example it can be seen how the "theory of generation" of St. Thomas, often considered insufficient and erroneous and in need of a deep biological revision, has—even without the aid of the microscope and knowledge of germ cells—grasped the truth and resolved problems which did not yet exist in St. Thomas' time or at least were not yet formulated. It is, in general, erratic to criticize the well-founded doctrines of theology solely on the basis of the changing opinions which physiology forms day by day.

In this regard, even the affirmation of Oietti that physiology has not yet spoken the last word, is similarly prophetic.

g. Summary

As a summary, it can be established that a profound knowledge of the biology of reproduction will not contradict the traditional doctrine of the disparity of sexes but will rather confirm it; thus it will in general confirm differentiation of the required conditions for the capacity for marriage—specifically, the absolute incapacity of the ectomized man, and likewise the capacity of the *mulier excisa*.

In the latter case, it is proper to make another distinction; only simple sterility is to be admitted in the *mulier excisa* if the vagina is not included in the extirpation. If the vagina is included, at least in a notable manner, as happens, for example, in the radical operations for carcinoma, by the methods of Wertheim and Schauta, then the requisites for matrimonial capacity are lacking and there is lacking the possibility of *penetratio debita* and *retentio seminis*. Here it is always a matter of a *vagina occlusa*. However, in such cases, there is no injustice to the woman in denying her the capacity to marry if for no other reason than because of the fatal basic disease which demands an intervention of such magnitude.

Declaring her impotent indicates the really human and social standpoint of the theory of difference.

In other cases, even from the social standpoint it is justifiable to determine the conditions required for matrimony in the case of the woman, by a criterion that is milder than that adopted for the man, since the woman belongs to the sex which has greater need of social protection.

The social, legal and moral importance of the problem entailed in the question of " impotency or sterility " can never be sufficiently estimated. It is not possible to overlook it, and a deeper consideration of the difficult matter is justified.

In the last analysis, the decisive question is that of the essence of marriage; whether this, according to its nature, exhausts itself exclusively in reproduction, or whether, beyond the reproduction which is common to all living beings, human matrimony also finds its justification in its own value. Otherwise, we are led with inexorable consequence to invalidity of marriage because of infecundity, if the *finis primarius*, declared to be the *finis essentialis* and *substantialis*, respectively, cannot be realized.

The absolute dominion of the *finis primarius*, as likewise its negation, would bring about an inversion of all the values.

At times, to combat certain attempts, it has been necessary to separate the secondary ends of marriage from the *finis primarius*, and to take a cautionary position. Moreover, when the *finis primarius* cannot be realized, through no fault of the married couple, it has seemed necessary to defend, against new currents of the times, even those values of matrimony which in a subsidiary manner touch upon the secondary ends of marriage.

There is reference here, above all, to the concept of marriage as an indivisible community of life (*individuam vitae consuetudinem continens*), as a *communicatio rerum humanarum et divinarum*. Moreover, matrimony is not merely an " institution of reproduction ", it is—even from the viewpoint of natural law—a bond of life, and a sacrament of supernatural origin; and because of this, it is a means of grace, and hence a help toward the mutual sanctification of the married couple. This is the *finis ultimus* of matrimony, the tending toward the *summum bonum*.

8. FACULTATIVE STERILITY (OBSERVATIO TEMPORUM)

(Periodic abstinence, " Time selection ")

a. Concept

Facultative sterility signifies infecundity freely chosen in conformity with one's desire. At first by facultative sterility was understood any desired birth prevention, according to the meaning given expression by Mensinga (1882), who adopted this designation for the use of the *pessarium occlusivum* he recommended. But the Catholic doctor Capellmann (1883) alluded by this expression to a method of birth limitation which concerned only the natural fluctuation of female fecundity and the avoiding of all the modifications of sexual intercourse contrary to nature and in themselves illicit.

By this method the integrity of marital intercourse is not affected; it is merely limited to the time when the capacity to conceive is diminished or suppressed; namely, to the *tempus ageneseos*. Since the time of Capellmann, by "facultative sterility" is meant the method introduced by him. In the literature of more recent times the expression " periodic abstinence " has come into common use.

b. Historical view

The cyclical fluctuations of female fertility were already known to the ancients.

The prescriptions of purity of the Mosaic law, especially those on cohabitation after purification (internal bath, Mikwe), cause one to presume that a precise knowledge of such fluctuations existed. It is certain that even Hippocrates and others knew of this. This knowledge later fell into oblivion and we find traces of it only in a few doctors (Fernel, Boerhave, Haller, Sims and others).

In 1883, Capellmann rediscovered and elaborated the data. According to Capellmann's concept, the time immediately after menstruation was to be considered the most suitable for conception. From that time on, according to him, the capacity to conceive diminishes up to a " minimum of conception " in the third week after the beginning of menstruation. In the last days preceding the next menstruation, it seemed to him to increase again.

Capellmann did not maintain that at any time conception was impossible, but merely that the probability was very negligible.

Capellmann's fundamental idea was correct, but the formulation and indication were certainly false. The errors committed in serious cases of illness (loss of sight as a result of glaucoma and pregnancy) brought discredit upon his theory and it was later unanimously rejected.

The most famous gynecologists supported the viewpoint that the woman is capable of conceiving at any time during her cycle.

New data in favor of cyclical variations of fertility resulted from the research of Siegel, Pryll and Jaeger during the war years 1914-1918. They succeeded in ascertaining " conception curves " which manifested evident fluctuations between an " optimum " and a " minimum " of the possibility of conception.

c. The new theories—Biological postulates

(a) Ovulation and menstruation

In the last twenty years, the research of Knaus has cast new light on the relationship between menstruation, ovulation and conception.

These relations were already studied even before Knaus. There was an attempt to seek a certain parallel between menstruation and the rutting (oestrus) of animals. But this did not succeed.

In any case a reciprocal influence of the cyclical processes which take place in the uterus (endometrium), in the ovaries and the so-called *corpus luteum*, was determined.

Menstruation was recognized as the breakdown of a process of proliferation. It was no longer considered, as at one time, the " incision of inoculation for the reception of a new bud," but rather the " abortion of an ovum not impregnated."

The relationship and connection between the phases of the cycle were recognized with greater clearness than before and the conclusion was drawn that conception was not possible without the discharging of an ovum capable of becoming impregnated (ovulation). Despite this view, the thought that the capacity for conception subsists in every phase of the cycle should preserve its validity since, on the one hand, the term of ovulation is variable and not determinable with precision and, on the other hand, the vitality of the ovum and sperm is not limited to a restricted period of time. Now the theory of Knaus is based precisely on these two preliminary questions:

(1) On the question of the life-duration of the germ cells;
(2) On the question of the moment of ovulation.

(b) *Life duration of the germ cells*

Up to a short time ago it was held that the life duration of the germ cells was very long. The research of the last decade (Hoehne and Behne, Hammond, Asdell and others) is unanimously agreed that this duration is notably shorter than was believed up to that time. The life of the sperm cell lasts at the most forty-eight hours, and that of the ovum only a few hours after follicle fissure. With the help of experiments of insemination of rabbits by means of a vasectomized male, Knaus verified and confirmed these results. The rabbit is suitable for such an experiment since ovulation is provoked in the rabbit through the sexual act.

(c) *The time of ovulation*

The time of ovulation was discovered by Knaus with the help of an experimental method (the so-called Knaus test). This is based on proof of the hindrance of the reaction of the uterine muscular system to the action of the hypophysis during the activity of the *corpus luteum*. With the help of this method, Knaus came upon the proof that, in a woman with a regular cycle of twenty-eight days, ovulation takes place at a definite point of time. Formerly Knaus estimated the fourteenth to sixteenth day of the cycle but recently, in general, the fifteenth day before the beginning of the immediately following menstruation. Recently, new and more precise " ovulation tests " have been discovered. They are based on the cyclical fluctuation of the rectal morning temperatures (basal temperature) and on the microscopic variations of vaginal secretion (" smear "), according to the method of Papanicolaou.

(d) *The theory of Ogino*

Before Ogino, the majority of researchers referred the term of

ovulation to the time of the preceding menstruation, although it
was already known that ovulation pertains to the immediately following menstruation. Ogino drew upon the consequences of this
knowledge. He was able to show that the disagreement among the
researchers concerning the moment of ovulation could easily be
resolved if one reckoned the latter by starting from the immediately
following menstruation. In this way, there arises a notable agreement; the term of ovulation lies between the twelfth and sixteenth
day before the beginning of the new menstruation. According to
the theory of Ogino, the last ten days of the cycle are practically
sterile. This sterile period should remain the same, even if the
duration of the cycle is subject to fluctuation, and should not take
part in the fluctuation.

(e) *The theory of Knaus and Ogino*

The theories of Knaus and Ogino have been united, and from
this point on we speak of the theory of Knaus—Ogino. The result
of this theory is evident: that impregnation is possible only during
the few days around the time of ovulation.

According to Knaus, in a regular cycle of twenty-eight days, the
first ten days and the last eleven days of the cycle would be sterile:
from the tenth to the seventeenth day there exists the possibility of
conception. According to Ogino, the last eleven days would, in
every case, be sterile.

This theoretical result is in practice subject to an important
limitation because of an indispensable addition—that is, the theory
holds to the degree that it is possible to exclude the disturbing
appearance of other factors.

d. Complications of the theory

Because of numerous factors, this theory, which at first seemed
so well founded, becomes complicated in its practical applicability.

(a) *The question of provoked ovulation*

According to Knaus, ovulation in the human species comes about
spontaneously and exclusively on the basis of endogenous cyclical
processes under hormonal direction. In certain mammals, especially

F*

in rabbits, there is instead another type of ovulation, that of provoked ovulation (violent).

Now in recent times, Stieve, Caffier and others have tried to produce proof against Knaus that ovulation even in the human species can be provoked by various exogenous factors. In particular, Stieve, making use of certain observations, has been able to show the great influence of the nervous system and certain mental processes on the female genital organs, particularly on ovulation.

From this it can at least be deduced that spontaneous ovulation is not the only type existing in the human species and that provoked ovulation can be determined beforehand through various factors.

Moreover, delays in ovulation through so-called displacement of phases (Riebold) are possible. Although Knaus might hold fast to his thesis of the independence of the ovarian function from the nervous system, the thesis must be revised upon taking into consideration various data which have in the meantime been accumulated.

(b) *The question of intermediate ovulation*

A further complication arises from the possibility of multiple ovulations within the same cycle. This possibility is definitely denied by Knaus.

The research of Samuels—who, by utilizing, with the help of the spectroscopic method, the fluctuations of the reduction time of the hemoglobin (from oxyhemoglobin to methemoglobin) for establishing ovulation (so-called cyclogram) considered multiple ovulation within any cycle as a normal case—does not have the unequivocal value of proof. The sources of error to which the method is subject are too great.

In recent times, Stieve and Caffier have studied this question anew and have been able to produce proofs in favor of multiple ovulation.

The same value of proof is found in the case of superfetation (successive conception after a fecundation had already taken place) confirmed by Runge.

Thus new researches have revealed complications which do not contradict *in toto* the theoretical foundation of the doctrine of Knaus, but make it seem very problematic.

These new researches have established the fact that there is no principal difference between spontaneous and provoked ovulation and that the possibility of provoked ovulation and of multiple ovulation must absolutely be taken into account. This is sufficient to limit the practical applicability of the method.

(c) *Further complications*

Further complications arise from the question whether the phase of the cycle during which the *corpus luteum* is active is effectively excluded from the other fluctuations of the total duration of the cycle, and whether it is always of the same length, or whether it is also subject to fluctuation.

These questions are very closely connected with that of so-called precocious and retarded conception—in other words with the question of the admissibility of the sterility of the postmenstruum and premenstruum respectively. Even the possibility of conception during menstruation seems to have been confirmed by the experiences of various researchers. Finally, it is still an open question whether it is actually possible to establish a rise of the cyclical curve during the last days of the same cycle. In regard to this question, it must be asked whether, in certain circumstances, the prolonged duration of the life of the sperm, because of a variation of acidity in the vaginal secretion during the last days of the cycle, must be considered.

From all these questions, which are far from being decided in a definite manner, there result many possible complications, so that the element of incalculability acquires an importance far greater than Knaus expected. In the light of an accurate criticism, there is little safety left in the method which is upheld especially in the popular writings. As a result of the various factors, the extension of fluctuation in the menstrual cycle is, even from the physiological viewpoint, somewhat wide. If fluctuations of pathological origin are added, the element of incalculability acquires an immeasurable importance—above all, in those cases which have greater need of reliable calculation: that is, in cases of serious illness.

How many problems arise even today in this matter can best be seen from the scientific works of Knaus himself—not from his popular work concerning fertile and sterile days and their " safe calculation," but from his principal scientific work: " Physiologie der Zeugung " (" The Physiology of Generation ").[1]

---

[1] Both published by Mandrich, in Vienna, 1949.

e. Criticism of practical applicability

(a) *General difficulties*

Difficulties increase as soon as we pass from the theoretic fundamentals to practical application. The frequent irregularity and fluctuations of the cycle in the same woman can definitely cause the reliability of the method to be called into question.

According to Stieve, in "ovarian-stable" types the probability of certain calculation is very limited. The healthier the woman is and the less perturbed her cycle is by sickness, by other exogenous factors and physical changes, the safer the method proves to be. As is natural, there will be less safety when the equilibrium of the vital processes is labile, thus above all, in women who are ill, as well as in those who do heavy work, in the undernourished, exhausted and in those affected by physical changes.

Moreover, the practical application of the method demands not a little intelligence and control, if the greatest possible security is to be obtained.

Knaus himself admits that the method is applicable only in "women genitally healthy." Hence its applicability is notably limited precisely in those cases in which its use would be necessary: that is, in sick women. In order to reduce failures to a minimum, Knaus prescribes that the method be used only when all the possibilities of fluctuation have been determined by means of cyclical ovulation for at least a year. But even then it is never sure that unexpected variations will not occur. A further limitation of the practical use of the method is based on the fact that it is necessary to have continuous and accurate medical supervision, which calls for a deep knowledge and long experience on the part of the doctor. And on the part of the patient, there is required great intellectual energy.

According to Knaus, the method is of service only to women "genitally healthy"; we must, however, warn also against its application to young and healthy married couples. (See *Limitation of the sphere of indication*, below.) The method is also subject to limitation in cases of women more advanced in age, because of the inevitably greater fluctuation of the cycle when approaching the climacterium.

Experience shows that conceptions taking place a little after the cessation of menstruation—that is, at the time of approach of the menopause—are not rare.

The deficiency of the method and the difficulties inherent in its application become more emphatic in those cases in which pregnancy should be avoided because of danger to life and health. In such cases, one cannot be content with the relative certitude of minimum conception. Here either absolute certitude or absolute abstinence is required.

(b) *Practical clinical experiences*

Face to face with the reports of positive results by some authors who can boast of special collective results and who can point to a series of successful results in the hundreds of thousands, with only a few sporadic failures, the following points are to be considered:

The greater the positive number reported, the greater must be the quota of healthy women to whom the method has been recommended. The greater the quota of sick women, the greater must the percentage of failures necessarily be; it will, however, be greatest when the doctors recommend the method only in cases in which, for serious health reasons, a sick woman must be protected from the dangers of a new pregnancy. There are a number of authors, worthy of belief, who in their report of negative results are forced to bring to attention the great numbers of failures, and included in these are some of a serious nature.

Among these are found both precocious conceptions in the postmenstruum as well as late conception in the premenstruum, and at times during the last days of the cycle.

The defenders of the method try to weaken the force of negative results by the following arguments: The accounts of the women are not reliable; they would often be interested in concealing the real term of conception; and it would never be possible to exclude extramatrimonial conception with certainty. In some cases, the method would not have been properly applied. In other cases, failures would be explained by unexpected disturbances of the cycle by phase disarrangement.

Finally, there is an attempt to weaken the value of the failures by pointing out that the number of failures are few in relation to the positive results. As a matter of fact, however, even if the theoretical fundamentals are confirmed, the practical applicability still could not bring that degree of certitude required when the theory is to be applied in favor of women with a grave health risk.

f. Disadvantages and dangers

While the defenders of the method extol its absolute harmlessness and deny any possible disadvantage, it must be said that the principal disadvantage lies in the fact that it promises a greater security than it can furnish.

Damage to health arises in cases in which greater consideration should be given; namely, when the method is to be applied to sick and suffering women.

But even for healthy women, the method is in the long run not so harmless and inoffensive as would be supposed from the fact that it has been extolled as a method " in conformity with nature " for the prevention of birth. In fact, there is a desire for maternity in healthy women. Experience shows that the *libido sexualis* in her reaches its greatest intensity in the phase of preparation for conception. This cyclical intensification of the libido has its own biological meaning. Now if the woman must, sometimes at the beginning of marriage, give up marital intercourse at the time when she has the greatest inclination for it and must submit to it when she does not desire it, it is very understandable that in the long run she would suffer from this. In this way, various functional disturbances would necessarily arise. Among these, the following have been seen to arise: dyspareunia, frigidity and *vaginismus*. In certain cases, this had led to a sexual neurosis which has developed into an anxiety psychosis, and these were removed only when the women freed themselves from the calendar and led a marriage life free of reservations.

Not a few cases of divorce are imputed to a prolonged " selection of time." It is therefore inaccurate to indiscriminately consider the method a "natural " means of birth prevention.

There is nothing natural in the calculated exclusion of conception, but rather an interpolation of the *ratio* (reasoning process) among the processes of nature which regulate themselves best when they can take place unconsciously and without being recognized.

g. Means of avoiding harm

From this viewpoint, the method can be fruitful merely in those cases in which it appears as a lesser evil in comparison to harm of another kind. When this supposition is present, one must have the greatest trust regarding both the reliability of the method and the manner of avoiding the above-mentioned harm. This calls for a restriction of the process in a twofold manner:

(1) In the reduction of the days in which conception could not occur;

(2) In the restriction of the so-called indications.

(a) *The limited (reduced) method*

The reduced method presents a way which is accessible in practice and which reduces to a minimum the factors of uncertainty connected with it, thus rendering it in practice more useful and reliable.

The condition *sine qua non* is the exact observation of the cycle for a sufficiently long period of time. The best way to attain such a result is to record all the important dates in a so-called menogram. Here belong not only the data concerning the duration of menstruation, but also the indication of its degree of intensity for each day and, further, precise data concerning each marital intercourse that has taken place, as well as data regarding the days in which the libido was more intense and the secretion (there is a so-called fluor of ovulation) greater; data regarding the so-called "pain of the intermenstrual period," and finally, data regarding all the other important factors (fatigue, excitations, etc.) which can influence the cycle. Such a menogram can also furnish conclusions of diagnostic importance. To increase the accuracy of the menogram, the new ovulation tests (basal temperature, analysis of secretion) which have been mentioned above must also be considered.

The use of such a menogram as a guide will not only help to ascertain the term of ovulation in a purely numerical manner, but also bring connected data into consideration.

Execution. On this basis, when the cycle has a certain regularity, one can determine not only the term of ovulation but also the variation which imposes itself from time to time.

However, we consider it too risky to trust in the sterility of the postmenstruum and hence we exclude (as possibly non-sterile) all the first half of the cycle including two to three days after ovulation.

In like manner, the last two to three days of the cycle must also be excluded since there is no definite assurance of their sterility.

In the normal cycle of twenty-eight days, only the twentieth through the twenty-fifth days, then, are to be considered sterile with a definite surety.

In an analogous manner, the days in question can be determined by other forms of the cycle. The greater the difference between the shortest cycle and the longest, the greater the number of days which can be considered sterile; and in the case of great fluctuation, the number can be reduced to zero.

The numerical relation of the fruitful days to the sterile is accordingly inverse to that indicated in the method popularized by Knaus. It is not a matter of only a few days of abstinence against all the remaining days of the cycle but, in reality, a matter of only a few days in which intercourse is permitted.

(b) *Limitation of the sphere of indication*

In close connection with this limitation affecting the method, there is present the limitation of the sphere of applicability. This comes into consideration only in cases in which, because of serious reasons, the woman must be protected against the danger of a new pregnancy—never, however, in cases in which such a reason is not present and even less when the danger is so serious as to imperil the life of the mother. In fact, in the latter case, we cannot even be satisfied with the relative safety which the limited method offers, but must, as already mentioned, demand absolute safety and hence absolute abstinence.

We must not forget that the limited method demands a great sacrifice on the part of the married couple and also requires a great measure of renunciation and strength of will which not all find in themselves. This method is merely designated for cases in which there is a serious indication. If a serious reason is lacking, and it is a case of a young and healthy couple, the method must not a priori be used. Young and healthy couples cannot easily claim a serious reason which justifies birth prevention.

When such a reason is lacking, they cannot avoid leading a married life according to nature, and they are not permitted to avoid its consequences. It is the duty of society to create such conditions that they need not escape the social effects of married life.

With older people, upon whom sickness and misfortune have left their mark, the application of the limited method is much more possible in view of the wounds which the struggle of life has inflicted upon them.

The approach of the climacterium diminishes at times the safety even of the limited method. In any case, greater service is rendered to married people who seek advice, by recommending this method with prudence and accuracy rather than by an uncritical generalization of the original method of Knaus and Ogino and of Smulders and Latz, without limitation and indiscriminately applied.

h. Sphere of application (Indications)

For abortion, as for birth prevention in all its forms, we speak of " indications," and principally three indications are distinguished : namely medical, eugenic and social.

(a) *Medical indications*

In regard to medical indications, it is to be noticed that it is preferable merely to speak of pregnancy complications for the mother. Such complications are to be faced by the use of all the means of therapy. In the matter of facultative sterility we must, in cases of proved danger, distinguish two groups of complications :

(1) The so-called relative, indications;
(2) The so-called absolute indications.

In cases of so-called relative indication, the application of the limited method is motivated according to the gravity of the complication, be it a *iusta*, a *iusta et gravis causa*, or a *causa proportionate gravis* in the terminology of moral theology.

The so-called absolute indication, as already mentioned, no longer comes into consideration in the sense of an " indication," but rather constitutes an absolute contraindication. This requirement may appear strict. Yet it must be realized that there are no other means of " contraception " which are absolutely safe and which, when used for a long time, are also harmless; so that even here there can be no other guarantee against the danger of death except complete abstinence. This sacrifice cannot be too high a price when the life of the woman is at stake but represents a command of considerate love.

(b) *Eugenic indications*

In the eugenic indications, the possibilities of application are subject to even more restricted limits. When there is a serious danger of transmitting hereditary stigmas a *iusta causa* can be present. But since the method demands not a small measure of intelligence and control, it cannot be applicable in cases of grave psychopathy, of defective intelligence (oligophrenia), of character degeneracy, etc. It can be considered chiefly when there exist certain bodily malformations in which one can be satisfied with the degree of safety offered by the limited method, since the danger of an occurring failure is not excessively as great as that of the case of manifest heredity. And in these exceptional cases, when an operation is possible, one can eventually seek surgical correction of the malformation.

For cases of medical and eugenic indication, the limited method does not offer absolute safety but, practically speaking, a sufficient safety at the most. This safety always becomes less the more serious the illness of the woman is and the more serious her general condition is. From this result limitations of the method's applicability.

If all of these elements are explained objectively and calmly to married couples seeking advice, those for whom the observance of the moral law is not merely an external form but an intimate need of the heart will gratefully welcome the suggested way, even if this requires greater sacrifice and renunciation than do other methods.

It must be remembered that the safety of a method becomes less the fewer limitations it demands.

(c) *Social indications*

The social indication is to be basically rejected. In regard to birth prevention because of social conditions, it must be stated that social conditions are to be combated by means of social legislation and other such provisions, and not by birth prevention.

The limitation of birth is not a remedy for social needs and, moreover, makes the social question insoluble through further complications. On the contrary, it does nothing but impede the true solution of the social problem. The social needs continue and are increased and perpetuated. (For further details see the next section.)

In abnormal times, as for example, in the last post-war period, with its almost insoluble problems and with a great number of marriages among the young, the social indication for selection of time can certainly become inevitable and present the only way out. But no attempt should be omitted to remove in the shortest possible time this condition of need, in order to procure for young married couples the possibility of a truly normal matrimonial life. It is not normal for young married couples to be condemned to consult the "conception calendar" all their life.

With the development of birth prevention almost to the point of a mass phenomena, there is, however, also presented in a more imposing manner, the unfavorable aspects of facultative sterility. We have shown that this method offers the greatest safety to healthy women and the greatest uncertainty to those who are ill.

The differentiated reproduction connected with it leads to a manifest "disgenetic" effect (contraselection), and precisely the more so the more it is transformed into a mass phenomenon as a result of propaganda. This can in time produce effects that are harmful to society.

This serious social danger remains the same whether it is actuated by illicit means of birth prevention or by "licit" means of periodic abstinence. The effect is the same in both cases.

Social indigence must be eliminated by other means than by indefinitely subjecting young couples to the "selection of time." The only remedy for these phenomena can be found in the establishment of social justice according to the meaning of the social encyclicals "Rerum Novarum" and "Quadregesimo Anno." It is not licit to silence the social conscience by the convenient manner of resorting to the subterfuge of birth prevention, not even by a method which the Church from the moral standpoint does not in se condemn.

i. The question of moral liceity

(a) *General view*

If the Church, on the one hand, has always most severely condemned birth prevention through contraceptives as an *abusus matrimonii,* an *onanismus coniugalis,* and has always considered it as a *res in se mala* (*intrinsecus mala*), so on the other hand, she has never a priori rejected the *observatio temporum.*

She definitely knows the strongly perturbing effect upon marriage and the harmful effect upon health caused by all contraceptives; but of greatest importance to her is the unchangeable commandment of God. In the *observatio temporum,* this commandment is not broken either by action or omission. If, in the *observatio temporum,* we can speak in general of an infraction of the moral law, this can take place only *per accidens*—that is, it can be verified only as a result of the particular circumstances of the case and the motives.

The desire to prevent offspring need not necessarily be immoral *in se;* it can be justified when a serious reason, a *causa iusta, iusta et gravis, proportionate gravis,* is present. In this case it is presupposed that the action is morally licit, that the means is not of an immoral nature, that it is licit or at least not illicit. Moreover, there is no doubt whatsoever that married couples can by mutual consent (*mutuo consensu*) give up the use of the marriage right (*usus iuris*), provided the right itself (*ius matrimoniale*) is not excluded by means of an agreement. If the right itself were excluded, then there would be a defect of the will to contract marriage (*defectus consensus*), and this would render matrimony null and its use illicit.

Since the *procreatio prolis* is the primary and not the exclusive end, then even secondary ends, in the right order and in the right subordination, justify the use of marriage. This latter cannot be illicit merely because there is temporary or permanent sterility.

Hence, according to the general doctrinal tradition, *copula inter senes et steriles, tempore praegnationis et menstruationis* (when based on certain presupposed prescriptions), *tempore lactationis,* etc., is licit. In regard to the *observatio temporum,* it must be noted that if it is licit to completely renounce the *usus matrimonii* by mutual consent, the renunciation of it in part—that is, the limiting of the use of marriage rights to sterile days—cannot be said to constitute per se a moral evil (Hejmeyer).

It is, however, not certainly licit to take matters lightly by applying this principle in general and without discrimination.

The application of the *observatio temporum* can be licit only within certain limits; its admissibility is bound up with certain presuppositions.

(b) *Requisites for liceity*

Among the requisites for liceity the most important is the existence of a justifiable reason. The moralists are not in accord in establishing the requirements for this point. The more rigorous view demands a *iusta et gravis causa*. The more moderate view is satisfied with a *causa honesta seu rationabilis*.

If we consider the import of the question, it seems more advisable not to take such requirements too lightly; here the principle *in dubio pars tutior est eligenda* could be applied.

Concerning the essential liceity of the method, the common opinion is that it is admissible under certain conditions. Only a few authors hold that the method is in general and indiscriminately permissible. In opposition to this vast laxity, some authors have come to take a rigoristic position which opposes its liceity.

Joseph Mayer has called attention to the fact that the mere external integrity of the act does not suffice and that even its internal structure must be irreproachable. In the *observatio temporum*, as well as in *abusus matrimonii*, the *finis operantis* is directed toward the same end—namely, the limitation of birth. This gives occasion to the adversaries of Catholic morality to accuse it of hypocrisy.

The arguments of Mayer are by no means to be taken lightly. They demand an integrity of internal intention as well as of external comportment.

(c) *Limits of liceity*

In accordance with the traditional teaching of the Church, the *observatio temporum* in se cannot be condemned since, if the requisites of a *iusta (et gravis) causa* are certified, the limits of liceity are not overstepped and every indiscriminate generalization is excluded.

The limits are determined by the following elements:

(1) By the harmful reactions upon the health and the intention of contracting marriage;
(2) By observance of the requisites of moral liceity;

Finally, the limitation is determined by the fact that the ecclesiastical magisterium has to the present time never declared an indiscriminate liceity in the sense of a *licet* pure and simple.

j. Doctrinal decisions of the Church

A fundamental decision of the Sacred Penitentiary of June 16, 1880, simply uses the negative formula: *inquietandos non esse*, and hence not a *licet*. The priest can indicate this recourse with prudence (*caute tamen insinuare*) to married people whom he has in vain tried to dissuade from matrimonial onanism (*quos alia ratione a detestabili onanismi crimine abducere frustra tentaverit*).

It is a matter, therefore, merely of a *medium cavendi onanismi* and not of a general permission. It is true that even in this way the danger of abuse is not excluded. But even in this case it must be said that *abusus non tollit usum*; the justified use of the method cannot be denied simply because the method is abused. In Noldin-Schmitt (1940), the indiscriminate divulgence of the method has been condemned: *propterea haec methodus non est indiscriminatim propaganda, sed solum in casu necessitatis consuli potest.*

The encyclical "Casti Connubii" has confirmed the liceity of the method within the designated limits. "Neque contra ordinem agere illi dicendi sunt conjuges qui, iure suo recta et naturali ratione utuntur, etsi ob naturales sive temporis sive quorundam defectuum causa, nova inde vita oriri non possit." ("It cannot be said that couples who use their right in a completely natural manner act contrary to the order of nature even if, in virtue of natural circumstances, a new life cannot be born.")[1]

Even here no positive liceity is expressed, but only a negative formulation. The words *recta et naturali ratione* require not only the external integrity of the act, but also the proper and natural attitude of the couple. The words *etsi ob naturales . . .* do not exclusively refer to the *observatio temporum*, but also include circumstances of another nature (*tempus praegnationis, lactationis, senium*, etc.), and certainly do not exclude the *observatio temporum*.

As a motivation the encyclical expressly recalls the secondary ends of marriage: "*mutuum adiutorium, mutuusque fovendus amor et concupiscentiae sedatio*": ". . . dummodo salva semper sit intrinseca illius actus natura ideoque eius ad primarium finem debita ordinatio" (*mutual aid, increase of mutual love and alleviation of concupiscence* "as long as the internal nature of the act and its due ordination toward the primary end are maintained").

The propaganda in favor of indiscriminately applying the

[1] Encyclical "Casti Connubii," N. 59.

observatio temporum appeals to the encyclical "Casti Connubii," by citing the above-mentioned passage apart from the remaining content of the encyclical.

When we are faced with this interpretation, we find it necessary to recall the rest of the encyclical and, in particular, the words to which so little attention has been given:

"Cum autem actus coniugii suapte natura proli generandae sit destinatus, qui in eo exercendo *naturali haec eum vi ac virtute de industria destituunt*, contra naturam agunt et turpe quid atque intrinsece inhonestum operantur."

("Any use of marriage in which, through human malice, the act becomes devoid of its natural procreative power is against the law of God and nature and those who dare to commit such actions make themselves guilty of grave sin.")

There can be no doubt that the abusive use of the *observatio temporum* falls within the object of the words *de industria destituunt*. For this implies a conscious, continuous and intentional frustration of the primary end of marriage.

An attempt has been made to appeal to the encyclical "Casti Connubii" in such a way that the words cited above would approve the predominance of the secondary ends of marriage. Against this interpretation, there is need to recall the last words of the mentioned passage, which expressly designate subordination: namely, the orientation toward the primary end of marriage as *debita ordinatio*.

A decree of the Holy Office on April 1, 1944, has completely clarified this point. To the question whether approval could be given to the opinion of certain modern authors who hold that the secondary ends of marriage are not essentially subordinated to the primary end, the creation of children, but have the same importance as the primary ends and are independent of them, the categorical answer " negative " was given.

A complete and clear answer on this point was given by Pope Pius XII in a discourse to the Congress of Midwives on October 29, 1951.

First, the Holy Father admonished the midwives to depend in this matter only on medical information worthy of belief and not on popular publications destined for indiscriminate diffusion among the people. Two things must be well distinguished: Concerning the question whether married people may use their marital rights even during the time of natural infertility, the Church has always taught that it is permissible, provided the marital right is used according to order. If, however, it is asked whether it is allowed to limit the use of the matrimonial right exclusively to sterile days, the following is established: If the agreement by the couple concerns not only the use of the right (*usus iuris*), but the right itself (*ius*), it would not only be absolutely illicit, but marriage would be invalid because of an essential defect of the matrimonial consent (*defectus consensus*).

The use of the " choice of time " (*observatio temporum*), in order to be licit, must always be based on a serious moral reason, sufficient and sure (*Basata, oppure no, su motivi morali sufficienti e securi*). The mere fact that the married couple performs the marital act according to nature does not suffice of itself to guarantee the rectitude of intention—*non basterebbe per se sola a garantire la rettitudine dell'intenzione*.

In order to ascertain whether these presuppositions are present, the conduct of the couple must be examined most attentively in each case (*la condotta degli sposi deve essere esaminata più attentamente*).

As a complement to this allocution, the Holy Father in another discourse, addressing the Italian family associations on November 5, 1951, added the following: "Hence in our last allocution concerning conjugal morality, we have affirmed the permissibility and, concerning the time, the limits—in truth very extensive—of a regulating of birth which, contrary to the so-called birth control, is compatible with the law of God. It can also be hoped, but in such matters the Church naturally leaves judgment to medical science, that science will succeed in giving to this licit method a sufficiently safe basis. The most recent information seems to confirm such a hope."

It is therefore established without doubt that the method of choice of time is in principle licit but surely not indiscriminately and in every case, and that its liceity can only be based from case to case upon morally sufficient and serious reasons and that the comportment of the couple must be accurately examined case for case. This is applicable without restriction even if science should give to this method a still surer basis than is the case today.

Those who do not give much thought to themselves and souls entrusted to them and indiscriminately counsel the choice of time should recall the grave words of the encyclical " Casti Connubii " which refer to frustrating the primary end of marriage: "They are blind guides of blind men. But if a blind man guide a blind man, both fall into a pit" (Matt. 15:14).

k. Pastoral viewpoints

The exhortation of the encyclical "Casti Connubi" which we have mentioned, together with the other warning to "caute tamen insinuare," manifest the way to be followed by pastoral prudence.

Noldin-Schmitt warns the priest that he himself should never give concrete advice concerning the *observatio temporum* but should only suggest that a trustful doctor be consulted. Nor is he to allow the distribution at the doors of the church of popular writings containing advice on "periodic abstinence" and stating that the method is recommended. These ideas at one time obtained such dissemination that it threatened to effect a serious danger to the Catholic concept of matrimony; to be the extension of a "masked Malthusianism" (P. Schmitz).

These dutiful admonitions are directed solely against abuse and irresponsible dissemination among the masses as well as against simplified popular expositions which do not take difficulties into consideration; which are not prepared for the complex matter; and hence can do nothing but lead into error. It is understandable how, from the pastoral viewpoint, severe criticism of the method has at times been disturbing. However, considering the extension of social needs and the *abusus matrimonii*, which in consequence of the latter has become a phenomenon of the masses, it is understandable that some shepherds of souls would feel grateful for the new method, which permitted an "accessible way out of the given problems of matrimony."

In the face of this, it was rightly pointed out that periodic abstinence cannot constitute a "way *out* of the problems of matrimony" but at most, a way which always remains *within* these problems, since the problems of marriage remain as such.

The defenders of the general spread of the method have appealed to Bishop von Streng of Basel, who, with regard to this question, declared: "The regulation of birth is licit and morally good when its reasons and means are morally good." However, it can be objected that the presupposition of morally good reasons is incompatible with the indiscriminate diffusion among the masses.

Moreover, the other affirmations made by the Bishop have been omitted and the above-cited words have been taken from the context of the same. He emphasizes the difficulties which arise from the irregularity and disturbances which are found even in healthy women, but which are greater in sick women.

In order that the method be applied effectively, it follows that it cannot be advised carelessly. He explicitly admonishes against the abuse of the method. Only to the well-intentioned and zealous ought this method not be precluded, and this with all reserve regarding the judgment on the effective success of the method, which is still placed in doubt by many specialists.

Von Streng recommends, above all, complete abstinence as the only absolutely sure way and at the same time, as a precious virtue and points out, against the modern aberrations, that this is possible and not seldom a duty.

Against the criticism of the method it has also been objected that it would lead to a transformation of material sins into formal sins.

Whether and when this danger exists, only the priest can judge, case for case.

Scientific criticism must serve truth and only by this can pastoral medicine truly serve pastoral theology.

Finally, even in this matter, attention must be placed on the attempt to defend the general spread of periodic abstinence by appealing exclusively to the secondary ends of marriage. Against this attempt to invert the hierarchic order, the most important points from the moral viewpoint have already been discussed. Recently, the decree of the Holy Office of April 1, 1944, has declared that the secondary ends of marriage are not independent of the primary, but are essentially subordinated to them (*essentialiter subordinati*). Thus the attempts which we have mentioned have been removed with unequivocal clarity.

l. A glance into the future

It is hoped that for the future the question of periodic continence will somewhat lose the importance it has had in the recent past and which it now has. The enormous losses due to wars and revolutionary movements may place a higher value on human life. The question of birth prevention and the means whereby this is brought about, may in the new social order no longer be so crucial as in the time of greater social need. With a change in social conditions, the *observatio temporum* will have a lasting importance only within those limits which the present exposition has tried to demonstrate.

9. ABUSUS MATRIMONII

a. Concept—Terminology

The question of *abusus matrimonii* (*onanismus coniugalis*) also embraces the problem of birth prevention—namely, of that obtained by illicit means.

When the means are licit (e.g., abstinence), there is no *abusus*. The problem of the diminution of births comes into consideration here as a sequel to birth prevention. As a pathological phenomenon verified in the organism of society, it must be treated in connection with questions of social hygiene and belongs more to Pastoral Hygiene than to Pastoral Medicine. In order to indicate in medical terminology *abusus matrimonii*, the following expressions are used: birth prevention, birth control, anticonception, contraception, etc.

The term "onanism" is frequently used in theological literature and corresponds exactly to the sin of Onan (Gen. 38:8-10).

All expressions which tend to hide or minimize the import of birth prevention and its essence as an abuse (*abusus sexualis*)—as, for example, the expression "planned parenthood"—must be completely rejected.

b. Nature of onanism

The essence of onanism consists in the deliberate transgression of the natural law willed by God. It consists in a frustration of the object of sexuality in general and especially of the primary end of matrimony (*finis primarius matrimonii*), which lies in the *procreatio prolis*. According to its essence, it is an action contrary to nature (*agere contra naturam*) through the conscious intervention of man in the natural functional processes. There is an attempt here to "separate pleasure from duty." But the feeling of sexual pleasure serves primarily, according to natural law, the ends of reproduction.

Even today it is true that God has punished with death the "sin of Onan," if not in the individual, in the people: *quod displicuit Deo et occidit illum propter hoc Deus.*

In accordance with this, the definition of moral theology is the following: "Onanism is a kind of copulation in which, generation cannot follow from the effusion of seed" (*Onanismus dicitur copula ita peracta, ut ex semine effuso generatio sequi non possit*— Noldin-Schmitt). This goes for all types of deliberate birth prevention.

c. Species and methods of control of conception

In a strict sense, the concern here is merely the prevention of conception. We therefore exclude the treatment of infanticide and abortion as rude methods of barbaric people in the limitation of reproduction and also the modern method of sterilization.

Contraceptive methods can be subdivided into two principal groups according as they are applied on the part of the male or on the part of the female. Further classifications distinguish:

Mechanical means;
Chemical means;
Biological means.

(a) *Methods used by the male*

(1) *Copula interrupta*

Coitus interruptus is historically the most ancient method; it is onanism in the strictest sense.

(2) *Copula tecta*

By *copula tecta* (on the part of male), also called *coitus condomatus*, is designated cohabitation with the use of membranes which work mechanically by covering and enclosing the *membrum virile*, within which the *effusio seminis* takes place.

These are also used as protective means against venereal infection. Because of this, they are said to be indispensable for sexual hygiene.

(b) *Methods used by the female*

Mechanical means

(1) *Copula tecta*

The best known means is the *pessarium occlusivum* introduced by Mensinga in 1882. This effects the hermetical enclosure of the uterine orifice against the vagina for the purpose of impeding the reception of sperm. Numerous modifications have arisen from this method.

(2) *Absorbent methods*

Many means with the use of tampons have been discovered, not so much for the purpose of effecting a hermetical enclosure as of completely absorbing the sperm.

(3) *Intrauterine methods*

These are based on the introduction of an instrument into the cervical canal of the uterus. These act not so much as a means of preventing conception as abortive means.

Chemical means

Their scope is the killing of the received sperm. This purpose is often hidden by recommending such means as "disinfectants," as a means of personal "intimate hygiene" of the woman, etc.

Biological means

By means of "biological" action are meant those means which pertain principally to the biological process of the maturation of the ovum, the ovarian cycle. These attempt either to arrest the maturation of the ovum itself or to transform the *congressus* into an infertile phase. This last method (facultative sterility or periodic abstinence) has been partly explained (cf. above).

There remain the methods of so-called temporary sterilization. Today, three methods are distinguished:

(1) Hormonal methods;
(2) Actinic methods (radiological);
(3) Surgical methods.

Up to now it cannot be said absolutely that the problem of temporary sterilization has been solved in a way so as not to raise objections.

By "combined" methods are understood those in which, in order to obtain greater surety, two or more of the cited methods are used at the same time, as, for example, the mechanical and chemical means,

(c) *Other methods*

The so-called *carezza* (*amplexus reservatus*) substantially consists in *actus imperfecti* and as such cannot be directly considered a species of conjugal onanism even if, according to scope and intention, it constitutes an *abusus sexualis*.

Even the so-called *copula dimidiata* must be judged in like manner. There takes place in this a partial retraction at the moment of the *effusio seminis* so that the *effusio* is still *intra vas naturale* in the proximity of the *introitus vaginae*. This tends at least to make conception more difficult.

d. Critique of the methods

The critique of the methods is limited to the purely medical viewpoint concerning safety and harmfulness.

(a) *Copula interrupta*

Copula interrupta is neither safe nor harmless. The harmfulness of the procedure is shown more clearly the longer it is practiced. Now this method is much used, since it can be employed at any time. Eventually this method produces grave harm, especially to the nervous system. Nervous disturbances in the sense of *neurasthenia sexualis*, disturbances of potency and feelings in both sexes are almost inevitable. Many authors place great importance on the lack of absorption of the sperm on the part of the woman. Very often there arises in the woman the specific syndrome of parametritis posterior. Moreover, even with the *effusio seminis ante introitum*, conception is always possible and this often leads to unjustified suspicion of the woman.

(b) *Copula tecta*

The *copula tecta ex parte viri* is considered by many as absolutely safe and absolutely harmless. This is completely inaccurate. Gynecological literature reveals numerous communications of damages. In the *copula tecta ex parte mulieris*, the harm is even more evident. If a *pessarium occlusivum* is to be efficient, a hermetical enclosure of the *portio vaginalis uteri* is necessary. Considering the smallness of spermatozoa, even such an enclosure does not assure absolute safety. The more the hermetical enclosure augments the surety, the greater becomes the danger of harm from obstructing the flow of secretion. If, finally, there is an attempt to avoid this harm by introducing a cervical pessary immediately before *congressus* and removing it immediately after, the danger of producing harm of a nervous and mental nature is increased.

There is also great insecurity when the introduction of the pessary is made by the woman herself or even when there is constant dependence on medical intervention. If the method is used for a long time, inflammatory ailments of the hypogastric organs are inevitable and this even when the pessaries are combined with "germicidal" (i.e., spermatocidal) chemicals.

(c) *Intrauterine methods*

This is so in a higher degree in regard to the so-called intrauterine pessaries. In the literature on gynecology, there are found numerous cases of severe harm to health through septic infections, and at times there is reference to a great number of fatal cases.

(d) *Chemical means*

The chemical means without exception do not guarantee a sure protection. They practically never succeed in killing all the sperm. Moreover, they often have the effect of injuring the sperm themselves. Fecundation, which may take place in spite of all, often leads to the birth of children with a germinal injury and of deformed creatures, etc.

Chemical means are truly and properly poisonous, and act in the sense of the so-called blastophthoria.

(e) *Methods of temporary sterility*

The same danger of germ injury is to be found in hormonal and actinic temporary sterilization. In particular, roentgen radiation has been found to be extremely harmful for the progeny. Moreover, it is impossible to so actuate a dosage of rays that injury would surely be avoided.

The surgical methods of temporary sterilization are not devoid of danger if for no other reason than that they require laparotomy.

A deficient effect can lead to extrauterine (ectopic) pregnancy or to permanent (irreparable) sterility.

The criticism of the methods from the medical viewpoint can be reduced to the following: There is no method of birth prevention which is absolutely safe and at the same time absolutely harmless, especially when applied over a long period. The degree of insecurity and of danger often proceed in a parallel manner.

Besides the primary and immediate effects, the mediate effects and the damage arising later should not be overlooked. A later effect which often occurs is secondary sterility. Moreover, serious effects in the mental sphere—above all, potency disturbance and neurosis—can often be observed.

There is scarcely a gynecological ailment which cannot be presented as a primary or secondary effect of the *abusus* (McCann, Barbe).

Once the method has been spread among the masses, social effects as well as individual effects can be established.

e. Social questions

The paradox of birth prevention as a phenomenon of the masses is that, even from the social viewpoint, it produces an effect contrary to that hoped for and that promised.

Just as it has been shown to be an illusion that the quality of the progeny can be bettered at the expense of quantity, so it is an illusion that social misery can be mitigated or removed by birth limitation and that the social question can be resolved by this means. Even in this matter, it has been shown that the opposite is the case: namely, that though the individual can procure more in a social sense, he does so at the expense of others. If, however, the matter is viewed in its entirety, it will be seen that there is no result other than that of perpetuating social misery, so that instead of resolving the social question by means of a just wage and just distribution of goods, it becomes incumbent upon the people who work honestly to have evasive recourse to something much more convenient, the prevention of birth.

In order to understand the impact of these things, there is need of explaining in detail the decrease of births, its causes and its biological, social and moral effects. This would be the task of social hygiene.

f. Judgment according to moral theology

(a) General view

Judging the problems from the purely natural and social view-point, it appears quite evident that *abusus matrimonii* is a grave evil. The gravity of the effects from a hygienic and social stand-point corresponds to the gravity of the evil itself. The judgment of moral theology is in complete accordance with these facts.

Moral theology considers onanism an action *contra naturam*, a *res in se* (*intrinsecus*) *mala*. Hence onanism is a *peccatum grave*. Its *malitia specifica* lies in the frustration of the *finis primarius matrimonii* and the following moral benefits: conjugal fidelity, health of the spouses, and the *bonum commune* (*societatis*). For this reason Holy Scripture designates it a *res detestabilis*. Moral theology has always condemned onanism as such, as *intrinsecus malum*, as *iure naturali et divino prohibitum* (St. Alphonsus, Gury, Ballerini, Lehmkuhl). Its intrinsic perversity cannot be changed by a motive that is in se irreprovable—as for example, the grave sick-ness of the wife (medical indication), danger of tainted progeny (eugenic indication), or penury (social indication).

Justified ends should be fulfilled exclusively by licit means: If the end is good but the means evil, the whole action would be evil (*non sunt facienda mala ut eveniant bona*).

This is so in greater measure when serious motives are not present but instead pretexts such as the following are found: fear of responsibility and sacrifice, egoism, convenience and the desire for pleasure.

The reasons for the intrinsic perversity of onanism which we have pointed out, have their basis in the natural order itself, in the *ius naturale*. To these are added others which are of the super-natural order: The profanation of matrimony as a sacrament; the rebellion of man against the divine precept *Crescite et multiplica-mini*, which is the indispensable condition for the complete execution of the command imposed on civilization: "Subdue the earth."

In the last analysis, it is therefore the *non serviam* which is behind this rebellion.

It is therefore a case of absolute misunderstanding of the situation to hold that the Church, in consideration of the circumstances of

G

the time, can and should mitigate its rigorous attitude toward this problem (Rauch).

The gravity and import of the moral disorder have been often misinterpreted, even by competent persons animated by a spirit of false humanitarianism. Thus the conference of Anglican bishops held in Lambeth, 1930, presumed to be able to pronounce, under certain presuppositions, the necessity of tolerating birth prevention.

On the contrary, the Catholic Church, despite the hostility of an epoch gone astray, has firmly held to correct doctrine. Time has shown her right. Even medicine, which for a decade declared birth prevention inevitable, has begun to give way in some instances to the conviction that its effects are pernicious. Thus, even in this sphere, the agreement of Catholic morality and science is being confirmed.

Imperialistic and military politics, which in recent times have tried to influence medicine and biology, provide a motivation which has nothing to do with Catholic morality. The Church is concerned with the commandment of God, the purity of matrimony and family, and with souls. The latter is concerned with social justice and not simply with the increase in the number of births. This latter is secondary and is spontaneously verified when the primary moral goods are respected.

(b) *Special questions*

(1) *Co-operation of the innocent marital party*

Formal co-operation, i.e., accompanied by internal consent, renders one an accomplice in any circumstance. Material co-operation, which is verified by mere tolerance without internal consent, is in general conceivable only on the part of the wife. If the husband seeks the *debitum*, using condomistic Onanism, a much more serious reason is required to permit a wife's rendering the debt than if the husband intends withdrawal. If he uses a condom, the wife must resist, even physically, unless a very grave cause excuses such resistance, e.g., physical harm or breakup of home. Even in such an extreme case, she must remain passive and take no deliberate pleasure as well as manifest her disapproval. If the husband contemplates withdrawal with semination *extra vaginam*, then the wife may permit intercourse and even, for her personal need, may request it since this act at least begins in a natural manner.

(2) *Copula dimidiata—Actus imperfecti*

The fulfillment and tolerance of *actus imperfecti* in marriage are not intrinsically illicit, especially if they can in any way contribute to the fulfillment of an essential end of matrimony. This need not absolutely be merely the *procreatio prolis*.

In regard to the method of *carezza (amplexus reservatus)*, which substantially consists in *actus imperfecti*, it can be rightly presumed that it is not in se illicit. Yet the inner structure of the action is at least very suspicious. Even if a direct *abusus matrimonii* does not exist, it approaches very closely the intention of procuring, by means of *actus imperfecti*, a *delectatio venerea minus plena*, without fulfilling the duty of *procreatio prolis*.

The *copula dimidiata* is neither to be considered a species of onanism nor an *actus imperfectus*. Yet in regard to the internal structure of the act, the same holds as for the method of *carezza*.

(3) *Lotiones post congressum*

Concerning the question of the moral liceity of douches immediately following *congressus*, the most reputable moralists expressly state that every attempt to eliminate the received semen (*expulsio seminis recepti*), either by douches or mechanical means, is illicit: "Every action by means of which there is attempted the expulsion of the received semen for the purpose of impeding conception is in se evil and constitutes a serious sin, and hence cannot be justified because of any kind of inconvenience. Such inconveniences can dispense from the marriage duty, but cannot render licit an action which is in se illicit."

There is only one exception and this is the case of violence outside marriage. "If it has not been possible to resist violence with violence, it is permissible to remove the semen by means of douche."

This is valid only within a short time immediately after the stuprum, because otherwise, in certain circumstances, an attempt at *procuratio abortus* would be present and this can never be licit.

From the medical standpoint, vaginal douches are considered "attempts with inadequate means."

(4) *Media cavendi onanismi*

When pregnancy exposes a woman to grave danger of life, the only permissible means of avoiding this danger is absolute abstinence.

When it does not seem possible nor necessary to observe absolute abstinence, there remains only recourse to partial abstinence: so-called periodic abstinence.

It is the task of the doctor to take into account the restricted limits within which it can be applied. Only within these limits can it act as a " medium cavendi onanismi."

(5) Co-operation of the doctor

Here the question to be discussed is that of finding out whether and up to what point the doctor can advise control of conception.

At one time it was considered unworthy of a doctor to dedicate himself to a study of such a question. In a time of social misery and moral confusion, he would abandon the sick, without counsel, to their spiritual needs and conflicts of conscience as well as to the most pernicious influences. In more recent times the old principle has been inverted, and it is required of the doctor as a duty to give patients more detailed counsel concerning control of concep-tion. That such behavior, from the viewpoint of Christian deonto-logy, is unworthy of a doctor, requires no special argument.

The proper attitude can only consist in this: that the doctor does not turn away from examining a question which admits of such responsibility. The doctor cannot take this matter lightly by omit-ting a discussion of this question and simply recommending birth prevention. Often he does not know what the effects of the words: " She should no longer have children," will have. With these words, he places his patients on the road to abuses and *abortus* and is responsible in conscience.

The doctor has, rather, the task of placing before the eyes of those seeking counsel the dangers of birth prevention. He should make it very clear that, in the long run, they themselves will be affected by the evil consequences.

He should renounce any ephemeral success and apparent popu-larity. He should have the courage to use all his authority in this question, as well in that of abortion, against the errors of a mentally morose and erroneous attitude, even at the cost of losing clients who do not wish to be instructed. Only in this way will he serve his patients as a true doctor.

In cases in which there is justification, but only in such cases, the doctor can and should discuss with the sick all the possibilities of avoiding conception, which are in accordance with the moral law and at the same time not of serious detriment from the hygienic point of view.

g. Doctrinal decisions of the Church

(1) A decision of the Sacred Penitentiary given November 16, 1816, treats of the co-operation of the innocent spouses and of the conditions under which there is not a case of formal co-operation.

(2) A decision of the Sacred Penitentiary given on February 1, 1823, examines the question of the circumstances in which a wife, who has tried in vain to prevent the abuse of marriage by the husband, is authorized to tolerate this abuse.

(3) One of the decisions of the Sacred Penitentiary most frequently cited is that of June 8, 1842, which, to the question of Bishop of Le Mans, answers that the wife is exonerated if she tolerates matrimonial abuse in a purely passive manner and for a grave cause.

The second part of the decision to the question whether the confessor has the duty in all circumstances to investigate whenever there is suspicion of matrimonial abuse answers that such a duty is not absolutely indispensable. This decision has been cited on many occasions but its meaning is often falsified, as if the Church agreed to *abusus matrimonii* and concedes to the spouses *bona fides* in all circumstances.

Such errors are diffused when ignorant or interested persons isolate and generalize decisions given for a special and determined case.

How wrong such an interpretation is can be clearly seen from the following decisions.

(4) A decision of the Sacred Penitentiary given on May 27, 1947, on the question whether absolution could be given to a woman when she herself desires *copula interrupta* and does not try to prevent it, although she is able to do so: answer, " negative."

(5) On May 21, 1851, and on April 19, 1853, the Sacred Congregation of the Holy Office decided in the same manner.

(6) Most significant are two decisions of the Sacred Penitentiary given on March 10, 1886, and November 13, 1901. They regard the question of the comportment of the confessor and his duty to question the spouses and, if necessary, to refuse them absolution. They show that it is erroneous to be content with the simple pre-

sumption of *bona fides*. A response of the Sacred Penitentiary given on December 14, 1876, states: *Non esse licitum favere poenitentium errori (circa onanismum) qui a multis bona fides dicitur, nec talem errorem creare.*

(7) A decision of the Sacred Penitentiary given April 3, 1916, declares that a woman threatened by her husband with serious threat may tolerate sexual intercourse in an onanistic way; on the contrary, under no circumstances, even under the threat of death, can she permit sodomistic relations.

(8) The Holy Office answered on November 22, 1922, a question of the bishops from the diocese of Utrecht. From this decision it is declared illicit for confessors to counsel and teach on their own the method of *copula dimidiata.*

The encyclical "Casti Connubii" has taken the position in a most ample manner in the question of *abusus matrimonii.* It solemnly condemns birth prevention by means of perverting the marriage act:

"At nulla profecto ratio, ne gravissima quidem, efficere potest, ut quot intrinsece est contra naturam, id cum natura congruens et honestum fiat. Cum autem actus coniugii suapte natura proli generandae sit destinatus, qui, in eo exercendo, naturali hac eum vi atque virtute de industria destituunt, contra naturam agunt et turpe quid atque intrinsece inhonestum operantur." (N.55)

("But there can be no reason, no matter how grave, that can render something intrinsically against nature, conformable to nature and morally good. And hence, since the use of marriage is, by its nature, directed toward the generation of children, those who, in using the same intentionally render it incapable of this effect, act contrary to nature and perform an evil and intrinsically immoral act.")

In regard to the position taken at the Lambeth Conference, it has been declared: If someone, deviating from the Christian doctrine transmitted by uninterrupted tradition, believes that he is able to officially and solemnly impart something different, the Catholic Church raises her voice against such moral decadence by reaffirming her mission of maintaining intact the purity of the matrimonial bond and again announces: "Quemlibet matrimonii usum, in quo exercendo, actus, de industria hominum, naturali sua vitae procreandae vi destituatur, Dei et naturae legem infringere et eos qui tale quid commiserint gravis noxae labe commaculari." (N. 57).

("Any use of marriage in which, through human malice, the act is made devoid of its natural procreative power, is contrary to the law of God, and those who dare to commit such an act render themselves guilty of serious sin.") Through the supreme doctrinal authority as well as solemn declarations *ex cathedra*, confessors are bound not to leave the faithful in error concerning this commandment of God, which imposes such grave duties, and not to allow themselves, through weakness, to yield to false opinions.

Against culpable silence toward certain errors, the encyclical reminds the shepherds of souls of their responsibility to God for the abuse of their ministry, recalling the words of God: "They are blind guides of blind men. But if a blind man guides a blind man, both fall into a pit" (N. 58).

"Si quis vero confessarius aut animarum Pastor, quod Deus avertat, fideles sibi creditos aut in hos errores ipsemet induxerit, aut saltem sive approbando, sive dolose tacendo in iis confirmarit, sciat se Supremo Iudice Deo de muneris proditione severam redditurum esse rationem, sibique dicta existimet Christi verba: 'Caeci sunt et duces caecorum: caecus autem si caeco ducatum praestet, ambo in foveam cadunt'" (Matt. 15:14).

"Should any confessor or pastor of souls, God forbid, lead the faithful committed to him into such errors, or confirm the same by either approving the same or culpably remaining silent, let him know that he will have to render severe account of his misuse of office to God, the supreme Judge. He will have to apply to himself the words of Christ: 'They are blind guides of blind men. But if a blind man guide a blind man, both fall into a pit.'" (Matt. 15:14).

These serious words pertain especially to the supposed pastoral prudence which, through motives of opportunity, omits the instruction which duty demands, and justifies this omission under the pretext of not wishing to change material sin into formal sin.

h. Pastoral considerations

The spiritual treatment of couples given to onanism calls without doubt for pastoral prudence and dogmatic firmness on the part of the spiritual director himself. It demands great knowledge, great tact, comprehension and firmness. In this sphere more than in any other, proper co-operation between priest and doctor can facilitate much the scope of both. The priest can and should know the definite results brought about by medical investigation and take these into account. The doctor must learn and recognize the primacy of morality and appreciate the fundamental laws of Pastoral Medicine, realizing that whatever is false from the moral point of view cannot ever be right from the hygienic standpoint. Otherwise, his counsel would have no value whatsoever; in fact, it would be harmful.

The doctor who possesses a deep scientific knowledge and who is familiar with the universalistic criterion of Pastoral Medicine can be of great help to the priest.

Proper medical information will give to the priest the beneficial and strengthening feeling of absolute agreement between Catholic morality and medical science. Thus the faithful collaboration of the doctor can be for the priest a comfort and help in one of his most difficult tasks.

In what concerns *bona fides* of the spouses there is almost always missing the essential requisite which, when present, would justify leaving the material sinner in subjective good faith.

Married people know most of the time very accurately what the problem consists in.

Despite our realization that social misery is often unbearable, and our understanding of human motives, abuse as such can never be condoned nor approved nor even tolerated by silence. The spouses who have learned the last details of the method are not ingenuous enough to be able to allege their *bona fides* in regard to the moral quality of the action. And if they are led astray through propaganda, there arises the precise duty of bringing them back to the path of the truth. In accord with the encyclical "Casti Connubii," outstanding moralists directly speak of a betrayal of office.

As a resumé, the following can be stated : In the question of birth prevention, the Church has found herself in the very difficult position of maintaining her point of view without compromise. She has been exposed to the most bitter criticism because of her supposedly inexorable rigidity and even inhumanity. It has been said that her viewpoint is incompatible with biological and modern medical knowledge and that she is opposed to the progress of humanity. However, the effects that have been verified have shown how properly the Church has acted, even in this field.

Facts have demonstrated that true science cannot lead to any other result but that of agreement with the Church; that only the

Church has been animated by benevolence toward man and represents authentic humanity.

Without doubt, Catholic morality requires heroism. But without heroism, the only way of salvation, that of "return to the thought of God," is not accessible. In order to attain this to the end, there is need of more than simple "heroism"; there is need of grace.

Therefore, whoever depends solely on the means offered by nature and does not consider the fallen nature of man, cannot by his own strength liberate himself from sin; and whoever fails to recognize the function of grace will find these problems insoluble. These can be solved only by adopting the universalistic criterion which takes into account the gifts of nature in their totality, as well as supernatural gifts.

2. Inviolability of Human Life

A. GENERAL PRINCIPLES

1. PRELIMINARY CONCEPTS

The right to life is " the original right that man has at generation and is the basis of all other rights." Hence the destruction of human life is an act which affects the most profound strata of individual and community life.

A living testimony profoundly symbolical of the fact that this act "affects the most profound basis" is the account of Sacred Scripture in which the first-born son of the first human couple, Cain, killed his brother Abel.

Considered in the light of depth psychology, the internal processes which preceded and followed the crime have found in this narration an imperishable representation that is universally and eternally valid.

In the general moral law of humanity, the Decalogue, God Himself has clearly and unequivocally pronounced: *Non occides.*

2. LIMITATIONS OF THE RIGHT TO LIFE

Every life is called into existence by God Himself. For the religious person this is the supreme foundation for the inviolability of the life of the human being. To one who does not recognize God, life is not sacred. He who offends against the sacred character of life infringes on the sovereign rights of God. Every life is sanctified through the sanctity of the Creator. All rights are derived from God, the Supreme Judge, who is the first Cause of all beings, of knowledge and love—the primary source of every right. Starting with this presupposition, we must determine whether and at what point the right to life has limits, over and above which man is not obliged to respect another's right to life; whether, in case of a conflict of rights, man may, given certain circumstances, injure the right to life of another.

The question of the limits of the right to life is one of the most difficult and most delicate questions of legal and moral philosophy. Basically different is the judgment when the question is a matter of the right to life of men versus the right of another kind of living being.

If the principle of indiscriminate inviolability of all life were extended to the extreme, as is held by Buddhism, then all human life would be extinguished. Man, in order to conserve his own life, is constrained to destroy vegetative and animal life. If and up to what point a limitation in favor of animal life is to be made, is a question that will be examined in another place. In any case, God has transmitted to man within certain limits the right of sovereignty over lower living nature. It is, therefore, permissible for man to make use of animals and plants as much as he needs to do so. The need as such designates the limits within which man must respect the right of animals and plants to life. Their right to life is thus only a conditional right, since otherwise every life would have to cease. In nature, according to the divine plan, one living being is dependent upon another.

Man is endowed with an immortal soul and so has a right to life that is basically an unconditional right, even though it is not an unlimited right. The limits here placed by the moral law will mean that under some circumstances the right is qualified and exceptions to the law must in justice be made.

3. LICIT CASES

Among the licit cases the most important are legitimate defense and the state of necessity. The fundamental illiceity of the destruction of life arises directly from the general moral recognition of all men, as well as from the revealed divine positive law: *non occides*. Hence the killing of an innocent person is, without exception, illicit.

a. Self-defense

The killing of an unjust aggressor (*iniustus aggressor*) is licit in cases of legitimate defense. Inasmuch as this seems to constitute a limit of the right to life, the right to legitimate defense is itself an expression of the right to life. The right to legitimate defense creates a motive of justification for the objectively illicit act. It removes from this act the illiceity as well as moral transgression, with the sole condition that the right to legitimate defense does not go beyond the proper limits, and that one who exercises legitimate defense does not go too far in the use of his right and does not become on his part an unjust aggressor. Both the positive juridical order and the moral order permit killing in legitimate defense.

b. Necessity

It is different in the case of necessity. Here the basis is an innocent conflict between two rights to life. In such a case, the question occurs for the most part in the following terms. May one life be sacrificed when, otherwise, both would be lost?

Well known is the ancient example of the " Plank of Carneades." Two shipwrecked persons struggle for a plank which can only hold one of them. May the one, the stronger, push the other into the sea so that both will not be lost?

A famous example of legitimate defense and the state of necessity at the same time is that of the *arcta via*. May a fugitive in order to save his life run over a child on a narrow street which does not allow any deviation? The moralists distinguish in this case whether flight arises from legitimate defense in the face of an unjust aggressor or as a result of a physical state of necessity. In the last case, the principle prevails that the child has an equal right to life.

In the often-discussed case of flight from hungry wolves, the answer is that it is never licit for parents (adults) to throw the child to the wolves to save their own lives. On the other hand, there is nothing against the father (or mother) sacrificing himself in order to save the spouse and child.

In the preceding example of the *arcta via*, there remains an unsatisfactory feature : the point that, in this flight from undeserved attack, the right of self-defense would be exercised not against an unjust aggressor. It would instead threaten an innocent third party. Another question usually associated with the state of necessity is the so-called valuation of goods. May minor interests be subordinated or sacrificed to greater interests? These two questions show that in the state of necessity there is consideration of something entirely different from the right of legitimate defense. The state of necessity can never in se remove illiceity from the act. It can, at most, eliminate "punishment" in the form of a positive right; public authority simply renounces, for reasons of equity, the right of punishment which was in se objectively present.

Hence extreme necessity can be, in a juridical and positive ordinance based on the natural right, merely a personal motive for exclusion from punishment, i.e., such as favors only the person affected. Inasmuch as the state of necessity is provoked by inculpable and elementary occurrences, it can, in certain circumstances justify the exclusion from guilt (motive of exclusion from guilt), but never to the point of excluding illiceity itself. The act, as such, is and remains illegal and morally illicit.

It is evident from this that the impunity (sanctioned by positive law) of an action resulting from a state of extreme necessity is not the same thing as moral liceity. Homicide, even if committed in extreme necessity, remains in se sinful. There is no state of necessity which can justify the killing of an innocent party: "Neque ullum adest 'extremae necessitatis ius' quod vocant, quodque usque ad innocentis directam occisionem pervenire possit" (Encyclical "Casti Connubii," N. 64).

Since it is a question of the right to life, not even the principle of valuation of goods can here be invoked (e.g., the question whether the life of the mother is more precious than that of the child). The right to life of two persons is equally sacred, and no public authority can give the right to violate it: *Res enim neque sacra utriusque vita, cuius opprimendae nulla esse umquam poterit ne publicae quodem auctoritate facultas.*

Finally, who can ever possess the norm to judge which of the two lives is, from the viewpoint of "valuation of goods," the more precious? Such a pretense would be presumption and would surpass every human capacity.

4. GENERAL MORAL PRINCIPLES

In order to judge an action from the viewpoint of Pastoral Medicine, the following general moral principles are decisive. The essential elements of a freely responsible human act (*actus humanus*), upon whose relation with the supreme moral norm the goodness or moral perversity of an act depend, are: the object, the end, the means, the motives and the circumstances of the act.

a. Object, end, and means

The object is that to which an act is intrinsically directed. It gives to it its moral, primary and essential qualifications (*ex obiecto*).

The end is to be understood as the end of the agent (*finis operantis*): that which the will of the agent strives to reach by means of the action. The end of the action in se (*finis operis*) is that to which the action is of its nature ordained and is identical with the object of the action.

The moral character of the action is determined in every case by the end:

(1) If the act is good *ex obiecto*, and the end is indifferent, the action does not become evil;

(2) An act, in se evil, cannot become good through a good end, but is and remains evil;

(3) An act, in se evil, is not changed by an indifferent end, but remains evil;

(4) An act, in se indifferent, acquires its moral character, above all, from the goodness or perversity of the end.

In regard to the relation between the end and the means, the following principles hold:

(1) If the end is good and the means good or indifferent, the act is good;

(2) If the end is evil and the means good, the act is evil;

(3) If the end is good and the means evil, the act is evil (*non sunt facienda mala ut eveniant bona*);

(4) If one of the elements of the act is evil, the whole act becomes evil (*bonum ex integra causa malum ex quovis defectu*).

b. Circumstances

The circumstances (*circumstantiae*) can influence the moral character of the act:

(1) An indifferent act (*ex obiecto*) can become good or evil *ex circumstantibus*;

(2) An act good *ex obiecto* can become evil *ex circumstantibus*;

(3) An act good or evil *ex obiecto* can acquire, *ex circumstantibus*, new goodness or new perversity;

(4) An act good or evil *ex obiecto* can become *ex circumstantibus* more or less good or evil;

In this last case, regarding evil acts one speaks of diminishing or aggravating circumstances (*circumstantiae imminuentes v. aggravantes*).

c. Moral systems

In doubtful cases, directives result from the moral system. The most important of these are: Tutiorism, Probabiliorism, Equiprobabilism and Probabilism. The question here is whether, in doubtful cases, one is obliged to follow the more rigorous interpretation (*pro lege*) or one may follow the more moderate interpretation (*pro libertate*). In definite cases of particular importance and responsibility, the rigorous principle *in dubio pars tutior eligenda est* is imposed. Moreover, the differences among the systems are characterized as follows: Absolute tutiorism teaches that the safer opinion is always to be followed even though the opposite opinion is very probable.

Mitigated tutiorism teaches that the safer opinion is to be followed unless the opposite opinion, *pro libertate*, is very probable.

Probabiliorism teaches that an opinion less safe (in favor of liberty) may be followed provided it is more probable than the opinion favoring law.

Equiprobabilism teaches that one may follow a probable opinion in favor of liberty when the opposite opinion favoring law is equally or almost equally probable.

Probabilism teaches that it is permissible to follow a less safe opinion favoring liberty provided it is solidly and certainly probable. The probability of an opinion is based upon the weight of the arguments, the strength of which merits the consent of a prudent person even if there exists the probability of a contrary opinion. Today, the majority of moralists follow the system of probabilism.

These distinctions, apparently theoretical and abstract, have great practical importance in the judgment of the moral liceity of medical intervention in controversial or doubtful cases. Moreover, the distinction between *voluntarium directum* and *indirectum* (*in causa*) is of importance.

This distinction has particular practical importance in all the medical interventions affecting the right to life.

5. DIRECT AND INDIRECT HOMICIDE

It is deduced from the general moral principles that a direct homicide (*occisio directa*) is present when the destruction of life is directly intended by the agent. It is irrelevant here whether the homicide is intended as an end or simply as a means.

Homicide is indirect if the action has a twofold effect (*duplex effectus*) and if its nature does not tend solely toward homicide; if it is not done with the intention of killing but death comes as a result of this act solely as a collateral effect (hence not *aeque certe et immediate*), even if this is foreseen or could be foreseen.

An example of indirect homicide would be the treatment of a pregnant woman, gravely sick, with medications which are indispensable in her case but which, in definite circumstances, can as a collateral effect bring about abortion—as, for example, quinine. The killing of the fetus as such is not intended, but at most is accepted as a lamentable and inevitable consequence.

An example of direct homicide would be the provocation of an abortion even if there is present the intention of saving or prolonging, by that means, the life of the mother. In such a case, the homicide as such is intended, and even if applied for a good end, it remains in se an evil means.

6. WAYS OF VIOLATING THE RIGHT TO LIFE—CLASSIFICATION

The violation of the right to life can refer both to one's own life and to the life of one's neighbor. It can consist in the destruction or endangering of life—in the destruction of the body or in the mutilation of bodily integrity.

The following concrete possibilities arise:

a. Destruction of life:

(1) One's own life;
(2) The life of someone else.

b. Mutilation of bodily integrity:

(1) One's own integrity;
(2) The integrity of another.

In both groups the possibility of cases in which illiceity is excluded must be examined.

The questions which are to be discussed here correspond to an important sphere of contact between moral theology on the one hand, and moral philosophy and philosophy of law and Pastoral Medicine on the other.

In the following pages, we will briefly consider, first, the questions limited to moral philosophy and philosophy of law, then those of Pastoral Medicine, as far as such a division can be rigorously effected.

The first question concerns the sovereignty of man over other living beings, and, at the same time, the question of carnal nourishment, which constitutes a hygienic problem.

The division thus contains the following themes:

I. *Questions of moral philosophy*

The right of conserving one's own life; the duty of self-preservation;

The right to kill animals; vivisection; protection of animals; protection of nature;

Suicide; self-mutilation; homicide at request; duel;

Vendetta of blood; capital punishment; war.

II. *Questions of Pastoral Medicine*

Infanticide; craniotomy; abortion; the right to operate; Sterilization; castration; euthanasia.

B. PARTICULAR QUESTIONS

I. Questions of Moral Philosophy

1. SELF-PRESERVATION

Just as man has the duty to respect another's right to life, so he has the duty to preserve his own life. Life was not given by himself, but was bestowed by God with the intention, above all, that he conserve it for the supernatural life. Man therefore has the right to self-preservation, but also the duty of self-preservation.

The duty of self-preservation also implies the observance of a healthy mode of life and, in particular, the abstaining from all that might have a harmful effect (excesses, narcotics), from endangering one's life without reason and weakening one's health and strength. Health is not only an object of right, but also constitutes a demand of duty.

This duty also includes the conservation of health, the integrity of the body and its members, which implies the proper use of the body and its members by avoiding every abuse.

In the conservation of one's health, man is obliged to use ordinary means. The obligation to use extraordinary means is not unlimited (e.g., undergoing operations).

In the present state of surgery and anesthesia, a surgical operation is no longer considered per se, as formerly, a *medium extraordinarium*; hence there may now be an absolute obligation to undergo a needed operation. There is not, however, an absolute obligation to undergo any very painful operation, any *amputatio notabilis*, etc. The duty of self-preservation also implies the procuring of all that is necessary for life (food, medicine) for oneself and for those entrusted to one's care (family, those requiring protection). There is therefore no doubt that, in conserving his life, man is authorized to make use of plants and animals. Whether the right extends to the point of killing animals depends on the question of whether and how far this is necessary. It is a question that cannot be resolved in a manner equally strict for all parts of the earth. In northern lands, especially in the Arctic regions, man depends much more on fish and flesh for food than in the fertile southern region.

The structure of human teeth in general corresponds, in its functional capacity, to both the herbivorous and the carnivorous. Hence, from nature itself, one cannot deduce general irrefutable arguments against the moral liceity of the use of meat.

The ascetical question of whether the renunciation of meat as nourishment must, for superior motives and in determined circumstances, be considered of higher merit, should not be confused with the moral question concerning the liceity of the use of meat, nor with the hygienic question of whether it is not more healthy for man to avoid nourishment from meat or to limit its use to the strictest necessity.

God gave man the right of sovereignty over the earth and living beings: "Fill the earth and subdue it, and rule over the fishes of the sea, and the fowls of the air, and all living creatures that move upon the earth. And God said: Behold, I have given you every herb-bearing seed upon the earth, and all trees that have in themselves seed of their own kind, to be your meat; and to all beasts of the earth, . . . that they may have to feed upon" (Gen. 1:28-30).

2. VIVISECTION

In the same manner, the question of so-called vivisection, i.e., of scientific experiments upon living animals, is answered. The term "vivisection," used to indicate this kind of experiment, contains a spurious element, since here there is no question of a "section" but merely of surgical operations on animals, for which anesthesia is used whenever possible.

Inasmuch as such experiments really serve the necessary ends of scientific investigation, especially conservation of the life and health of man, and inasmuch as these are indispensable—i.e., they cannot be substituted for by any other means of equal value in resolving scientific questions—their use cannot be morally illicit. But this is so only within indicated limits. When these are used merely for scientific demonstration—as, for example, in lectures— they are to be rejected inasmuch as the didactic end can be equally fulfilled by other means. In this case, illustrations or films can serve the purpose. Experiments performed without necessity during class merely tend to diminish in students the respect for life.

In this connection there arises the position to be taken in questions concerning the protection of animals and the protection of nature.

Every torment inflicted upon animals comes not only from the lack of love for living beings, but also from lack of respect for the Creator. This respect must also determine one's complete attitude toward nature. But there are exaggerations in this matter which are based on an erroneous attitude. Where the limits between man and the world of beings inferior to man are not exactly determined, the falsely understood *Tat twam asi* ("You are this"), raises the animal to the same degree as man, and at the same time lowers man from the position given him by nature.

The more animal life is protected, the more man loses the protection which is necessary for him and the picture of man becomes devaluated and destroyed. Thus, this concept—related to Buddhism—definitely exercises an action adverse to life and culture.

The true protection of nature must rest on respect for God and upon the just view of the position that man has in nature. A protection of nature which rests exclusively on legislative and penal sanctions will always be insufficient, and often arises too late to avoid destruction of the most precious treasures of nature. *Quid leges sine moribus?* (Mai).

It is the task of education to inculcate, from earliest youth, this respect and love in hearts and thus there will spontaneously result an interior attitude: *Ama—et fac, quod vis* (St. Augustine).

3. SUICIDE

a. General view

Man has not given life to himself—it was given to him as a mission. Hence suicide is not only an infraction of the fifth commandment and of the love commanded by God, and a violation of the duty of self-preservation, but is also a violation of the sovereign rights of God and hence a sin against the first commandment. Inasmuch as it is committed by one who despairs of God's mercy, it is a sin against the Holy Spirit.

Man does not have absolute sovereignty over life, neither his own life nor the life of another: We are not lords over life and death. The immorality of suicide is obscured in the conscience of man when suicide is represented as an heroic act, or at least as an indifferent act euphemistically called "free death." This designation is intended to emphasize liberty on the part of man in ridding himself of life. Actually there is reference here to nothing else but the liberty of opposing one's human will to the will of God.

The ennobling of suicide by considering it an act of liberty is opposed directly to the Christian philosophy of the cross—that is, to unconditional submission to the will of God and the humble proposal to carry the cross no matter how heavy it may be.

The heroism of patient suffering is today less highly evaluated than the heroism of action, even if it is the unruly action of self-destruction.

b. Criteria of distinction

These general criteria retain their validity even apart from the consideration that there are numerous cases of suicide in which the person committing suicide does not have full or exclusive responsibility. Suicide committed in the state of endogenous depression is caused by a morbid (pathological) mental disturbance (psychosis), and hence is carried out without free determination of the will, without responsibility (imputability). Even so-called diminished imputability can reduce freedom of will to a point of eliminating almost all responsibility.

Cases of this type are often connected with phases of female sex life (psychosis of menstruation, of pregnancy, puerperal and lactation psychosis): psychosis in moral depression arising from the climacterium.

The suicides of students, which are not rare, can also be associated with the mental disturbances of puberty.

Moreover, there are not a few suicides in which the true and proper fault is imputable more to someone else than the one committing the suicide. This can be designated as (indirectly) induced or (passive) suicide. These suicides can be classified as " short-circuit actions " arising during a state of thoughtlessness similar to that provoked by shock (Pintachovius). These cases, together with suicides arising from a state of depressive melancholy, of obsessive neurosis, or hysterical syndromes, represent cases of notably diminished imputability; while the premeditated suicide, in which a life full of failure comes to termination, definitely represents nothing but a flight from the consequences of a course of life.

Recently, various attempts have been made to present suicide in certain circumstances as a duty, as for example, when committed as a means of putting an end to life which has become useless and " without worth " and which can only be a burden to parents or community, etc. (Cf. *Euthanasia*.) (Here the use of " hara-kiri " among the samurai is to be recalled: a form of suicide employed in a pagan cult.)

c. Particular cases of suicide

To the cases which demand a different moral evaluation belong those in which suicide constitutes the sacrifice of one's life for the salvation of others, either the people or the Fatherland.

The sacrifice of one's life for a higher end is permitted insofar as in it an *auctoritas divina* can be recognized: the sacrifice of life by a soldier, a miner or fireman to save his fellow men, his comrades; the sacrifice of a doctor who has risked his life through dangerous experiments, on the success of which the cure of his fellow men can depend. However, mere ambition must not be the motive.

When a married or single woman commits suicide to avoid dishonour, the moral responsibility of death will fall, in the first place, on the culpable person, and this also in cases in which a person is led to desperation and suicide through the fault of another.

d. Social factors

In recent years statistics have shown that the tendency to suicide has increased, especially in large cities and industrial centers. The causes are many and diverse. There is no doubt, however, that social causes play an important role in cases in which various social needs, employment, requirements for family life, etc., are not fulfilled.

The continuous increase in suicides among women is, without doubt, attributable to the increase of the number of women engaged in industrial work outside the home. This social causal factor is to be combated only through social measures.

The other principal factor for the numerical rise of suicide is to be found in the mental sphere and in one's outlook on life. The extirpation of religion is principally responsible in this case. Whenever an attempt has been made to give practical help by establishing places of consultation and aid for such people, it has been seen that the matter is possible only if, together with the attempt to alleviate the social need, there is also an attempt toward a psychoreligious reconstruction. Only when this is so will the help be assured.

4. SELF-MUTILATION AND VOLUNTARY LESION

The causes of voluntary lesion are principally of a twofold nature: first, the attempt to remove oneself from a burdensome or insupportable obligation, something that is frequent in war but found even in the field of labor; second, to procure for oneself or one's relatives certain advantages through receipt of a pension, a premium of security, etc. Here belong the not entirely rare cases of insurance fraud. The methods and the possibilities of voluntary lesion are extraordinarily diverse. The immorality of the action presents many aspects: besides the infraction of the commandment of self-preservation, there is the violation of moral imperatives, more or less obliging in conscience and, in many cases, also, the element of fraud. In very rare cases there arises the motive of injuring or making another ill, as happens in voluntary lesion through sexual motives.

Regarding voluntary lesion or consent to illicit lesions, the encyclical "Casti Connubii" declares: ". . . Ipsi privati homines in sui corporis membra dominatum alium non habent quam qui ad eorum naturales finis pertinet, nec possint ea destruere aut mutilare aut alia via ad naturales functiones se ineptos reddere, nisi quando bono totius corporis aliter provideri nequeat" (N. 71).

(". . . The same private men have no other dominion over the members of their body than that which pertains to their natural end, and they may not destroy or mutilate or render them in any way inept in the performing of their natural functions except in the case where the good of the entire body cannot be provided for by any other way.")

There can be a licit case, then, when the good of the entire body, the *bonum commune*, cannot be safeguarded by any other way, as, for example, when, in case of necessity, one amputates his hand in order not to endanger his life through gangrene or infection (sepsis).

5. SOLICITED HOMICIDE

From what has been already said, even death at request is illicit. Basically this kind of death does not differ from suicide; it merely makes another person an instrument and therefore represents a *suicidum mediatum*. The actions of the executor are to be judged according to the same criteria which hold in the question of euthanasia. (Cf. below.)

6. CAPITAL PUNISHMENT

From the viewpoint of moral philosophy, capital punishment is considered an emanation of the right to life and death delegated by God to the supreme authority of the state, a right which, in the patriarchal epochs of pagan Rome, the father of the family (*pater familias*) had as an expression of his regal power (*ius vitae ac necis*). Christ Himself recognizes this power of state authority. When questioned by Pilate: " Dost Thou know that I have power to crucify Thee? " He answered: " Thou wouldst have no power at all over Me were it not given thee from above " (John 19:10-11).

Arguments against capital punishment cannot be based on the fact that legitimate state power does not *have* the right, but only on the doubt as to whether men are capable of exercising such a right with true justice and of not abusing it.

One of the most serious arguments against capital punishment is undoubtedly that in case of judicial error the punishment is irreparable. Less decisive is the other principal argument that capital punishment removes the repentant delinquent from the possibility of conversion and self-improvement. As a matter of fact, the delinquent who is truly repentant can acquire great merit by accepting his punishment and can thus save his soul.

If the problem of capital punishment is viewed exclusively from an earthly point of view, there can be no argument in its favor. If it is looked upon merely as a social measure of safety or as a means of intimidation, experience shows that this means alone is not sufficient to efficaciously limit criminality and to reduce the number of those who are guilty of capital crimes and who constitute a danger to the community. Moreover, the possibility of abuse would make this punishment seem absolutely unacceptable if there were not other viewpoints capable of giving it sense. But these are exclusively supernatural considerations. Among these is the power of earthly authority as a participation in the justice of God. This implies a tremendous responsibility before God. Under this view, capital punishment can be morally justified and can have meaning, if the delinquent suffers death as an expiatory sacrifice for the violation of the right to life committed by him; if he accepts the sacrifice of his physical life in order to save his supernatural life, as did the repentant thief on the cross: ". . . We are receiving what our deeds deserved " (Luke 23:41).

Hence, since the execution of a capital sentence is truly, from the moral viewpoint, of a purifying nature, the Catholic chaplain of a prison can often give instruction, spiritual consolation and assistance which make the delinquent see the punishment as a just expiation. Then, and only then, has capital punishment meaning, and then only can it be transformed into a last earthly benefit for the delinquent inasmuch as, in place of a disturbed earthly life, there is opened up, through the purifying power of death, the passage into supernatural life. However, where the power of the state is not founded upon God, the supreme source of right, the state does not have the right to inflict capital punishment, not even upon those who have committed the most serious crimes.

7. THE JUST WAR

The exclusion of illegality from homicide in wartime is based, as in the case of capital punishment, partly on the principle of the legitimacy of the state authority, by whose order homicide takes place and partly on the principle of the right of legitimate defense. The concept of a "just" war is based upon a superindividual extension of the right to legitimate defense—that is, upon a legitimate collective defense against an unjust aggressor (*iniustus aggressor*).

Up to the present time, moralists are not in accord on the possibility of a "just" war. The most that can be admitted is that a truly "just" war, if one can speak of such, is actually extraordinarily rare. The theoretical possibility of a legitimate defense of the community cannot be absolutely denied. But, in such a case, what counts most is the nature of the goods which are at stake.

Even if history offers numerous examples of war waged through unjust motives, there are but few cases of legitimate defense, of occasions when it was truly necessary to fight in order to save supreme goods. For all other wars in which there has been an attempt to give justification by considering them as *ultima ratio regum*, the following words of Christ are applicable: "All those who take the sword will perish by the sword" (Matt. 26:52).

8. DUEL, MENSUR, AND VENDETTA OF BLOOD

The right of a just war is not applicable to the duel. At the most, it can be applicable to that form of duel which ancient history offers as an example in which two rulers fought each other in place of their people in order to avoid the general shedding of blood.

Dueling is, in se, not intrinsically homicide, but the endangering of one's life or the life of another and is often followed by homicide.

The Church has always opposed dueling; she condemned it in the ancient form of the "judgment of God" (ordeal), a form like that mentioned above, in which two commanders fight as representatives of their armies; moreover, the Church opposed the development of medieval tournaments and, above all, the so-called duel of honor, which arose from the code of honor of a chivalry that deviated from the original idea and established the wild custom of the post-medieval universities.

The duel was condemned as early as 1560 by Pius IV, and after him by Benedict XIV in the bull "Detestabilem" of 1752.

In a decision of the Congregation of the Council on June 13, 1925, the Church compared the "mensur" of qualification (in use among students) to the duel, since it led to an erroneous concept of honor and hence seems preordained toward the duel.

The idea that offended honor can be satisfied only by bloodshed is still more unjustified and immoral than the vendetta of blood.

II. Questions of Pastoral Medicine

1. INFANTICIDE

a. Concept

By infanticide is meant, according to law, the killing of a newly born child on the part of the mother at the moment of birth or immediately after. It is irrelevant whether the child was mature (*partus maturus*) or still immature (*partus praematurus*). What is essential is merely that it was capable of living and actually lived at the moment of the killing.

Hence, the proof that the child lived (breathed) is of decisive importance for the report.

b. Penalty

In nearly all penal legislation, infanticide is punished more lightly than common homicide inasmuch as the mother kills her child at the moment of birth or immediately after. This "datum of privileged fact" prevails, according to German law (#217, Penal Code), for the "illegitimate" mother and favors only her, while the penal codes of other states punish legitimate mothers with a lesser penalty than that imposed for common homicide. However, it may be more severe than that imposed on the illegitimate mother (thus #139 of the Austrian code).

In the same manner abandonment of a child is punished—an act which leaves the child so that he is exposed to the danger of death and his rescue is exclusively left to chance (#149, Austrian Penal Code). This crime is committed by anyone who exposes, in a dangerous place, a child of such an age that he is in need of help.

c. Questions of legal medicine

At one time, besides abortion, which is dangerous to the life of the mother, infanticide was the only means of eliminating an undesired progeny. In the great majority of cases, infanticide had to do with children born out of wedlock. Among certain people infanticide or abandonment of the child is prevalent when twins are born (because of the suspicion of illegitimate pregnancy and, in part also, because of ideas proper to magical pagan cults, such as attributing twin births or other multiple births to diabolical influence). Abandonment also occurs in some places in the case of malformation and even in the case of an excessive number of female births. The motives posited for this procedure are neither concordant, clear nor explicit. In former times, infanticide was punished by death, often in cruel form (impalement or being buried alive).

The milder form of punishment dates back to the French Revolution. Inasmuch as the milder form definitely favors unwed mothers, psychological and social motives are brought into consideration. This is so solely because the deed takes place at the moment of birth or immediately after, since only at this moment can the decision and determination of the will be influenced in a manner so intense that diminished responsibility can be presumed.

At a later point of time, when it can be presumed that the deed was done with full determination and intention, the full punishment for homicide intervenes.

Thus, in the mitigation of punishment, the following are taken into consideration: the affective state following birth, the motives, the so-called fear of dishonor, etc. From the legal viewpoint the question whether the child was still alive after birth can present serious difficulty. For the most part, such a question is posited solely concerning respiration and is decided with the help of the test of " floating " the lungs, stomach and intestines, the results of which are not completely certain. An examination of details of this test would take us too far. Of importance is the question of establishing at what moment the child can be considered born. According to some legislation, the child can be considered born as soon as a part of the body comes to light.

According to English law, a child is considered born alive if it is still living after the complete separation from the mother (cutting of the umbilical cord). For the deed of infanticide, it is for the most part irrelevant whether the child is capable of living, i.e., can continue to live independently.

Inability to live can be taken into consideration as a motive of mitigation in establishing the measure of punishment.

For the rest, the norm is that, according to physiological principles, the object must be considered a human creature; hence, an object so irregular that the possibility of its continuing to live seems excluded (a high court decision of July 9, 1897). Thus, we can speak of infanticide even when it is a case of a monstrous creature (*monstrum*).

In certain circumstances, it is very difficult to distinguish whether there is a case of so-called " precipitated birth " or " deliberate birth " of the child—as for example, if birth takes place in a toilet or in a liquid-containing bucket. It is not always easy to destroy the presumption that the mother in her excitation did not realize that she was going through the labor pains of birth.

On the contrary, if the ligature of the umbilical cord is omitted, for the most part the intention of killing the child is evident. This deliberate omission of assistance necessary for birth (passive infanticide) has in the past played an important part.

d. Social questions

From the social viewpoint, an attempt has been made to combat infanticide by the institution of foundling homes. Especially in Latin countries, the system of foundling homes was connected with that of the so-called wheel (*torno*), a system which leaves unknown the name of the mother as well as that of the child. Without doubt it cannot be denied that the objection posited against the foundling homes are in a certain manner justified: These are antiquated institutions surpassed by far and made superfluous by the modern care of the newly born, and they have a tendency to suffocate the sense of responsibility, to contribute to the increase of illegitimate births, and to impede the prospect of matrimony for the unwed mother (in comparison to the father of the child). Moreover, in the system of anonymity it is never possible to know the true origin of the child.

Where the conditions are fortuitous, there is no reason for not establishing more modern institutions as a substitute for foundling homes. But where proper conditions do not exist—above all, where conditions of life are more primitive—the foundling home (because it preserves anonymity) seems to be the only possibility of efficiently combating infanticide and abortion (cf. *Abortion*). And that will generally be the case in missionary regions.

In certain missionary regions, the abandonment of the newly born children increases in a frightful manner. With primitive people, and even with somewhat civil or cultured people, China not excluded, the abandonment of female children is not rare.

In an analogous tendency regarding the minor value attributed to female births, there is also the effect of the ideas of Islamism, namely, of the Koran. On this basis, in the dangerous missionary regions it seems to be of extreme importance that well-directed foundling homes and orphanages be established and maintained.

e. Canon and moral law

Canon Law and moral law do not add a particular crime of infanticide under the category of homicide, but consider the former under the latter as *occisio innocentis*. The manner of judging the guilt more mildly takes into consideration—inasmuch as is necessary—only the circumstances (*circumstantiae*) and the "impediments to freedom of will."

2. KILLING OF THE FETUS (CRANIOTOMY, ETC.)

The killing of the mature child in parturition (craniotomy) in order to save the mother when serious obstetrical complications present themselves represents, for the doctor, the most serious conflict of conscience imaginable. The same can be said regarding the killing of the immature fetus in the uterus: *procuratio abortus*. Attempts to justify this violation of the right to life by means of theoretical construction have not been wanting.

a. Attempts to justify

(a) *Theory of legitimate defense*

The so-called theory of legitimate defense proceeds from the hypothesis that the mother finds herself in the state of legitimate defense before the fetus when she is in a situation which is an impediment to birth. Prescinding from the fact that the fetus is never an *iniustus aggressor*, with like reason it can be said that, in regard to its right to life, it finds itself in the state of legitimate defense against the mother, especially when the impossibility of birth depends upon the physical conditions of the mother (for example, restriction of the pelvis). The two hypotheses are equally erroneous.

(b) *Theory of necessity*

The theory of the state of necessity is based upon a more just premise, inasmuch as there is question here of the conflict of two a priori equal rights to life. Now, in relation to the theory of the evaluation of goods, it is argued as follows: Since the life of the mother is to be considered the most precious, when the conflict of the two rights to life are verified, that of the fetus is to be sacrificed in favor of that of the mother. Against this, the Church declares that both rights are equally sacred; it follows that there can be no state of necessity that can authorize the killing of the innocent.

(c) *Theory of the voluntarium indirectum*

The hypotheses that in craniotomy and in similar interventions (abortion) there is question of a case of *voluntarium indirectum* (*dolus indirectus*) is based upon the presumption that the intention of the doctor is not directed to the killing of the fetus, but exclusively to the saving of the mother. The killing of the fetus is simply an inevitable consequence of the operation and deplorably permitted. Not even with this theory can the problem be resolved. The action itself is, according to the nature of the operation, directly and essentially ordered to the killing of the fetus. The killing represents the premise for the attained end. It is difficult to imagine a more evident *occisio directa* than that of craniotomy and embryotomy.

(d) *Theory of the conscientia perplexa*

The hypotheses that the immorality of the action can be mitigated inasmuch as it is a case of *conscientia perplexa* cannot be entirely excluded, at least for certain cases of craniotomy. But this does not permit a generalization and hence does not permit a general justification. Only an experienced moralist can judge when, in an unforeseen case (*casus improvisus*), the doctor can appeal to a *conscientia perplexa*. When the corresponding conditions are present, there is lacking the freedom required for the basis of a *peccatum formale*: " . . . *in huiusmodi casu deest libertas necessaria ad peccatum formale*" (St. Alphonsus).

Hence in no case does the doctor have the general authorization to kill the fetus whether at the moment of birth or before, no matter what the stage of pregnancy.[1]

b. Premature birth

In contrast to craniotomy and abortion, in provoked premature birth, there is question of a fetus already viable even though not mature. Consequently, with regard to artificially provoked premature birth, there is, by the nature of the intervention, no violation of the right to life, even if, in a concrete case, the child is born so weak that it succumbs to the influences of extrauterine life. The essential fact is that it has reached such a degree of maturity as to render possible the conservation of life.

3. SURGICAL OPERATIONS

a. General view—Right to operate

Basically, every intervention upon the integrity of the body— whether one's own body or that of another—represents an illicit corporal mutilation and hence a violation, or at least a danger, to

---

[1] The question of craniotomy as well as that of abortion and other interventions is here only briefly mentioned in relation to the right to life in view of the general norm. The pastoral-medical evaluation of these interventions is explained in detail in the exposition of the complex obstetrical problems.

which one's own or another right to life is exposed. Every surgical operation is objectively an attempt upon the integrity of the body. There arises here a question up to the present not yet resolved in a completely satisfactory manner, that of knowing what are the elements which give to intervention the character of illiceity and what are those that transform it into a juridically and morally licit action.

(a) *Theory of consent*

Many have seen the decisive elements in the consent of the mutilated person: *volenti non fit iniuria*. This idea does not touch the essential point. The theory of consent cannot alone justify the intervention.

Proceeding from this, the attempt has been made, for example, to explain that in abortion the consent of the mother is the determining justifying motive. The argument has been based on "the right over one's body," in virtue of which the woman herself could decide whether she would like to become a mother or not. But here—prescinding from the fact that such a right over one's own body and life holds only within restricted limits—it is not a matter of a decision about her body and her right to life, but a question of the child's right to life, which is here injured. The mother has no right over the life of the fetus, but only a delegated power, the abuse of which renders her morally culpable and juridically punishable.

(b) *Theory of professional right*

Also unsatisfactory is the theory of the medical professional right. According to this theory, the doctor, because of a particular professional right, would be authorized to procure any intervention which he, according to his scientific criterion, held to be necessary.

Related to this is the theory of professional duty, according to which an action of the doctor conforming to duty cannot involve a punishable fact (cf. Lilienthal). The theory of professional right would constitute for the doctor a norm of particular right and would thus place him above the general juridical order. Thus an important power would be entrusted to him, the abuse of which could have extraordinary and dangerous consequences. This, unfortunately, has been the case at times when the doctor acted by delegation of the state's power.

(c) Theory of consuetudinary right

There is no basis for the legality of medical intervention even if one seeks such a basis by holding that the legality rests upon consuetudinary right, for this constitutes too uncertain and variable a foundation for the decision of problems of so great importance. Moreover, this theory could apply at most to the legal aspect of the question, but not the moral aspect.

(d) Theory of the therapeutic end

In practice, the theory of the therapeutic end, which departs from just, fundamental ideas and approaches juridical positivism, has shown itself to be of relative value.

According to this theory, the therapeutic end as such authorizes the intervention of the doctor and removes the character of illiceity. The state recognizes this end. Such recognition by the state is expressed by the maintenance on the part of the state of medical institutions and schools of medicine. Hence the state cannot punish an action determined by an end that it recognizes and intends to be realized.

Even here, the presupposition of liceity is the consent of the mutilated person; without this, even an operation intended for therapeutic ends would remain a violation of personal rights.

The consent, in unison with the therapeutic end, has a justifiable effect, but only within the limits of juridical and moral order.

An intervention in itself illicit or immoral cannot become licit.

b. Forced interventions

(a) Forced treatment

We can speak of forced interventions when the will of the patient is against the intervention and can be overcome only by violence. It is irrelevant that the intervention affects only the bodily integrity and does not affect any other right to life.

There are cases in which resistance must be overcome as when, in children, the unconscious, the drunken, the mentally ill, etc., there is lacking the capacity to make a declaration of will in a validly legal form and at the same time a delay would be dangerous.

Here the consent of the sick person can either be substituted for

H

by a legal representative, or, when this is lacking, consent can be presumed.

When the danger is imminent and serious, it is understood that the doctor can intervene without consent of the patient and even against his manifest will or that of his relatives; for example, when an unreasonable mother refuses to give consent to tracheotomy for her son sick with diphtheria.

If, in the case of a narrow pelvis, the doctor performs a Caesarean section in order to save the life of the child, he does not commit a punishable act, even if he does this against the desire of the mother and her relatives—who perhaps demand craniotomy—since here the case of absolute necessity in regard to the child is verified.

Forced intervention in the strict sense refers more to other questions: above all, when intervention is executed under delegation of the coercive power of the state.

Here one must see whether the intervention as such is morally licit *ex obiecto*, whether it is unobjectionable, and, under certain circumstances, what are the superior interests of the *bonum commune* which can justify the violation of the free determination of the will (e.g., vaccination).

In this case, attention must also be given to the degree of danger present because of the intervention. The necessity of narcosis can, in determined circumstances, be a plausible motive for the refusal of a forced intervention. When it is a matter of an intervention in se morally illicit, the forced execution of the intervention can be a circumstance which quantitatively raises the moral perversity of the action in the sense of an aggravating circumstance.

(b) *Mutilating punishments*

Regarding the justification of forced intervention and mutilating punishments, the encyclical "Casti Connubii," No. 69-71, states:

"Publici vero magistratus in subditorum membra directam potestatem habent nullam; in ipsam igitur corporis integritatem ubi nulla intercesserit culpa nullaque adsit cruentae poena causa, directe laedere et attingere nec eugenicis, nec ullis aliis de causis possunt umquam."

("Public authority has no direct power over the members of its subject; if there is no guilt and no motive exists for the infliction of corporal punishment, the same cannot ever, in any way, directly mutilate or affect the integrity of the body whether for eugenic or any other reasons.")

When, therefore, guilt is not present and there is no reason for inflicting corporal punishment, authority cannot, for any motive, affect the integrity of the body—not even for eugenic reasons—as, for example, in legal sterilization.

In answer to the question whether a temporal judge can do harm to a person in order to prevent damage in the future, St. Thomas states that certain measures of security are permitted but claims that it is never licit for a judge to inflict upon an innocent person corporal punishment consisting of death, mutilation or flagellation. "Nunquam secundum humanum indicium aliquis debet puniri sine culpa, poena flagelli, ut occidatur vie mutiletur vel verberetur" (St. Thomas, *Summa theol.*, IIa IIae, qu. 108, a. 7 ad 2).

Hence the possibility of a mutilating punishment for certain crimes, e.g., the punishment of castration for sexual delinquents, does not seem definitely excluded. However, it is another question whether such a punishment fulfills its purpose and is significant. Under no circumstances are mutilating interventions of the innocent licit for the sole reason of prevention—for instance, the prevention of hereditarily tainted progeny.

(c) *Forced eugenical and criminological intervention*

Among the forced interventions or operations the principal ones are eugenic sterilization and criminological castration. Any operation by means of which the capacity to procreate or conceive is suppressed or destroyed represents, from the objective viewpoint, a grave bodily mutilation (*mutilatio gravis*).

Generally speaking, distinction is made between sterilization and castration. In castration the germinative glands are surgically removed or made incapable of functioning through irradiation. But in sterilization the germinative glands are preserved with their internal secretion. Only the conduction of the germinative cells is interrupted. In regard to sterilization and castration for therapeutic ends, no serious problem exists. It is definitely permissible when it is a necessary remedy that cannot be effectively substituted for by any other measure; thus, for example, castration in cases of malignant tumors of the testicles and of the ovaries, etc.

More difficult than the question of therapeutic castration is that of criminological castration; as a punishment for serious or habitual sexual delinquency, namely, as a means of security and prevention, as prescribed in some legislation.

That castration as a punishment for one who is culpable is not illicit has already been mentioned—without considering in detail the question of the efficacy and barbarous character of the punishment. What has been stated is valid only for crimes already committed and is not valid if it is a matter of simply preventing possible or future crimes (so-called prophylactic castration). The question whether castration as a punishment fulfills its end or whether it even can fulfill its end is to be treated in connection with the medicopastoral evaluation of other surgical operations.

4. EUTHANASIA (DESTRUCTION OF A LIFE "WITHOUT VALUE")

Euthanasia is the extreme consequence of a series of postulates which represent an ideological unity and which are directed against the sacred character of life: birth prevention, abortion, sterilization, suppressive selection. The rational principle common to all these postulates is an absolutely temporal intention; a materialism not always well dissimulated; the idea of an unlimited autonomy of man, with the elimination of a supernatural moral law and of responsibility before God as Creator, Legislator and Supreme Judge.

Passing over the apparently harmless postulates—such as the licit alleviation of pain in incurables—there is the attempt little by little to attain more ample consequences; the concession of stronger doses of narcotics to "shorten the suffering" of incurables and dying persons, going as far as exterminating the insane and idiots who are designated as "useless human remains," as having "useless existences," etc., and finally eliminating the old and defective.

The initial postulate to "help the dying" is transformed finally into an open destruction of life. The apparent humanity of the motive reveals itself as crass materialism.

The utilitarian arguments here presented are not in fact tenable from the economic point of view, at least not for the keen, who are not deceived by initial apparent success. "The calculation is false" (Walter). The financial burdens which have to be faced in regard to the sick and those who have need of care are by no means unproductive. The care of the incurable produces effects of great moral value. Hospitalization can appear more expensive than sterilization and euthanasia only when considered in a superficial manner. The inevitable caution against boundless abuse demands immense sums, or the abuse devours human lives in so great a number that the moral corruption and the destruction of the social order that follow lead to damage much greater, and the presumed utility is paid for at too great a price.

If free way were given to euthanasia, neither the danger of abuse, even of licit curative methods, nor that of fatal errors would be excluded.

The mere possibility of an error in diagnosis and prognosis would suffice to completely change the relationship between the patient and doctor. This is the most disastrous aspect of euthanasia. Confidence in doctors and clinics would be forever destroyed. All the assistance given to the demented through the incessant labor of generations of altruistic psychiatrists would be destroyed by a single stroke. Not only would institutes of cure be discredited, but also asylums, old folks' homes and hospitals; and confidence in these and in doctors would be lost. The presumed "humanitarianism" has revealed itself in truth as a destruction of all true human sympathy.

The sacred character of life is the basis of medical morality. The doctor is not the lord of life and death. A conscientious doctor will always refuse to assume the role of an executioner, even if there is the attempt to glorify him with rhetorical exaltation and if there is attributed to the "selectionist doctor" the greatest dignity, and if, in his hands, the greatest power is placed.

Finally, even in the mental life of the apparently mentally dead, there are many unsolved enigmas. In many cases surprising facts have become known by discovering before imminent death a richness of mental life—buried under the surface—that was hidden in completely demented persons. We also do not know what takes place in the dying. We merely perceive that the last moments are of decisive importance. These last moments can bring to many dying persons a great amount of grace and can still save an apparently lost soul.

When a man believes himself authorized to shorten, even by a few seconds, the life of his fellow creature, he deprives him of these decisive moments of grace—and in so doing, possibly still thinks that he is benefiting him.

From the higher supernatural viewpoint there is no useless life. For to the apparently most desperately sick apply the enlightening words of St. Thomas: *Melius ei sic esse quam penitus non esse.* (" It is better for him so to be than absolutely not to be.") In order to understand this correctly, one must be able to understand that every " esse " represents a participation in the being of God. Only from an ontological-metaphysical viewpoint can the extreme profundity of these mysterious words be comprehended—words which to human pride (which does not gaze beyond things earthly) appear to be foolish and scandalous, but which in reality, arise from a most profound wisdom and the highest illumination.

Thus, in conclusion, we return to what we established in the beginning—namely, that the right to life is the most original right of man and the basis of all the other rights of man—whether considered in the sense of natural law or positive law. There is no defense of the rights of man if, from the beginning and to the end, there is no respect for the right to life, and, in consequence, respect for the Creator and Preserver of life. The right to life is of *iuris divini* and hence absolute, universally obliging and inalienable.

3. Medical Operations

~~~~~~

A. OBSTETRICAL OPERATIONS

1. CRANIOTOMY

a. Concept

By craniotomy in the medico-pastoral sense is meant the killing of a mature child, carried to full term or quasi-full term, perpetrated at birth or a little before the beginning of birth itself.

In this concept are contained all those obstetrical operations which reduce the dimensions and divide in part the body of the child, whether they affect the head itself (cranium), as in craniotomy in the strict sense, or another part of the body—inasmuch as they have by their nature the killing of the child as the inevitable effect.

Hence, cleidotomy, which consists in dividing the clavicle for the purpose of diminution, would not be contained under this concept, since the death of the child is not absolutely inevitable.

The operations mentioned are supposed to serve in the saving of the mother's life when parturition is impossible without them.

b. Methods

It is the common end of all the methods to reduce the dimensions of the child's body. We distinguish between the methods which affect the head of the child and those which affect the torso of the child.

(a) Methods which affect the head (craniotomy in the strict sense). The classical form of craniotomy is the perforation of the head (perforation) commonly associated with the reduction of the cranium by means of crushing instruments (cephalotripsy) or a combination of perforation and crushing the base of the cranium (cranioclasis, craniocephaloclasia, etc.). In this group, the method of removing the head (decapitation) is also included.

(b) Methods affecting the torso (embryotomy in a wide sense, embryulcia). These include evisceration: the emptying out of the thoracic and intestinal viscera; the dismemberment of the fetus (embryotomy in the strict sense), the cutting of the vertebral column (rachiotomy), etc.

c. Spheres of application (Indications)

The interventions mentioned have had in obstetrics two principal spheres of application: restriction of the pelvis or disproportion of dimensions between the head of the fetus and the pelvis; and the presentation of the fetus in such a position as to render birth impossible.

(a) Disproportion of dimensions. Such a disproportion does not necessarily depend upon the restriction of the mother's pelvis (more frequent form: pelvis flattened by rachitis); it can also be caused by hyperdimension of the child's head (hydrocephalus), or by the deformation of the pelvis or head.

(b) Positions which render birth impossible. Among these, that which occupies the first place is the so-called protracted transverse presentation, in which there is danger of a rupture of the uterus which would be mortal and also, in certain circumstances, the so-called mentoposterior of the face and front (with chin directed toward the back).

Craniotomy can be taken into consideration in order to facilitate birth when the child is already dead. If the death of the child is definitely confirmed, the above-mentioned operations no longer form the object of medico-pastoral problems: whatever no longer lives cannot be killed.

d. Medico-pastoral judgment

(a) *The question of conflict*

In cases of this kind the doctor finds a serious conflict of duties, if the obstetrical situation has reached the point where it appears to him evident that there is no way out but to sacrifice the life of the child in order to at least save the life of the mother—since otherwise both lives would be lost. The attempts to solve such a conflict theoretically have already been studied in relation to questions pertaining to the right to life. We have been able to show that it was not possible to resolve the conflict in a satisfactory way, either by the theory of legitimate defense, or with that of the state of necessity, or of the *voluntarium indirectum*. Not even the appeal to the *conscientia perplexa* in certain particular cases can indicate the solution. It cannot be applied in general.

Basically craniotomy constitutes a *homicidium directum* and concretely an *occisio innocentis* and, because of this, constitutes a *peccatum grave contra quintum preceptum*. Moral theology teaches that an action in se bad (*res in se mala*)—the killing of the child— is not permitted, not even for a good end: to save the mother: *Non sunt facienda mala, ut eveniant bona* (" Casti Connubii," N. 66).

Hence, there seems to be an irremediable conflict between the demands of medical science and Catholic morality and the doctrine of the Church.

(b) *Doctrinal decisions of the Church*

Comprehending well what is involved in such a question we can understand how the Church has not up to now and never will be able to answer the question of the liceity of craniotomy with any answer other than a *non licet*.

The moral norm in question pertains to natural rights and to Divine law. Hence it has an absolute and immutable value.

The Church cannot bring about, by means of her decisions, any modification of the natural law. Save in the holding of this principle, the decisions made up to now manifest great circumspection in their formulation, which acquire ever-greater resoluteness with the progress of surgical obstetrics.

A decision of the Sacred Penitentiary of September 2, 1869, and one of November 28, 1872, use the formula: *Consulat probatos auctores sive veteres, sive recentes et prudenter agat.* (" Consult authors of approved worth, whether old or modern, and act with prudence.")

The Holy Office, on May 28, 1884, answering the question whether it is permitted to perform an operation which brings about death,

H*

uses the formula: *Tuto doceri non posse.* ("It cannot be taught in conscience.") Similar is a decision of August 14, 1889. More decisive was the refusal in a decision of July 24, 1895, and one following on May 5, 1902. Finally, in a decision of May 4, 1895, this refusal was again expressed in the clearest manner.

A decree of the Holy Office of May 28, 1884, in answer to the precise formulation of an appeal, again replied with the formula: "Tuto doceri non posse."

While the preceding questions exclusively limit themselves to the problem of craniotomy and of embryotomy, the greater part of the succeeding questions pertain to the problem of *procuratio abortus.*

In this regard, reference must also be made to the attitude of the Code of Canon Law concerning *procuratio abortus.* This logically applies also to the *occisio foetus* in birth. According to canon 985, those who have committed an intentional homicide or have procured an abortion (if this is effected) incur incapacity to receive Orders. The same goes for all the accomplices.

According to canon 2350, # 1, all those—the mother not excluded —who have effectively procured an abortion, automatically incur excommunication, without the express sentence of the judge.

According to canon 985, there is *irregularitas ex delicto* for those *qui voluntarium homicidium perpetrarunt aut foetus humani abortum procuravint, effectu secuto, omnesque cooperantes* ("those who have committed voluntary homicide or effectively procured abortion, and all their accomplices ").

According to canon 2350, #1, they incur an *excommunicatio latae sententiae: procurantes abortum, matre no excepta—effectu secuto* ("persons who procure abortion, the mother not excepted, at the moment the crime takes effect ").

The affirmations of the encyclical "Casti Connubii," (N. 64) have recently acquired fundamental importance:

"At quae possit umquam causa valere ad ullo modo excusandam innocentis necem? . . . Sive ea matri infertur sive proli, contra Dei praeceptum est vocemque naturae: 'Non occides!' Res enim aeque sacra utruisque vita . . . neque ullum adest 'extremae necessitatis ius' . . . quodque usque ad innocentis directam occi- sionem pervenire possit."

("But what reasons can have the force to make in any way excusable the direct killing of the innocent? Whether it is inflicted on the mother of the child, it is always against the commandment of God and the very voice of nature: 'Thou shalt not kill!' In fact, the life of the one and of the other is equally sacred; the destroying of either can never be conceded to any power, not even public authority . . . , and there does not exist a 'right to extreme necessity' which can extend to the direct killing of the innocent.")

Even the allocution of Pope Pius XII to Italian obstetricians given October 29, 1952, can be considered a fundamental doctrinal decision of the Church. In this allocution, the Pope again declared that, according to the Catholic moral viewpoint, the question of deciding which of the two lives is the " more precious "—whether that of the mother or that of the child—cannot be established in obstetrics. In the encyclical "Casti Connubii," Pius XI made it clear that the two rights to life are equally sacred and that here the principle of " valuation of goods " has no place.

The task of obstetrics can consist only in using all means possible to save both lives, that of the mother and that of the child. Because of its interpretation, this allocution has given rise to public discussion. It has been affirmed that the Pope declared that the life of the child has, in certain circumstances, precedence over the life of the mother. The Church has been accused of immolating the life of the mother. In England a movement was started to exclude Catholic obstetricians from the exercise of their profession for reasons of social security: it was declared " intolerable and monstrous " to force a woman to be assisted by a Catholic obstetrician who is obliged to act in conformity to the dictates of the Pope.

In reality, this allocution of the Pope which has been so furiously attacked has declared nothing more than what the Catholic Church has always taught by means of official moral theology and all the doctrinal decisions pronounced up to the present time through the supreme ecclesiastical authorities of the Church (the Roman Congregations), including the Holy Office. It is a matter here of the supreme principles of morality which are absolutely indestructible.

(c) *The solution of the conflict*

The most serious reproaches have been raised against the Church because she has not, at least in the case of extreme necessity, declared and affirmed by an unequivocal *licet* that the doctor is authorized to kill the child in order to save the mother. This has led to a direct exclusion, from the exercise of obstetrics, of Catholic doctors who obey the commandment of the Church.

In contrast, the development of events up to the present time has demonstrated that the Church, with her prudent reserve (*tuto doceri non posse*), has been very wise. A *licet* would have given sanction to craniotomy as well as abortion. The right to life of the fetus would have been left without protection.

Holding firmly to the illiceity of this, the Church has contributed in giving to medical science a motive for an otherwise insoluble conflict; a conflict which would have inevitably weighed heavily upon the conscience of a doctor animated by sentiments worthy of his profession.

Modern surgical obstetrics in its more recent developments has sided with the Church. At present, craniotomy is in practice substituted for by the modern methods of Caesarean section. If craniotomy is still practiced, it is dependent on the inefficiency of the obstetrical organization and, above all, on the fact that the obstetrician has occasion to visit the pregnant woman in a stage when it is no longer possible to have a Caesarean section and no other alternative remains but craniotomy.

Moreover, the greater possibility of an operation for the enlargement of the pelvis (pubiotomy, hebeosteotomy, etc.) has made craniotomy more superfluous.

In order to remove the deficiencies which still persist in obstetrics —deficiencies partly due to regional difficulties—it simply suffices to give systematized and organized assistance to pregnant women in the form of obstetrical prophylaxis.

Because of the surgical and prophylactic progress of obstetrics, craniotomy today has almost completely disappeared, since there are sufficient hospitals with experienced obstetricians and specialists.

Craniotomy can, without difficulty, be completely obliterated by a continuous improvement of these institutions.

In modern obstetrics, without doubt, a new and higher respect for the right to life of the child can be noticed. The terrible effects of the mass destruction of human life, a condition seen in wartime, has contributed, perhaps, toward a greater appreciation of human life and the right to life.

With the abandoning of craniotomy, the classical problem of Pastoral Medicine has found a satisfactory solution. This shows that the immutable principles of the Church can be in absolute agreement with those of science, provided that science strives to increase and deepen its realizations.

2. PROCURATIO ABORTUS

a. Concept

Unlike craniotomy, *procuratio abortus* involves the death of the immature fetus, not yet viable, in any stage of its development from fecundation to the moment in which the viability begins.

The beginning of viability takes place from the twenty-eighth week of pregnancy. The duration of pregnancy is calculated to be forty weeks.

If the fetus is immature but viable, we speak of a *partus praematurus*. If it is before the beginning of viability, we speak of abortion. Abortion and *partus praematurus* can be included under the concept of *partus immaturus*.

b. Classification

In the matter of abortion we distinguish:

(1) Abortion which takes place spontaneously without external provocation (*abortus spontaneus*).

(2) Abortion induced by an external action (*abortus provocatus*).

From the clinical viewpoint, we distinguish:

(1) *Abortus imminens*. In this case it is still possible to arrest the process by an adequate treatment (repose in bed, strict diet, sedation by means of narcotics).

(2) *Abortus progrediens*. If hemorrhage is copious and there is present an aperture of the uterine orifice, the expulsion of the fetus can no longer be avoided.

(3) *Abortus incompletus*. The fetus is dead and for the most part expelled; some parts of the fetus and the related membranes of the ovum, the chorion, the placenta, etc., still remain in the uterus and are to be removed.

(4) *Abortus completus*. The fetus and all the residue of the ovum have been expelled or removed.

The clinic further distinguishes between aseptic and septic abortion. Spontaneous abortion generally follows an aseptic course. Infection easily follows provoked abortion, and even in spontaneous abortion infection from specific germs is possible. Septic abortion is generally criminal abortion. Forensic medicine distinguishes, in provoked abortion, between criminal abortion and the interruption of pregnancy by medical indication (cf. below).

Moreover, forensic medicine also acknowledges an *abortus simulatus*. Finally, we mention *abortus habitualis*, which is a particular form of spontaneous abortion. It is frequently the effect of syphilis but at times arises from a constitutional defect (infantilism). From the point of view of Pastoral Medicine, the criteria of classification mentioned are irrelevant except when distinguishing between *abortus spontaneous* and *abortus provocatus*. Only the last enters into the concept of *procuratio abortus*.

c. Viewpoint of Pastoral Medicine

The forensic distinction between criminal abortion and therapeutic abortion in legal medicine, pastoral medicine and moral theology is relevant in treating of a difference of motives and also for other circumstances which aggravate the guilt—as for example, the particular defect of conscience in the execution, which admits of an increased danger to the life of the mother.

In the case of criminal abortion, besides the motives mentioned in reference to infanticide, the desire for money plays a principal part. In medical abortion as in craniotomy, the motive is to avoid a danger, certain or presumed. Even here the motive of money is not always to be excluded.

The difference of motives is worthy of consideration from the viewpoint of penal law. In the case of the state of necessity, intervention effected for the purpose of saving the mother is not punishable. This does not mean that it is morally licit. The difference of motive has, from the viewpoint of moral theology, the significance of aggravating or diminishing circumstances of guilt.

For these reasons, the criteria of classification adopted by Pastoral Medicine cannot be the same as the clinical ones and those adopted by forensic medicine.

Pastoral Medicine concerns itself essentially with *abortus provocatus*. Pastoral Medicine must judge the external fact from the point of view of the *occisio fetus directa*—whether, from the point of view of forensic medicine, it is a matter of legally punishable criminal abortion, or a matter of an interruption of pregnancy prescribed by the doctor and not subject to punishment. From this point of view, Pastoral Medicine must also reject the term "interruption of pregnancy."

This extensively used term is not only logically inaccurate, but also erroneous. Moreover, it dissimulates the essence of intervention and obscures the significance and importance of abortion, thus blunting the conscience. The expression "killing of the fetus" would be more accurate. This would always allow the possibility of distinguishing whether it is a matter:

(1) Of a premeditated and criminal intent to kill;

(2) Of feticide effected by the doctor in good faith, with the intention of saving the mother.

For Pastoral Medicine, both *procuratio abortus* and *craniotomia* fall under *occisio foetus directa*. In obstetrics, the two interventions assume a different position.

d. Methods

Two principal groups of methods can be distinguished in *abortus provocatus*:

(1) Internal means (dynamic); medicaments, toxics (ergot, rue, juniper, sabina, apiol, etc.). An efficient dose of these will for the most part provoke a general intoxication.

(2) External actions (mechanical means); blow, shock, maltreatment, thermal and electrical stimuli.

The direct interventions (surgical) pertain to the second group. They include:

(1) Operations to open the cervical canal; taper-shaped laminae, instruments of dilatation (Hegar's dilators, metreurynter; in more advanced stages, colpeurynter, etc.).

(2) Operations for the purpose of mutilating or destroying the ovum—puncture of the membrane, intrauterine injections.

(3) Surgical methods in the strict sense:

(a) Through vaginal passage (colpotomy—*sectio vaginalis parva*).

(b) Through abdominal passage (laparotomy—*sectio caesarea parva*).

Forensic medicine distinguishes between medical and quackish methods. Typical methods of this latter type are practically all the "dynamic" means, whether "adequate" or "inadequate", and in the last case for the most part toxic. Moreover, the introduction of a catheter (so-called method of midwives), injection of liquids in the uterus by means of a syringe (auto-abortive method) are very dangerous to life.

In general, it can be stated that methods do not exist which are not dangerous, even when feticide is brought on by a doctor. Any abortion means for the mother danger to life or serious harm to health.

e. Dangers

Even if the technical perfection of the methods excluded such dangers as:

(1) Serious violent mutilation of the uterus of the vagina and the annexed parts, and;

(2) Primary septic infection—

there would still remain a series of dangerous elements which no technical progress could ever eliminate, since they are inherent in the very nature of the intervention. They are the following:

(1) The danger of secondary infection and later damages. One of the more frequent later effects is that of secondary sterility. Moreover, complications of the ulterior parts often arise, as also does an accentuated tendency toward extrauterine pregnancy.

(2) The dangers of a disturbance of the internal secretion. While, in the natural course of pregnancy, the transformation of the activity of the endocrine glands arises in a gradual manner, in abortion the function is abruptly interrupted. Thus it often has persistent effects. This danger is especially serious if pregnancy is interrupted during the early stages.

(3) The danger of later mental damage. This is more frequent and more serious than generally believed. Often this concurs with the somatic disturbances already mentioned. Even without these, there are depressions, feelings of sin and guilt and deep neurotic complexes. Often, after induced abortion, a psychosis arises, and at times even suicide occurs.

The effects just mentioned can never be definitely excluded, even in those cases in which doctors declare that abortion was necessary and the operation is performed by specialists in the aseptic surroundings of a hospital.

In this regard, the experiences of Russian gynecologists during the years 1917-1932 are instructive and valuable, and found expression in the first Pan-Ukrainian Congress of gynecologists which took place in Kiev in 1927.

In reference to this, an eminent clinical gynecologist has stated that the task of the gynecologist is to heal sick women and not to make healthy women sick. Hence it can be stated that there is no operation so contrary in essence to the true task of the doctor and the true concept of professional duty than that of abortion.

f. Indications

(a) *General view*

We wish to emphasize, above all, that when we speak here of "indications," we use the term solely in its usual sense. From the viewpoint of Pastoral Medicine, the use of the concept of "indication" must be rejected, as also the expression "interruption of pregnancy." They cause confusion concerning the nature and import of the operation and also weaken the conscience and lead it into error.

By "indication" the scientific motivation for a therapeutic therapeutic operation in conformity with law is meant. Hence abortion cannot be put on the same plane with any other operation or therapeutic measure. Here there is an essential difference. Abortion can never be considered a true therapy. It is, rather, always the admission of an absolute failure—it is a bankruptcy of true therapy. Thus we speak of "pathological complications of pregnancy" when there is treatment of the medical aspect of the so-called indications; we speak of the state of necessity inasmuch as the penal aspect is considered, and of *casus perplexus* in treating of the theologico-moral question in order to establish whether, in exceptional cases of absolute necessity, subjective guilt could be lacking.

The predominant opinion in medicine since 1900 has tended to see everything as a system of "indications." In this system, three principal groups can be distinguished:

(1) The medical indication. This seeks to protect the life and health of the pregnant.

(2) The social indication. This seeks to eliminate the social conditions of misery.

(3) The eugenic indication. This seeks to prevent tainted offspring.

Near these three principal groups has been placed another group of indications under the fallacious name of "ethical indications."

This includes cases of so-called state of necessity in regard to honor, danger of suicide, pregnancy as a result of criminal acts: incest, rape, etc.; sometimes even cases of "contamination of race" have been included.

Within the medical indications there is the further distinction of:

(1) The "absolute" indication: danger to the life of the pregnant woman which cannot be eliminated by any other means ("vital" indication).

(2) "Relative" indication: danger to life which is not absolutely certain, and danger, more or less serious, to health. If it is a matter of preventing a possible damage, one speaks of "prophylactic" indication. The "relative" indication admits of every degree, from the most rigid use of the indication to the least serious, so that finally it serves as a mask and a scientific pretext for the practice of abortion by unscrupulous doctors.

(b) *Medical indications*

(1) *General view*

Numerous maladies pertaining to all the specialties of medicine have been designated as medical indications. The most important are the following:

(1) Toxic pregnancy;
(2) Psychosis of pregnancy;
(3) Pulmonary tuberculosis;
(4) Heart disease;
(5) Renal disease;
(6) Metabolic disturbances, endocrine disturbances;
(7) Diseases of the nervous system;
(8) Organic diseases of more diverse types.

To this can be added a type of "indication" represented in all the groups, based upon the unlimited extensive interpretation. It could justly be called the species of "fantastic indications."

(2) *Critique of the medical indications*

In general, in regard to the medical indication, it can be asserted that the more deeply this question is studied, the more clear are the ideas acquired concerning the nature of the operation, its methods and dangers; and the more these are contrasted with the dangers that are believed to be eliminated by means of the operation, the more clearly is it evident that this calculation is erroneous.

The complications of pregnancy, which can in certain circumstances be a serious danger to the pregnant woman, and which are impossible to eliminate without abortion, are reduced to a minimum. And even this minimum could be eliminated by persistent progress in therapy and above all by the instituting of preventive assistance for the pregnant. If even today, in exceptionally rare cases, there are residual complications which do not yet seem to be overcome, this is nothing but a proof of the failure of therapy and of the insufficiency of actual knowledge. On the other hand, recourse to abortion in the great number of cases is more dangerous than the disease which it pretends to avoid. It is unthinkable that an existing illness could be cured by this intervention.

Up to now, no woman has been made better by an abortion, whereas numerous women have, because of abortion, become sick and weak. In numerous cases it has been observed that abortion has provoked substantial aggravations and deadly effects whether as mediate effects or as later effects.

On the whole it must be held as a general principle that the maladies of pregnancy are to be treated and possibly healed; pregnancy should be maintained at least until the fetus is viable.

In particular, regarding the indications, the following are to be observed:

(1) Toxic pregnancy. Pernicious vomiting (hyperemesis gravidarum) can for the most part be successfully cured. Hospital care and removal from environmental influences are important.

The "nervous form" reacts well to general treatment and psychotherapy. In the form of purely mental origin the vomiting should cease at the latest at the first movement of the child, about the beginning of the twentieth week, when maternal love is awakened.

The " toxic form " is more difficult to treat, but even this can be successfully treated (hospital treatment, insulin, infusion of glucose; hesperedin, diet). Only in exceptionally rare cases is there little success in stopping progressive marasmus of unfavorable prognosis. In such cases not even abortion saves the life of the mother.

Toxic preëclampsia can be treated in a hospital with good probability of success, since the urine and blood pressure are held under constant control. It pertains to the second half of pregnancy, with the result that, in case of necessity, when there is imminent danger, artificial premature birth of a living child is possible.

(2) Psychosis of pregnancy always requires reclusion and treatment in a hospital, especially when there is danger of suicide. In these cases, pregnancy is often brought to termination. Acute psychosis generally departs after birth. But abortion brings about danger of a much more serious mental change.

(3) Pulmonary tuberculosis represents the most diffused indication and is most abused. There has been a complete change of outlook on the part of specialists in pulmonary tuberculosis. Up to a short time ago, it was held in good faith that in these cases abortion was definitely necessary. It was not always easy to distinguish the involuntarily erroneous diagnosis from fraudulent premeditation. No other indication has been so abused as this. This is a typical example of how with good will one of the most diffused indications can completely disappear. It is a known fact that treatment in a sanitarium offers great probability of success in any stage of pregnancy of the tuberculosis patient. Treatment with streptomycin, which for the most part has positive success, is added. Light cases show in pregnancy a marked tendency toward a cure. However, the serious cases are never helped by abortion, but often rapidly become worse because of the weakening of resistance. In serious cases, the greatest danger presents itself during the last weeks of pregnancy because of the obstacle to respiration constituted by the elevated position of the uterus. In these cases provocation of premature birth after the twenty-eighth week has a more favorable effect than abortion.

In absolutely desperate cases, neither this nor any other means can save the life of the mother. Hence all that is possible must be done to save at least the life of the child.

(4) Heart disease. In this case, *mutatis mutandis*, the same application is to be made as for cases of pulmonary tuberculosis. It is

not difficult, by means of hospital treatment, to preserve pregnancy up to the viability of the child. It is important to avoid uterine contractions by surgically provoking a premature birth.

(5) Renal disease. In regard to diseases of the renal parenchyma the same is applicable as in the cases of toxic preëclampsia and of heart diseases. Even here there is danger only toward the end of pregnancy. The diseases of the renal pelvis (*pylitis gravidarum*) can for the most part be favorably influenced by hospital treatment (disinfection of the urine, catheterization of the urethra, eventual washing of the renal pelvis).

Only in extremely rare cases does therapy fail and life become endangered by urinary sepsis (urosepsis) or by the simultaneous danger of an intestinal occlusion from toxic agents (*ileus gravidarum*). However, this danger is never present before the twenty-eighth week. Hence even here, in cases of necessity, it is possible to obtain a remedy by a surgical premature birth.

(6) Metabolic disturbance. Diabetes (*diabetes mellitus*) is a typical example of how the progress of science can eliminate an indication. Modern hospital treatment—with precise examinations, control of the sugar contained in the blood, diet, insulin therapy, etc.—always makes it possible to conserve pregnancy up to the viability of the child.

(7) Diseases of the nervous system. Here the following are given as "indications": Multiple sclerosis, poliomyelitis, tabes dorsalis, and tumors of the brain.

In cases of multiple sclerosis and in paralysis from the tabes or poliomyelitis, it is possible to conserve pregnancy at least up to the time of viability of the child and then to operate without uterine contractions by means of local anesthesia. Tumors of the brain, inasmuch as the operation cannot be deferred, must be operated on even if there is danger of indirectly provoking an abortion.

(8) Organic diseases. Only in most rare cases does amaurosis of pregnancy bring on permanent blindness. But even in this lamentable case it is not justifiable to sacrifice the life of the child in order to save the eyesight of the mother. The same goes for the dangers to which the sense of hearing is exposed—for example, progressive otosclerosis.

In regard to the so-called obstetrical indication there is nothing more to add to what has been said in regard to craniotomy.

Just as, through surgical obstetrics, craniotomy has been eliminated, so also the progress of therapy and prophylactic assistance for the pregnant will cause the last remnants of the medical indications to vanish.

(c) *Social indications*

In general, in regard to the " social indications," the following are to be considered: The social conditions of misery should be combated by means of social hygiene, social assistance, social politics and not by feticide.

Muckermann has posited an annihilating criticism to the so-called social indication: " A child cannot be condemned to death because it is impossible to nourish it." Even Reichel called the "social indication" a "license to murder."

The remedies that can be applied are contained above all in the encyclical "Quadragesimo Anno." In practice, it essentially considers a "family wage," rightly understood, a just wage, due to every workman who works full time, and advocates, along with this, social institutions to compensate for the burden when the family increases to the extent of surpassing the mean. All those whose families do not exceed the mean have the obligation of contributing to these institutions ("compensation chests"), and those whose families exceed the mean have the right to receive from this compensation.

Moreover, the guarantee of the "right to work" as well as sound politics seem essential for protection from unemployment. We shall consider this question more in detail when we consider the question of birth decrease.

(d) *Eugenic indications*

In general, the following can be said of the eugenic indications:

When hereditary prognosis has in a certain case been absolutely established, no positive law and of course no natural law and, least of all, no natural or supernatural moral law can ever sanction the destruction of a life already procreated.

If what has been anticipated in the primary explanations of the eugenic indication were confirmed and if such an indication were acknowledged, other arguments opposing the destruction of a life "without worth" (so-called euthanasia) would be superfluous.

In particular, the arguments against the eugenic indication of abortion are the same as those posited against eugenic sterilization (cf. below).

(e) *Ethical indications*

In general the following can be said of the eugenic indication: It would be a singular denial of the essence of ethics to pretend to eliminate a crime and its consequences by committing another crime.

In particular, for the most important cases the following can be said:

(1) The danger of suicide does not justify abortion, but merely makes necessary the internment in an appropriate institution. Abortion is the worst means that can be imagined for eliminating the danger of suicide. In certain circumstances it can even provoke the most serious depression, with a tendency toward suicide.

(2) The so-called indication by violence—actually of tragic frequency during military occupation following wars—is often closely connected with the so-called indication by suicide. The question would be judged with greater calmness and more objectively if examination of it were not disturbed by sentimental elements of a purely subjective nature. If what has been said in regard to the question of the medical indication is recalled to mind, it will be acknowledged that even in these cases no benefit is rendered to women. Even in these instances the evil is limited when the woman, against her will, brings the child to term once she has conceived it. Then she can decide whether she wants to keep the child or consign it to trustful hands—whether in a public or private charitable institution or to private persons.

In cases of imposed maternity, there is no obligation to keep the child and to educate it personally. If the woman keeps the child and admits the same into her family, this action on her part certainly constitutes a heroic sacrifice and an example which will bring upon her the blessing of God.

It is then a supererogatory service which goes beyond simple duty. Duty itself does not demand on the part of the mother more than the bringing to birth the life that she has conceived. It is the duty of the community—in particular of all charitable institutions—to efficaciously help women by forming institutions to which a child can be entrusted in conscience and which will furnish satisfactory conditions for the child.

In regard to the other cases which we have studied under the concept of the medical indication (so-called state of necessity of honor, contamination of the race, etc.), there is nothing more to be added to what has already been asserted.

In résumé, with reference to the indications which have been considered, it is to be noticed that if the questions relating to the right of life and its natural derivations are well understood, their importance will be definitely acknowledged.

g. The question of legal liceity

We have seen that the legal liceity or "non-punishability" of medical abortion is in no way identical with moral liceity. In certain penal legislation the doctor who performs the abortion is in general not punishable. It is usual to express such an exemption in a particular legal disposition for doctors. It is evident that such a particular disposition which confers upon the doctor power over life and death is incompatible with natural law.

This leads to abuses and the more so with the extension of the social and eugenic indications.

Another way of guaranteeing impunity to the doctor in the case of serious medical indication is that followed by the Austrian Penal Code and the penal law of certain other states. The penal sanction, in the special legislation regarding abortion (#144 of the Austrian Penal Code), threatens both the doctor and the co-operators with the same penalty. However, on the strength of the general legislation concerning the state of necessity (#2 of the Austrian Penal Code), the doctor can claim impunity if there exists a serious medical indication. Since even here there exists the possibility of abuse because of fictitious indications, in certain countries measures have been taken to combat abortions permitted for the slightest reason. German legislation has tended more to legally establish and recognize the medical indication, by establishing certain "posts" which were to determine the indication. The decisions made were of rigorous observance for the doctor. In case of positive deliberation there existed for the doctor a juridical duty to fulfill the abortion.

The way followed by Austrian legislation to protect embryonic life was more just (Law of November 1, 1938). It merely introduced "centers of examination." Their task was not that of establishing an indication but only to examine and see whether, in a concrete case, all the possibilities of conservative therapy were used. If this were so, then the doctor had full freedom of action. If he intervened he could make use of the protection accorded him by paragraph #2, but only if the opinion of the post or center of examination was given. If he did not intervene, he could not be cited for the omission.

In certain countries, there has been at times an attempt to abrogate wholly or partly the penal legislation against abortion. Prescinding from the fact that abolition of juridical protection of the fetus signifies a serious violation of the right to life—and hence, of the natural law—the effects of the liberty conceded to abortion and its legalization were absolutely unfavorable.

The experience of countries in which legalized abortion was temporarily permitted has shown that the greatest damage to the health of women was caused by this, and everywhere it was necessary to abrogate the decrees. It has been confirmed that when the penal law does not punish, nature itself punishes.

h. The question of moral liceity

In regard to the question of moral liceity in the killing of the fetus, nothing essential can be added to what has been posited in regard to craniotomy. In both cases, the problems that must be judged from the moral point of view are basically the same.

At most, a doubt may be possible inasmuch as there have been authors who did not admit of a *homicidium* in the *procuratio abortus*—at least in the early stage of pregnancy, since they did not consider the fetus yet a *homo*. In fact, the distinction between a *foetus animatus* and *foetus non animatus* was made in the past. This distinction was based on the opinion held by Aristotle, according to whom the *anima rationalis* as a specific vital principle of man does not dwell in the fetus from the beginning. Animation took place in the masculine on the fortieth day and in the feminine fetus on the eightieth day after conception. On the basis of this opinion, the killing of the fetus before animation was not to be considered *homicidium*. Prescinding from the fact that there are no substantial reasons for such a differentiation between the sexes in regard to the question of animation, today even the hypothesis of a successive animation is no longer generally held in regard to a specifically human soul. Even if the *anima rationalis* begins to function notably only later, the soul, as the *forma corporis*, as the vital principle, acts from the first moment of fecundation and precisely as a specifically human soul.

Even if, from the beginning, there exist *in actu* only the vital vegetative and sensitive functions, the rational powers of the soul are present *in potentia* from the beginning. The human soul is a unified and indivisible vital principle. If the unity and indivisibility of the human soul is eliminated, the doctrine of the *pluralitas formarum* with its consequences would prevail.

Following Aristotle, St. Thomas also held the doctrine of a successive animation but with reasons of greater depth. On the other hand, Albertus Magnus made use of all his authority in favor of a simultaneous animation, i.e., in favor of animation by the *anima rationalis* from the first moment of conception. Most modern authors, biologists and doctors, as well as theologians, hold the view of simultaneous animation. It would be completely erroneous to hold that the opinion of St. Thomas on successive animation is definitely outmoded and can no longer be held as a *sententia probabilis*. Even if the exposition of all the arguments pro and con would lead us too far, yet it can definitely be established that the most recent results of biology and psychology are very spontaneously and easily reconcilable with the hypothesis of successive animation as well as that of simultaneous animation.

No matter how this controversial question can be resolved, in any case this is at least certain: that the illiceity of the killing of the fetus even in the first stage of development is in no way affected. In fact, from the moment of fecundation the human embryo is a specifically human embryo, a *homo in potentia* which can become nothing else but a human person. Whether the killing of it is represented as a *homicidium perfectum* or a *homicidium attentatum* and *anticipatum* is irrelevant.

Hence the distinction between *homicidium anticipatum* and *homicidium proprie dictum*, on which St. Alphonsus Liguori ingeniously based the illiceity of the *occisio foetus nondum animati*. In general, there is no such thing as a *foetus non animatus*. The fetus lives from the first moment, and life without animation is in general not conceivable.

A further consideration results from realization of the ideology which includes all violations of the right to life.

The acceptance of the moral liceity of abortion would annul all the arguments against forced sterilization and euthanasia, and finally against the destruction of human life arising from mass elimination and war. If we do not want the last effects, we cannot accept the first error, which makes falling into the last effects inevitable. If respect for the right to life does not begin with embryonic life, which is most in need of protection, all the consequences that have been mentioned are inevitable. Whatever a just theoretical meditation on the problems has for a long time acknowledged has been terribly confirmed by historical reality.

i. Doctrinal decisions of the Church

The Church, by her doctrinal decisions relating to this and like questions, has always clearly and unequivocally defended and protected the right to life, even of man not yet born. She therefore merits the gratitude of all who take to heart the true dignity of man. Instead of this gratitude, her position meets with unreasonable and often inimical criticism.

If this position could, even in good faith, be considered as hardness, time has shown that its effects have been very beneficial and that a deviation from them has caused unhappiness and worse misfortune than that which it was hoped to avoid.

The doctrinal decisions referring to craniotomy are valid partly *implicite* and partly *expressis verbis* even for *procuratio abortus*. Any doubt concerning these is removed by a decision of the Holy Office, July 24, 1895, and that of May 24, 1898.

In recent times the encyclical " Casti Connubii " has clarified the stand taken by the teaching office of the Church and has presented a particularly penetrating view of the question of medical, social and eugenic indications for abortion. The essential elements of the doctrinal declarations regarding the medical indications have already been explained in treating of craniotomy.

In reference to the social and eugenic indications the following is mentioned :

" Quae autem afferuntur pro sociali et eugenica indicatione, licitis honestisque modis et intra debitos limites, earum quidem rerum ratio haberi, potest et debet; at necessitatibus, quibus eae innituntur, per occisionem innocentium providere velle absonum est praeceptoque divino contrarium, apostolicis etiam verbis promulgato: 'Non esse facienda mala ut eveniant bona.'" ("Casti Connubii," N. 66.)

("Thus the social and eugenic indications can and ought to be taken into consideration, provided the means are licit and honest and within the proper limits; but in the state of necessity upon which these indications are established, with the killing of the innocent, this is repugnant to reason and contrary to the divine precept promulgated by the words of the Apostle: 'One ought not to do evil in order to obtain good.'")

Regarding the necessity of protecting the fetus by penal legislation, the following is declared:

"Iis denique qui apud nationes principatum tenent feruntque leges, oblivioni dare non licet auctoritatis publicae esse, congruis legibus poenisque, innocentium vitam defendere, idque eo magis, quo minus ii, quorum vita periclitatur et impugnatur, se ipsi defendere valent, inter quos primum sane locum tenent infantes in visceribus matris abditi. Quod si publici magistratus parvulos illos non solum non tueantur, sed legibus suisque ordinationibus permittant atque adeo tradant mediocorum aliorumve manibus occidendos, meminerit, Deum iudicem esse et vindicem sanguinis innocentis, qui de terra clamat ad caelum." ("Casti Connubii," N. 67.)

("Finally, those who have the supreme government of nations and legislators must not forget that it is the duty of public authority to defend by opportune laws and the sanction of punishment, the life of the innocent; and thus the more so, the less the endangered life is able to defend itself. And here of greatest importance are children whom the mother still carries under her heart. If the public power not only does not defend these creatures, but also by law and decree leaves or rather puts them in the hands of doctors and others to be killed, it should remember that God is the judge and avenger of innocent blood which cries from the earth to heaven.")

j. Summary

Even *abortus artificialis*, like craniotomy, can definitely vanish through progress in therapy and the systematic construction of prophylactic assistance for the pregnant. It is clear that progress in science contributes toward definite victory over abortion.

Even in this question, there is no unsurpassable contrast between the demands of science and the moral doctrine taught by the Church. Moreover, the Church merits gratitude from science, since holding tenaciously to its *non licet* always gives science new impulse toward progress; this culminates in the definite overcoming of an imperfection in the therapeutic methods which conflict with the moral law.

A time will come when it will no longer be understood how it was ever possible that in an era which is considered progressive the killing of the fetus by doctors could have become so extensive.

Despite the great technical and mechanical conquest, the future will have to consider this era as the period of the most lamentable errors in all the history of medicine. On the contrary, it will be considered a great moment when the universalistic criterion of Pastoral Medicine is acknowledged by all.

3. GRAVIDITAS EXTRAUTERINA (FOETUS ECTOPICI)

a. Concept—Classification

By extrauterine pregnancy is meant any pregnancy that takes place outside the normal place (*graviditas ectopica*). The uterine mucus (endomentrium) prepared by the cyclical processes is the only physiologically suitable place for the reception of the fertilized ovum (nidation). Nidation that takes place in any other place is abnormal, "ectopic."

Classification

Apart from the most important form, which is that of "tubal pregnancy" (*graviditas tubaria*: nidation in the Fallopian tubes), the following are the less possible forms of ectopic nidation:

Graviditas isthmica: Nidation within the isthmus of the tube near the upper part of the uterine orifice.

Graviditas interstitalis: Nidation within the muscular stratum of the uterus near the isthmus of the tube.

Graviditas intraligamentaris: Nidation within the ligaments of the uterus (generally in the ligamentum latum).

Graviditas ampullaris: Nidation in the abdominal extremity of the tube (ampulla tubae).

Graviditas ovarica: Nidation in the ovary proper.

Graviditas abdominalis: Nidation in the free abdominal cavity.

b. Causes—Frequency

At one time it was held that ectopic pregnancy was rare. *Graviditas tubaria* is relatively more frequent than the other forms, and the most rare is *graviditas ovarica*, and finally extremely rare is the *graviditas abdominalis*. Tubal pregnancy has become more frequent since around 1914.

Prescinding from the fact that diagnosis is today more simple, it is unanimously admitted that the principal cause for this increase is found in the frequency of the inflammation of the oviducts (salpingitis, adnexitis). Its cause is further found, above all, in the enormous extent of *abortus, abusus matrimonii* and gonorrhea. On the other hand, tubal pregnancy can occur even in cases without inflammation.

c. Dangers—Progress

Every ectopic pregnancy entails a serious danger for the pregnant woman. Only in exceptional, extremely rare cases can the pregnancy continue to develop undisturbed. In most cases, the ovum is prematurely unfastened or broken.

In tubal pregnancy there are two possibilities:

(1) Gradual distension and loosening of the ovum accompanied by slowly progressing and uncontrollable hemorrhage: internal rupture of the fetal membrane (tubal abortion).

(2) Sudden rupture accompanied by very serious signs of shock and often by an internal hemorrhage of the free abdominal cavity, which constitutes immediate danger of death: external rupture of the fetal membrane (tubal rupture).

Tubal pregnancy always represents a complication of pregnancy dangerous to life, but of special danger is the tubal rupture, in which, if there is no immediate intervention, the pregnant woman inevitably succumbs because of internal hemorrhage. In rare cases—often without anticipatory diagnosis—the ectopic pregnancy can develop to maturation. In these cases, it is a matter of forms of *graviditas ampullaris* and *graviditas ovarica* or *abdominalis*. Even when the ectopic pregnancy develops to maturity without disturbance and, consequently, without being realized, new dangers present themselves: birth in a natural way is impossible. It can come about only by means of laparotomy.

Laparotomy in a case of abdominal pregnancy is more difficult and dangerous than a common *sectio caesarea*. This is due to the fact that the placenta, often dissolved into numerous shreds, develops in the peritoneum, either in the parietal peritoneum or in the visceral lining of the abdominal organs. Hence the mortality is greater in this operation than in the Caesarean section. The great number of cases of terminated births and fortunate outcome for the mother and child has already been mentioned.

d. Judgment of Pastoral Medicine

In consideration of the grave dangers, Werth in 1904 established the following principle: In whatever phase an ectopic pregnancy is diagnosed with certitude, the ovum is to be treated as a malignant tumor; i.e., it is to be removed as soon as possible.

On the contrary, moral theology even in this case holds to its fundamental principle, that the direct killing of man is never permissible: *Numquam licet directe occidere hominem.*

There seems to be an insuperable problem here that renders the judgment of Pastoral Medicine particularly difficult. But even this difficulty finds its solution in an objective examination of the facts.

First, we must depart from the fact that the diagnosis of ectopic pregnancy is often very difficult. It is relatively easier in the case of tubal rupture. Even here, there is no other problem for Pastoral Medicine than that of saving the mother; the doctor not only can, but must intervene and do so as soon as possible. There are no preoccupations on the part of moral theology since the doctor is authorized to presume with moral certitude that at the moment of hemorrhage the fetus no longer lives, but is lost: thus, he must no longer preoccupy himself with the life of the fetus.

The same thing holds in the case of so-called tubal abortion. Even here, hemorrhage is the essential symptom which leads to the diagnosis; and with every strong and protracted hemorrhage the death of the fetus is to be definitely presumed. The difference between this and the former case is only this, that it admits of a longer waiting period, especially when the diagnosis is not completely clear and definite. The matter is different when the fetus is alive—that is to say, in ectopic pregnancy without disturbances. Here the diagnosis is very difficult. In most cases, the diagnosis is not generally established in the early stages, but only when the pregnancy is far advanced. In such cases, it is not possible to foresee the effects that immediate intervention would have on the living but not yet viable fetus. Though laparotomy is inevitable in every case, the most opportune thing is to postpone it until the fetus is viable or until the regular termination of pregnancy.

The difficulties and dangers, sometimes greater than those presented by a simple Caesarean, must be faced in the interest of saving the life of the child. This requires that the interests of both mother and child which are at stake are to be equally weighed.

What is more, the increasing number of favorable results for both mother and child proves that the advances of technical surgery resolve even this problem in a satisfactory manner.

It is natural that as soon as the diagnosis of an extrauterine pregnancy is established, the pregnant woman is to be taken to a hospital in order to operate on her as early as it seems necessary. As soon as hemorrhage takes place, there is present the right and duty of operating.

Modern surgical obstetrics has no longer reason to hold the radical view of Werth, who in 1904 had no moral justification, still less clinical justification. So there is no reason to consider the standpoint of Pastoral Medicine incompatible with that of clinical medicine when the advancements of the latter permit treatment in such a way as not to raise any objections.

e. Doctrinal decisions of the Church

The pronouncements of the Church and of Catholic moralists concerning direct attack of the surgeon on the fetus or direct removal of a nonviable fetus, clearly show all such acts to be immoral.

Years ago medical experts held that ectopic pregnancy constituted a grave and present danger to the mother, and moralists permitted excision of the Fallopian tube, even though the death of the fetus would result. This is *indirect abortion* and morally it is justified by the rule of twofold effect. Reliable medical opinion as to the mother's danger suffices.

4. ARTIFICIAL PREMATURE BIRTH

a. Concept

By artificial premature birth (*partus praematurus artificialis*), we mean the process whereby the viable but not yet mature fetus is extracted before the regular termination of pregnancy (*partus maturus*).

In general, the earliest point of time is considered to be the twenty-eighth week of pregnancy. A fetus born before this time remains alive only in an exceptional case. (The recognized minimum weight at birth is 600 gr.) Practically speaking, the twenty-eighth week of pregnancy can be considered the minimum limit of viability and the weight of 1000 gr. for birth. The more the premature birth approximates the minimum limit, the more difficult is the bringing up of the child and the preserving of its life.

The nearer the premature reaches the fortieth week, the more favorable are the prospects of life for the child. Its fate depends in great measure upon the care and assistance that it is given.

b. Methods

As in artificial abortion, the method can be divided into:

(a) Internal, medicinal methods (dynamic means);
(b) Surgical, operative methods (mechanical means).

(a) *Medicinal methods*

The application of dynamic methods is more successful the closer to the natural end of pregnancy is their use. These methods tend to stimulate the uterine contractions. The preparation of the uterus is less the further the moment of birth is from the termination of pregnancy.

I

The following must be essentially taken into consideration:

(1) Purgatives;

(2) Stimulants for uterine contractions (quinine, hypophysis, extracts from the thymus and hypophysis);

(3) Uterine tonics.

(b) *Surgico-mechanical methods*

(1) Intestinal enemas;

(2) Electrical irritation of the uterus;

(3) Mechanical shaking (vibratory massage, the apparatus called the " Seistes " of Gauss);

(4) Insertion of a bag (procteurynter, colpeurynter, metreurynter);

(5) Rupture of the amnion (puncture of the fetal membrane);

(6) Operative methods:

(aa) Vaginal operation (*sectio vaginalis parva, hysterotomia vaginalis anterior, Dührssen*);

(bb) Abdominal operation (laparotomy), " sectio caesarea parva ").

The various methods can be combined.

c. Sphere of application (Indications)

In modern obstetrics, artificial premature birth has lost much of its former sphere of application. At one time it was principally used in cases of narrow pelvis in order to avoid craniotomy or Caesarean section. Since its results in regard to the vitality of the child left much to be desired (in accentuated cases of restriction of the pelvis, the operation had to be necessarily anticipated) and, since it was difficult to select the right moment and adequate methods, artificial premature birth has been used less often than formerly.

This is chiefly attributable to the favorable results obtained with the Caesarean section (*sectio caesarea*) which, in case of restriction of the pelvis, has as a method of choice absolutely supplanted artificial premature birth.

On the other hand, another indication of premature birth acquired ground slowly but constantly: as a means of eliminating *abortus artificialis* in the case of pregnancy complications.

This was so especially in cases of tuberculosis, heart deficiencies, kidney troubles, etc., in which the greatest danger for the pregnant is present during the last weeks of pregnancy because of the higher position of the uterus (cf. above).

In such cases, premature birth in the form of the so-called vaginal Caesarean section (*hysterotomia vaginalis anterior*) can have an extraordinary benefit and can save the life of mother and child.

The operation is technically very easy: It consists essentially in a medial incision of the anterior lip of the mouth of the uterus and the cervical canal, or of the anterior wall of the uterus to the internal mouth of the uterus, with the removal of the vesical wall. This permits the emptying of the uterus within a few minutes without contractions, which is of great advantage especially in cases of heart lesions, imminent danger of eclampsia, etc., in which cases contractions constitute a particular element of danger. Technically there is no difficulty and danger since the medial incision is exact and the suture is very simple.

A definite advantage of the method is this, that the operation can be done even with local anesthesia, thus rendering narcosis superfluous which, in certain circumstances (e.g., in the case of heart defects), constitutes an additional burden. It would be desirable that this valuable method be an object of greater attention than formerly as this would lead to the complete elimination of abortion in obstetrical therapy.

d. Judgment of Pastoral Medicine

In the case of pelvic restriction, artificial premature birth as alternative to craniotomy or the Caerarean section is at present rejected in favor of the Caesarean section, since this latter assures more extensively the right to life of mother and child.

On the other hand, its value in the form of *hysterotomia vaginalis*, in case of imminent complications of pregnancy after the twenty-eighth week, cannot be sufficiently estimated. Some authors have expressed an unfavorable judgment concerning the rearing of children born prematurely, especially from the viewpoint of the selective hygiene of the race. On this point, the following is to be observed: Without doubt the rearing of premature children demands unusual care and effort. The difficulties and probable success stand in inverse relation to each other, the earlier the premature birth takes place. The fate of children born prematurely depends greatly upon care and assistance given.

It is indispensable that these cases be given closed hospital care. The most suitable are the institutions which have the equipment and materials needed for the care of premature children. The question whether the use of these means for a human being of "lessened worth" is justified is a question that can be posited only by that very utilitarian materialism which has denied the same care to the infirm and mentally sick and has proposed euthanasia.

On the other hand, it can be established that when the initial difficulties of care are overcome and the premature child has reached the stage of development of the child born at full term, its successive bodily and mental vitality need not be in any way compromised and its future activity in life can be outstanding.

Besides this, the consideration of the right to life is sufficient to call for the use of all the means of assistance; these always bring a great compensation, not always materially but in an inestimable and immaterial manner.

e. Doctrinal decisions of the Church

A decision of the Holy Office given on May 4, 1898, answers the following questions:

(1) "Eritne licita partus acceleratio, quoties ex mulieris arctitudine impossibilis evaderet foetus egressio suo naturale tempore?"

(2) "Et, si mulieris arctitudo talis sit, ut neque partus praematurus possibilis censeatur, licebitne abortum provocare aut ceasaream, suo tempore, perficere operationem?"

(3) Concerns "praegnatio extrauterina," already considered.

The answer is expressed as follows:

(1) Partus accelerationem per se illicitam non esse, dummodo perficiatur iustis de causis et eo tempore et modo quibus, ex ordinarie contingentibus, matris et foetus vitae consulatur.

(2) Quoad primam partem, negative, iuxta decretum fer IV. 24 Julii 1895 de abortus illiceitate. Ad secundum vero quod spectat,

nihil obstare, quominus mulier, de qua agitur, caesareae operationi suo tempore subiciatur.

The translation of the questions is as follows:

(1) Is acceleration of birth licit when, because of the restriction of the mother's pelvis, the birth of the child at the natural time would be impossible?

(2) And, if the restriction of the mother's pelvis is so great that the birth of a premature child appears impossible, is it permissible to provoke an abortion or to realize in time a Caesarean section?

The answer:

(1) The acceleration of birth is not of itself illicit, provided it is done through justified motives and in such a manner that, in the normal course of things, provision is made for the health of the mother and child.

(2) In regard to the first part: negative, according to the decree of July 24, 1895, in regard to the illiceity of abortion. To the second part: It is perfectly permissible to have the mother undergo a Caesarean section at the proper time.

Hence the following principles are valid for the provocation of artificial premature birth:

(1) The operation is not in se illicit.

(2) In order that it be licit, the following conditions are to be verified:

(a) A just cause (*iusta causa*—in medicine: a serious indication).

(b) The right point of time.

(c) Execution through proper methods which offer a greater guarantee to the life of the mother and child.

These principles are in perfect harmony with the natural principles of medical science and modern obstetrics.

5. CAESAREAN SECTION (SECTIO CAESAREA)

a. Historical view

Caesarean section is one of the oldest operations of obstetrics. It was practiced by different people from remote times for the purpose of saving the surviving fetus by extracting it from the dying or apparently dying mother.

According to tradition, a *lex regia* which prescribes the section upon the deceased mother goes back to Numa Pompilius.

Legal dispositions of this type, which have kept the name *lex regia*, have been retained in the codices of various countries up to the present time (e.g., Austria).

According to a more ancient tradition, the name of the operation arose from Julius Caesar, who was extracted from the body of his mother by means of the section (*ex matris utero caesus*) and thus the name " Caesar " is synonymous with " born by means of a section."

The operation was later called *sectio caesarea*, expressed in German as *Kaiserschnitt*. We omit here more recent attempts to explain the term.

Up to recent times, the Caesarean section performed upon a living mother was rightly considered one of the most dangerous in obstetrics. Before the era of narcosis and asepsis, it was for the mother equivalent to a death sentence. Küstner justly observes that in the ancient " classical " Caesarean section " the blood of a hecatomb flowed."

One has to know this in order to understand the repugnance of former times toward this operation and to realize how pressing then were the problems connected with craniotomy.

Only modern methods of surgery have removed the dreadful aspects of this operation.

b. Concept

By Caesarean section, in the sense of modern obstetrics, must be understood that surgical operation in which access to the uterine cavity is established by opening the same by means of an incision.

c. Classification—Methods

These are the possibilities:

(1) Caesarean section with mature child;

(2) Caesarean section with immature child (so-called small Caesarean section, *sectio parva*).

The access can be obtained:

(1) By means of laparotomy (*sectio abdominalis*);
(2) Through the vaginal passage (*sectio vaginalis, hysterotomia vaginalis*).

Further divisions according to the technique of the operation (transperitoneal or extraperitoneal; corporeal or cervical Caesarean section) are irrelevant from the point of view of Pastoral Medicine.

But more important is the distinction between:

(1) Conservative methods and;
(2) Mutilating methods (radical).

To the latter belongs the method of Porro, once much discussed and today no longer used (cf. below). This is today largely supplanted by special methods which permit a conservative procedure (without removing the uterus) in the case of infected contents of the uterus. At present, precedence is given to abdominal, transperitoneal, and cervical Caesarean section. Their success is excellent for the mother and the child.

d. Spheres of application (Indications)

From the viewpoint of Pastoral Medicine, there is little to add to the obstetrical doctrine of indication. For this, the following principle is basic: In a conscientious direction of birth, neither the life of the mother nor the child should be lost through the procedure. While at one time the Caesarean section was used only in consideration of the child (indication in favor of the child), with increased security for the mother the question has also acquired spheres of application in consideration of the latter (maternal indication).

In case of necessity, it permits the fastest emptying of the uterus. Such expanded indications are: hemorrhage in the case of *placenta praevia*, premature loosening of the placenta, eclampsia.

The vaginal method permits birth by Caesarean operation almost without danger and within a still shorter time when a most rapid operation is important.

Naturally, the indispensable condition in which this operation can be fulfilled is the presence of a narrow pelvis.

Obstetrics distinguishes further:

(1) Relative indications;
(2) Absolute indications.

As relative indications are considered those in which the Caesarean section comes into competition with diminishing operations (craniotomy).

In case of absolute indication (extreme narrowness of pelvis) the Caesarean section is the only mode possible for the liberation of the fetus.

Pastoral Medicine cannot admit this distinction since, together with the Caesarean section, other mutilating operations would be justified. In time, even obstetrics will take this point of view.

e. Medico-pastoral questions

Various serious questions arise:

(1) Is a pregnant woman bound in conscience to undergo a Caesarean section in order to save the child:

(a) Only when the prognosis of the operation is favorable;
(b) or also when the prognosis is unfavorable for her?

(2) Is the doctor obliged in conscience to apply this method or let it be applied by another authorized doctor?

(3) In case of necessity, is it licit to have a person who is not a doctor execute the same?

(4) Is it licit for the doctor to refuse to take care of the pregnant person when she refuses to undergo the Caesarean section and insists on craniotomy?

(5) Is it licit for him, in this case, to perform the Caesarean section against the will of the pregnant person and her relations?

The answer to:

(1) When the prognosis of the operation is favorable, there is no doubt that the answer is in the affirmative. When the prognosis is unfavorable, it can be objected that the mother must conserve her life for the already existing children. Yet she cannot do this at the price of the life of a child. Finally, not even craniotomy is absolutely devoid of danger for the mother. On the other hand, even an unfavorable prognosis does not imply absolute certainty of death. But even if this were so, the following principle still prevails: *Numquam licet directe occidere hominem.*

(2) It must be affirmed that there is a duty of conscience on the part of the doctor. He is also obliged in conscience to perform the

operation only when he possesses the necessary skill; otherwise, he is obliged to have it performed by a specialist.

(3) Today, in civilized countries and in normal times, the situation is not imaginable in which a doctor who does not have surgical experience would find himself without aid in conditions under which he must take into consideration the question of the Caesarean section upon a living mother in order to save the child. The means of transportation and the telephone almost always offer the possibility of procuring aid. If, however, all these possibilities are lacking, we may concede a case in which a doctor who does not have surgical experience finds himself faced with the question whether, omitting the operation, he will let the mother and child die or attempt to save her with an immediate operation or at least save the child—in the face of danger that the mother will die in consequence of the operation because of inadequate surgical care.

If, in such a situation, it is judged that the doctor is obliged in conscience to operate, he cannot, in the case of an unfavorable outcome, be reproved for lack of skill. If, however, the situation is an absolutely desperate one, there is no reason, *necessitate cogenti*, why the right to help in necessity must be expected only from the doctor. Anyone, even a person other than a doctor, who has courage has the right to act. In fact, there are known cases in which simple barber-surgeons have performed the operation with success, and against expectation there was happy outcome for the mother, notwithstanding the fact that the operation was performed and care conducted in the most primitive manner. This should not give occasion for misunderstanding. A general recommendation is not to be found in these words. It is a matter merely of a question of conscience for cases of extreme necessity which must be decided according to conscience. The priest can only be advised to refrain from any part in this operation. A failure would affect him in a twofold manner. Besides, he could always be reproved for his incompetency.

Hence we omit to give, as certain old works do, a detailed description of the manner of effecting the Caesarean section. What is necessary is explained under *Sectio in mortua*, below.

(4) The conscientious doctor not only can, but must refuse to treat the pregnant woman who refuses to undergo a Caesarean section and insists on craniotomy—and this even when there is danger of being called inhuman. He must have the courage to insist

I*

on an "either-or." The woman and her relatives must know that he is absolutely in earnest and does not intend to practice craniotomy. They will eventually give in.

(5) In case of extreme necessity, the consent of the woman and her relatives is not required for Caesarean section. Juridically the consent refers only to the sphere of the rights of the one who gives it.

The pregnant woman has no right to dispose of the life of the child. If, in order to save the life of the child, the doctor operates against the will of the mother and relatives, this is an attack upon the rights of the mother and in se illegal—but the doctor can have recourse to the right which is given him by the state of necessity and the urgent need of the child who is in danger. From this point of view, the Caesarean section assumes a juridical position different from that of any other operation.

The doctor can defend himself against civil action by adducing proof of the testimony of indication and the irreproachable execution.

f. The Porro operation

The Porro operation, from the pastoral-medical viewpoint, occupies a special position. In this operation, after the Caesarean section has been performed, the *corpus uteri* is removed (*defundatio seu supravaginalis amputatio*). The operation causes subsequent sterilization and castration, since with the uterus the ovaries are also removed; hence it constitutes a *gravis mutilatio*.

This operation is performed, on the one hand, to eliminate the uterus as a source of hemorrhage or infection and, on the other hand, with the primary or secondary intention of preventing further pregnancies. In consideration of the latter effect, the special position is justified. In regard to its moral liceity, the following is to be mentioned: A *gravis mutilatio* is, according to the predominant doctrine, permitted only insofar as it serves to save life and the danger cannot be removed by some other means. Hence, if the operation is performed merely to impede a new pregnancy, to remove the danger of a new Caesarean section, it is illicit. But, if it can be considered as the only possibility of saving the mother from a hemorrhage and infection that can endanger her life, it is licit.

Since the Porro operation, which has for its purpose the avoidance of infection, has become superfluous because of new methods (cf. above), its sphere of medico-pastoral application has become restricted. With this, the condition for its moral liceity—namely, the impossibility of saving the life of the mother by any other method—is removed: *Licitam tunc esse tantum, cum agitur de servanda vita, quae aliter servari non potest.*

g. Sectio in mortua et moribunda

(a) *Sectio in mortua*

These are the requisites for the application of *sectio in mortus et moribunda*: The fetus must be viable (at least twenty-eight weeks old) or at least it must be considered possible that it lives. Any degree of probability, however small, suffices. In cases of chronic illness and prolonged agony, the child generally dies before the mother. On the other hand, the child's prospects of life are more favorable the sooner or more sudden is the death of the mother, and most favorable when the mother in good health dies of a violent death (accident). The operation is to be performed as soon as possible after the death of the mother.

Justification of the operation: The objection that the operation is too gruesome and affects the feelings of the relatives is unfounded. In general, this opinion arises simply from a lack of proper evaluation of the life of the child after the death of the mother. It is precisely here that it is important not to give way to false sentimentality. The life of the child is to be saved. Strength of character is required in order to firmly maintain these principles. The doctor should consider the reproaches and hostility that will arise. In general, he will also be accused of religious fanaticism. All these difficulties should not dissuade him from the fulfillment of his duty. No one knows what possibilities are hidden within the child. But prescinding from this material value, there remains the duty of conserving the life of the child at least up to the time that he has received Baptism. One must have the courage to lead men back to the sensibility of these values which today are so often forgotten.

An objection which is more frequent is the presumed uselessness of the operation. Here it is well to recall that already in 1758 Cangiamila informed the profession of a great number of cases in which it was possible to save the life of the mother.

Although the guarantee of his authority has been doubted, we can appeal to numerous trustworthy reports of modern and most recent times.

The best way of overcoming the objection that the mother may only be "apparently dead" and may die from the effects of the operation is that the doctor scientifically and conscientiously carry out his duty of determining the death of the mother and perform the operation in the same way he would perform it upon a living woman. Therefore he cannot wait so long that even the life of the child is definitely lost.

(b) Sectio in moribunda

In regard to the dying pregnant woman, objections appear more justified. In each case the decision remains a question of conscience and in every case is a very difficult decision. Fundamentally, not even the moral liceity of the *sectio in moribunda* can be doubted. Even more than for the *sectio in mortua*, the doctor has the duty of executing the operation with the same accuracy he would use upon a living person. This is so especially in regard to the attention given the umbilical cord (double ligature), after birth and wounds. Hence the following objections merit special consideration:

The operation seriously offends justified sentiments (Capellmann —Bergmann). It is very difficult to select the appropriate moment: "Sometimes one operates on the dying mother only to extract a dead child. . . . At other times one operates upon an apparently dying mother whose death does not come from the illness with which she is affected and in whom the Caesarean section increases the danger represented by the present illness. These difficulties are the reason for inducing one to abstain from operating in the majority of cases." (Capellmann—Bergmann.)

(c) Attitude of the priest

In general, the priest is strongly warned to abstain from the fulfillment of a *sectio caesarea in mortua* and more than ever *in moribunda*, or directly *in viva*.

(1) The operation may prove extremely upsetting to a priest not accustomed to surgery. If he becomes uncontrolled, all is lost and nothing is gained.

(2) The operation is dangerous, requires a certain knowledge, courage and ability.

(3) Because of its bloody character, and because it pertains to the genital sphere, it is not free from a certain lack of decorum for the priest.

(4) It can give scandal, and harm can come to the prestige of the clergy.

It is therefore impossible that the execution of the *sectio ceasarea* be imposed as an obligation upon the priest. Its performance by him is to be viewed basically as a general prohibition.

There are cases of necessity in which all considerations—even those of clerical decorum—must become silent, and hence the priest cannot be reproached when he does what his conscience dictates.

Nor is he to be reproached if, in consideration of the difficulties which present themselves and because of his incapacity and the effects that can arise, he does not enter into the task.

h. Doctrinal decisions of the Church

The position taken by the Church in regard to the Caesarean section arises fully from the decrees concerning craniotomy.

The position regarding the Porro operation is derived from the reasons already given.

In regard to the *sectio in mortua*, there are basic decisions which also determine the attitude of the priest.

The Roman Ritual prescribes that, in case of the death of a pregnant woman, the child is to be extracted and, if alive, he is to be baptized:

"*Si mater praegnans mortua feurit, fetus ab iis ad quos spectat, extractus, si certo vivat, baptizetur absolute.*" The same is literally expressed in canon 746, #4, CIC.

Important here is the prudent choice of the words *ad quos spectat*. They are not prejudiced against the choice or exclusion of determined persons. Above all, they allude to the experts whose professional duty it is to perform the task. But in the absence of these same, other persons are not excluded. Thus, a situation is imaginable in which even the priest can be the one *ad quem res spectat*. The question can be considered controversial. Probable arguments can be posited in favor of the contrary opinion.

In favor of this is the ancient decision of the Holy Office on February 15, 1780, and a recent decision of December 13, 1899.

This latter regards a case in which a priest, in the absence of a doctor, performed the *sectio in mortua*. The child lived and was baptized. The pastor was accused, absolved by the tribunal, but subjected to disciplinary sanction by the administrative authority. To the question whether the pastor acted rightly an answer was given, referring to the decree of February 15, 1780, to a Vicar Apostolic in China, which dealt especially with conditions in missionary regions.

In it we read that the prescription of the Roman Ritual was nowhere rigorously followed, was not promulgated, and hence was not strictly binding. There is danger, it was pointed out, that atrocious calumny will be excited against religion (*atroces calumnias contra religionem excitandi*) and serious consequences will arise from it. The answer therefore insists on the necessity of acting wisely and prudently, lest in winning few souls, many may be lost: *Caute prudenterque agendum . . . ne, cum paucos quaerimus, multos amittamus.*

Nevertheless, great effort should be made to make known all that is prescribed in the Roman Ritual. It is the duty of missionaries to instruct, gradually and with circumspection, the natives and to make them understand the necessity of saving the child. On the other hand, the missionaries are advised in certain cases to abstain from becoming enmeshed in these matters and not to excessively insist on the execution of the *sectio caesarea*.

In general, the following can be stated: The priest must, as much as is possible (*regulariter saltem*), refrain from the execution of the operation. He has no obligation to perform it personally. It is generally and absolutely forbidden for him to do it.

The following is especially established for mission lands: In this case, the opinion that a decree of the Holy See prohibits the operation is not accurate. It only calls attention to the particular difficulties which present themselves in missionary regions. Yet even in those regions there is the possibility that a situation may present itself in which, even for the missionary, there remains nothing else but to personally operate.

Normally he should instruct and spread the necessary knowledge for execution of the operation. In order to fulfill this task, he himself must possess the knowledge.

6. ANESTHESIA IN BIRTH

Here we do not discuss whether narcosis and other methods of anesthesia used in operations are licit or not. This is outside the discussion: There are always difficult operations that involve great responsibility, and in these the doctor is not only authorized, but obliged to use every means to eliminate pain. It is brutal to make a simple application of forceps to the lower section, to say nothing of more difficult operations, without the use of anesthesia.

The problem under discussion is that of establishing whether it is justified to claim, in general, as a right for the one giving birth, the elimination of birth pains or to deny the same.

The defenders of anesthesia in general—even in normal birth— argue in the following manner: There is no reason why every mother should not enjoy the benefit of a painless birth even in the case of a normal birth. All should benefit from technical and scientific progress. Moreover, the desire of women to have children would be strengthened, for one of the principal reasons for the repugnancy to have children is found in fear of birth pains. Pain as such is not a universal commandment of nature. The words of Scripture: "In sorrow shalt thou bring forth children" (Gen. 3:16) does not signify the prohibition of anesthesia.

On the other side it is objected: Birth is a natural process. It is neither justified nor wise to intervene in this process which normally takes place in the best manner without the action of man, at least in cases where there is no absolute necessity.

Such a necessity could certainly be present in the case of pain that is extremely intense, as in the case of extreme sensibility of the nervous system. Then the process is no longer normal. As long as it proceeds in a normal manner, any human intervention is more harmful than useful. Finally, birth pain has itself a deeper meaning. It is important that women consciously experience the mystery of maternity. The pains of giving birth are quickly forgotten, but from the psychological view they consolidate and deepen maternal love.

Thus the arguments given by both sides are probable and worthy of serious consideration. In practice, the application of anesthesia is not as simple as it seems. This is based on the fact that at the moment the pains arise it can never be definitely known how long they will last and what course they will take.

If, from the first moment, all possible methods in the application of anesthesia were used to remove all pain, it could still be in a case of protracted birth that the anesthesia could no longer be applied with the necessary effects at the time when it was most necessary.

It is definitely licit to apply a light *narcose à la reine* during the expulsive contractions and a so-called narcosis of transition. Morally licit—in fact directly of obligation as a duty of charity— is the elimination of pain in all the pathological processes of birth which deviate from the norm, which have begun with pain more intense than the normal.

It is a probable opinion that in normal birth the use of anesthesia is not morally illicit.

It is impossible to establish at what point normality begins and to what limits the pains are normal. One can only proceed from case to case. Moreover, the picture can be disturbed and changed deeply at any moment in the giving of birth. Even a valiant and resolved woman can weaken in the last moment of the transition. Since in the individual case it is almost impossible to trace the limits of the normal and pathological, it is also impossible to have the question of moral liceity depend upon so uncertain a criterion. So we can hold that, even in normal birth, anesthesia is in se not illicit. It is merely advisable to strengthen in women a feeling for the moral value of conscious support of the normal pain of birth—i.e., that not exceeding the limits of toleration.

7. BAPTISM IN BIRTH—BAPTISMUS IN UTERO

We are not discussing here the Baptism, in case of necessity, of the child immediately after birth who is delivered alive but is of weak vitality. This is no problem but a duty easily understood by the Catholic doctor, midwife or nurse.

Here we treat of the difficult medico-pastoral problem of establishing whether there exists an unobjectionable possibility of administering Baptism to the fetus *in utero* in the case of threatening complications and the danger of intrauterine death of the fetus. Prescinding from the necessity of Baptism for salvation and the fact that the spiritual life constitutes a good that is superior to temporal life, some authors have recommended the Baptism of the child in the mother's womb in case of imminent danger of death for the fetus or when the obstetrician is compelled to resort to craniotomy.

In view of the moral illiceity of craniotomy, the preceding Baptism of urgency is in se irrelevant.

An *occisio directa* is as illicit for a baptized child as it is for one unbaptized.

It is a moral duty for a Catholic doctor to preoccupy himself with the Baptism of urgency in any case of imminent danger of death for the newborn child as well as for the fetus not yet born.

This duty exists even in the case of an aborted fetus, including those in the earliest stages of gestation, and this always conditionally: *si vivis*, or *si capax es*.

Regarding the Baptism, the following is to be noted:

The baptismal water must moisten the body of the child at whatever point. It is not sufficient that it wet the membranes of the ovum or the placenta. Canon 746, CIC, prescribes:

#1. "Nemo in utero matris clausus baptizetur, donec probabilis spes sit, ut rite editus baptizari possit."

#2. "Si infans caput emiserit et periculum mortis imminet, baptizetur in capite, nec postea, si vivus evaserit, est iterum sub conditione baptizandus."

#3. "Si aliud membrum emiserit, in illo, si periculum mortis imminet, baptizetur sub conditione; at tunc, si natus vixerit, est rursus sub conditione baptizandus."

#4. "Fetus, in utero baptizatus, post artum denuo sub conditione baptizari debet."

#1. "An infant shall not be baptized while still enclosed in the mother's womb as long as there is probable hope that it can be baptized when born."

#2. "If the infant puts forth the head, it may be baptized on the head in case of imminent danger of death, and the Baptism shall not afterwards be repeated conditionally if the child lives."

#3. "Should any other limb emerge, the infant may be baptized on that limb conditionally, if the danger of death is imminent; but if the infant is born alive, it must be baptized again conditionally."

#4. "If the fetus was baptized in the mother's womb, it shall, when born, be baptized again conditionally."

In order to perform the Baptism of *partus nondum editus* the following methods have been recommended:

(1) Rupture of the ovular membranes and the simple *ablutio* or *aspersio* of the part of the body which presents itself;

(2) Aspersion by means of an injection syringe:

(a) Through the vaginal tract across the ovular membranes;

(b) Through the abdominal wall, uterus and ovular membranes;

(3) Aspersion by means of tubular instruments (*siphunculus*).
The last-mentioned method should at the present time be completely abandoned if for no other reason than that its asepsis is doubtful. Only the methods of (1) and (2) can be seriously considered. The method of (2b) is to be rejected as dangerous and suspicious; moreover, the necessary and required aspersion of the body with baptismal water is not sure.

Whatever method is to be chosen, the doctor is to note the following:

(1) He must fulfill the requirements regarding the forma and *materia sacramenti*;

(2) He must comply rigorously with the medical requirements of asepsis in order not to endanger the mother.

8. THE CO-OPERATION OF NUNS IN OBSTETRICS

With all respect to the consecrated traditions which are contained in the rules of Orders, the fact that their rule prohibits some nuns from assisting in obstetrical operations is a deficiency. Historically, such a prohibition is completely comprehensible. Even from the psychological point of view, there are elements which justify it— above all, the fact that nothing makes the religious more conscious of the burden of her sacrifice than participation in the experience of physical maternity. Actually the nun takes part in this experience in maternity wards.

This prohibition cannot be justified on the basis of *indecentia* or *inconvenientia* alone. Much is demanded of the nuns in surgical operations of every kind. Often in public hospitals, they must also be witnesses of operations that are questionable from the medico-pastoral viewpoint, so that the question of co-operation can become very serious.

On the other hand, co-operation in obstetrics can present an experience of great moral value. Obstetrics is perhaps the most difficult department of all medicine, but rightly understood it is without doubt the most exalted. Participation by the nursing Sisters can be of benefit not only to the mother, but eventually to the nuns themselves, provided they assist in the wards in an unobjectionable manner and according to the norms of Pastoral Medicine.

It is further to be considered whether in the countries where the service is needed the Orders of nursing Sisters should educate midwives among the nuns and allow them to take examinations given by the state.

The conference of bishops held in Fulda in 1922 established for the nursing Orders directives which permit promising developments. In the meantime, the development of the question of nuns in obstetrics has made notable progress, and in many countries as also in many Orders a happy solution *via facti* has been found.[1]

9. THE QUESTION OF CO-OPERATION

The question of the limits of moral liceity in co-operation is of great importance not only for the nursing Sisters, but also for lay nurses, assistants and helpers, especially in regard to the objectionability of certain operations from the medico-pastoral viewpoint. It is therefore necessary to know the principles of moral theology on this point.

We must distinguish between:

(1) Direct and indirect co-operation (*cooperatio immediata seu mediata*).

(2) Formal and material co-operation (*cooperatio formalis seu materialis*).

Cooperatio mediata is further divided into: Proximate and remote co-operation (*cooperatio proxima seu remota*).

Formal co-operation, which implies internal consent to the illicit act, as such is always illicit.

Direct co-operation is, according to the *finis operis*, equal to formal co-operation and is therefore likewise illicit.

---

[1] NOTE. On February 11, 1936, the Sacred Congregation of the Propagation of the Faith released an Instruction to religious institutes of women regarding the assistance they might thenceforth give mothers and infants in mission lands, thereby releasing them from the former prohibition against their assisting in maternity cases.

Simple material co-operation is in se illicit, but can *per accidens* be licit, provided it does not accord in intention with the illicit act of the agent and there is present a *causa proportionate gravis.*

The danger of losing one's position is also to be considered a *causa proportionate gravis* when it is a case merely of *cooperatio materialis* or *remota.*

On the other hand, formal co-operation cannot be justified by any reason, however serious.

The question of co-operation has become in the last decade particularly serious. In some countries Catholic hospitals have been forced by public authority to permit in their places operations causing sterilization, provoked abortions, etc.

In view of such a situation there can be no doubt that, because of grave scandal and danger to the faith, the norms which regulate the co-operation of doctors and nuns are to be observed more rigorously than formerly.

B. OPERATIONS ON THE REPRODUCTIVE ORGANS

1. GENERAL VIEW

The operations which we are to study here belong, insofar as they refer to operations on women, to the branch of gynecology and, insofar as they refer to operations on men, to the branch of surgery or urology.

For Pastoral Medicine there arises the need of comprehending the gynecological operations and those of sexual surgery from a common viewpoint.

As a general principle which Pastoral Medicine is to follow in judging the operations upon the human genital organ, the following can apply:

Any operation favorable to the purpose or end of human sexual life, natural reproduction, has in its favor the presumption of moral liceity.

Any operation which is contrary to the end of natural reproduction has against it the presumption of moral illiceity.

An operation which favors natural reproduction will therefore lose the character of a morally licit action only through the particular circumstances of the case—for example, when the action itself is intentionally turned toward extramarital or adulterous reproduction. The possibility of abuse is per se no reason against moral liceity: *abusus non tollit usum.*

Hence an operation, in se licit, which serves to aid reproduction, cannot become illicit merely because account must be taken of the possibility of abuse. It is only that the preoccupying character of such an operation increases with the increase of the probability of abuse. Of decisive importance for the moral judgment of any action are, beside the object, end and means, the motives which determine the action and the circumstances which accompany it.

In this regard, we must refer to the general principles of moral theology.

2. GYNECOLOGICAL EXAMINATION

A requisite for every medical therapeutic measure is an indisputable diagnosis. A requisite for a sure diagnosis is an accurate examination. Every medical examination begins with the external inspection of the organs; only then does the examination with the aid of sense of touch (palpation) follow; and to complete the examination recourse is had to such methods of acoustics as auscultation percussion (even for the abdominal organs). Finally, special methods such as radiological examinations (for example, hysterosalpingography, etc.) may be used; also functional examinations with the aid of perfected physiological, chemical and biological methods.

a. Execution of examination

The individuality of the gynecological examination lies in the circumstances of the situation. It requires not only a special technique, practice, experience and ability of judgment, but much tact and comprehension of the psychological circumstances and moral responsibility.

The examination will often be considered embarrassing, and yet it is most important. Nothing should be omitted and it should be exact and complete. Moreover, gynecological examinations should take place in the quickest and most discreet manner possible.

The bimanual palpation is the specific method for the gynecological examination. This should furnish a plastic image of the condition of the internal organs. In this case, the "external" hand is *quasi* more important than the "internal." This latter must, as much as possible, introduce two fingers, for this facilitates the stereoscopic "vision with the fingertips." If this is not possible, the examination is to be done *uno digito*. With virgins and children, the examination is made per rectum.

The vaginal examination is to be excluded when it is unnecessary.

When it is a matter of obtaining a judgment concerning the condition of the female genital organs, the method is absolutely indispensable and no other can be substituted.

When there is only a suspicion of a genital disease, and there is a bearing of such disturbances on the entire organism of the woman, the omission is to be considered a grave technical error.

It is, however, clear that its application is not indifferent: just as this examination cannot be omitted when it is indicated, so also it must be avoided when it is avoidable. A necessary examination ought not to be omitted; an examination that is not necessary should not be performed.

It is desirable that at least every first examination be made in the presence of a trustworthy witness (nun, assistant). It is better if this is done with optical separation and without acoustical isolation—for example, by means of a curtain. But unfortunately, this cannot always be realized.

An examination effected in narcosis should never be made without witnesses. There is the danger of serious accusations on the part of hysterical patients as well as erotomaniacs.

The danger of *motus inordinati* for a conscientious doctor is in general not so great as is often presumed. The *motus inordinati* is repressed by the exclusive thinking on the object to be fulfilled more than by habit. He who is completely taken up in a matter is not led to indecent thoughts. There is, however, a danger for the doctor when certain erotomaniac patients repeatedly request gynecological examinations.

As soon as the doctor notices this, he should refrain from these examinations and should make them only when necessary and then in the presence of an assistant.

If the patients no longer go to him, the doctor shall not lose much. The doctor must not only use every means of avoiding any pain during the examination, but must also do all that is possible to avoid the awakening of involuntary, erotic sensations. Otherwise, these can cause incalculable harm.

In whatever circumstances, care must be taken that in the examination virginity be respected.

In regard to a virgin, if an examination by means of a speculum is inevitable, this fact should be made in writing with a citation of the witnesses in the clinic record and the reason for the operation should also be registered.

In case of necessity, a medical declaration should be made.

The same should be done in all operations in which the integrity of the hymen is to be sacrificed. Whenever it is possible, a special instrument is to be used (speculum for virgins).

b. Questions of moral theology

The gynecological examination is treated in Capellmann—Bergmann under the title *tactus et aspectus impudici.*

If an abusive examination can be included under this concept, such a general summation is not acceptable, either from the viewpoint of honest gynecology, or from the viewpoint of Pastoral Medicine.

The same can be said when Capellmann—Bergmann speaks of a " more than necessary decency."

Indecency is never necessary and whatever is necessary is not indecent. It can, at the most, become indecent through the circumstances.

It is clear that a doctor goes against moral duty when he performs examinations which are not necessary or makes necessary examinations in an indecent manner.

It is right to say that each individual case is a matter of conscience for the doctor and that the avoidance of consent in *motus inordinatos*—at least in the beginning—is merely an *internum* of the doctor.

"He is to remember that he also has the duty to respect the verecundia and conscience of his patients and that his manipulations can provoke *motus carnales* in himself and in his patient." (*loc. cit.,* p. 234.)

If the doctor by his examination intentionally provokes these *motus carnales* and a *delectatio venerea*, he is guilty of a serious sin.

In regard to the question whether a woman has the moral obligation of submitting to an examination, the following is to be noted.

According to the opinion of the ancient moralists, the woman is not obliged, not even to save her life, to submit herself nude to the eyes and hands of the doctor (surgeon): *nec etiam ad vitam sibi servandam, nudam se oculis et manibus chirurgi subiicere.*

However, it must be noted that in former times the surgeons constituted a category inferior to the *medici puri.* The gynecological examination was, for the greater part, entrusted to the midwives, later to the gynecologist, and its actual importance developed relatively late. In order to evaluate the importance of the modern gynecological examination, it is sufficient to recall the task of the present-day fight against cancer. This will be all the more successful the more general becomes the conviction of the value of an early examination when the primary symptoms are suspected.

Since the conservation of one's life and health constitutes a moral obligation, especially when it refers to persons who have to fulfill toward others other important duties of education, maintenance, etc., the thought of these duties will overcome the repugnance, in se justified, toward examination. Inasmuch as this represents the only means of fulfilling such duties, it is not only not sinful but meritorious, and moreover, can become a duty from the viewpoint of the fifth commandment.

3. OPERATIONS ON THE HYMEN

a. Defloratio artificialis

Artificial defloration by means of an incision of the hymen can appear indicated when the *immissio membri* becomes impossible because of the rigidity of the hymen.

One cannot be too reserved in establishing an indication. The rigidity can in reality be due more to a "potency weakness." In *vaginismus*—an expression used to express a disturbance of potency in women—the *discisio hymenis* is of doubtful efficacy insofar as the disturbance is often due to mental causes. When the prognosis for the elimination of the difficulty by means of an operation does not appear absolutely favorable, the operation should rather be discouraged, since, in case of a canonical process for a dispensation from *matrimonium ratum non consummatum*, the difficulties of proof can become uselessly aggravated to the point of rendering it impossible.

The operation is, however, justified when a favorable prognosis is given—in cases in which natural defloration meets with difficulties beyond the normal and, on the other hand, the consummation of marriage can be facilitated by the operation, in se very modest. Since this serves toward the consummation of marriage, its moral liceity is beyond doubt.

According to Cardinal Gasparri, the wife is directly obliged—*probabilius*—to submit to the operation, when this renders the *consummatio matrimonii* possible. If she refuses, she loses the right to claim nullity *ex capite impotentiae viri*.

Recourse to the operation is not justified when it is not a matter of consummating the marriage and when the operation is not necessary and scarcely offers a possibility of success.

Grotjahn has held that the *defloratio artificialis* should completely take the place of the "violent, barbaric defloration which often produces a psychic trauma." To justify his position, he states that an occlusive pessary is possible only in a deflowered woman.

Other authors have held the same for propaganda purposes and have spoken of a "debarbarization of the sexual life." They have placed in doubt the value of virginity with the purpose of eliminating an important assurance that prematrimonial sexual commerce has not taken place.

There is no need to explain in detail that these tendencies are to be rejected from the standpoint of Pastoral Medicine.

b. Plastic suture of hymen (Reparatio hymenis)

While, on the one hand, the general postulation of artificial defloration was raised, contemporaneously there arose the appeal for a surgical method of repairing a broken hymen by means of a plastic suture, thus simulating integrity. As long as virginity is esteemed as a good, dissimulation by means of deceiving practices will be used to hide the loss of this good. The moral illiceity of this operation is beyond doubt.

From the juridical standpoint, the doctor renders himself guilty of complicity in a fraudulent action.

This is a matter of a fraudulent and surreptitious action, which is punishable as "deception in marriage"; and, according to most civil laws, it constitutes a reason for the impugnability of marriage. According to Canon Law, on the basis of surreptitious consent, a lack of consent because of an error *redundans in errorem personae*, can come into question.

4. CIRCUMCISION

a. Circumcisio praeputii

In *circumcisio praeputii*, we must distinguish the *circumcisio ritualis* practiced among the Jewish people and other Oriental peoples (still traditionally performed in certain Christian tribes) and *circumcisio therapeutica*, which is a surgical method used in certain cases of phimosis, etc.).

The ritualistic circumcision is to be understood as essentially a symbolic act of sacrifice.

Those attempts at explanation which attribute to circumcision only a hygienic or biologico-sexual signification are incomplete in their interpretation. It is certain that circumcision, especially in the Orient, also has a hygienic value; perhaps it even has utility from the standpoint of sexual physiology, since it dulls the sensibility of the glands, thus diminishing the danger of a *eiaculatio praecox*. It would, however, be erroneous to hold that it has no other signification.

A Christian doctor can perform a therapeutic circumcision only in those cases in which it is established that it constitutes the most simple surgical method in relation to other methods. There are no moral objections to this operation, but only motives of devotion.

b. Circumcisio puellarum

The *circumcisio puellarum* is only of ethnological interest. It is practiced among some people of lower degree of civilization, more in the form of *circumcisio* or *excisio clitoridis seu nympharum*.

Among the other "sexual operations" of ethnological interest are suturation or infibulation. The latter is also practiced among men, in general, for the purpose of impeding premarital and illegal sexual relations. Certain other operations serve the purpose of increasing erotic excitation; still others, such as the operation of "mica" (slitting of the male urethra—artificial hypospadias), have the purpose of birth control. Knowledge of these operations is especially necessary for the science of the missions and for the missionary doctor.

5. OPERATIONS IN CASES OF GENITAL DEFORMITIES

a. General concept

If deformities in general are considered as serious signs of degeneration (since for the most part they are caused by damages of hereditary disposition), this is true also in great measure for deformities of the genital organs. Hence all attempts at surgical correction are to be considered with the highest skepticism. And there is reason for serious preoccupation when there is the intention of rendering artificially possible a reproduction which nature itself seems to exclude.

It is necessary to carefully examine whether and when one can assume, both morally and hygienically, the responsibility of operating. Whether it is a case of eliminating an impediment which is opposed to reproduction and conforming with nature or whether it is a case of rendering artificially possible a reproduction which does not correspond with nature. It is the task of the marriage counselor, conscious of his responsibility, to discourage marriage in these cases.

Only operations of the first type are morally and hygienically justified.

b. Special cases

(a) *Uterus duplex*

In certain cases, the unification of the two halves of the *uterus duplex* (Strassmann operation) has led to the normal course of birth of a child. Such cases are justified as regards the method, but not in a general sense—only case for case with accurate discrimination.

(b) *Vagina artificialis*

Plastic operations for the construction of an artificial vagina have been considered and performed both in the case of primary congenital defects (atresia, aplasia) as well as in cases of secondary, acquired occlusions (brought on by injury, burning, etc.).

Justification: When it is a case of secondary defects, with normally functioning organs, these operations can be upheld. G. A. Wagner has stated that, in a case of this kind, a woman gave birth to three healthy children.

In the case in which the internal organs are atrophied, the operation cannot be permitted simply with the object of freeing the patient from the "feeling of inferiority" and to engender an illusory "joy of living." Such persons are objectively unfit for marriage. The *vagina artificialis* (mostly formed through intestinal transplantation) is not a *vas naturale*. It is therefore a case of *impotentia coeundi* in the canonical sense *ex parte mulieris*; matrimony in the sense of Church law could not exist and the sexual act would have to be considered as an unnatural act.

In a case in which the operation was successful (Latzko), a woman married without her husband becoming aware of the eliminated defect. Such a marriage is null in consequence both of the *impedimentum impotentiae* as well as that of defective consent (cf. above). Operations performed for the purpose of forming a *vagina artificialis* can be upheld only in rare and exceptional cases when they serve to render possible the fulfillment of the primary end of matrimony, the *procreatio prolis*.

This is so only under the condition that the normal functioning of the internal genital organs is certain. If the external defect was acquired in a secondary way, the substitute formation of the vagina through transplantation may be considered a *vas naturale*, since this at one time existed before the operation.

(c) *Vagina duplex artificialis*

On the part of some gynecologists (Zomakion, Haendly), a recommendation has been made to form artificially a *vagina duplex* to protect the woman from pregnancy without removing permanently the capacity to conceive. By means of the operation a septum is artificially formed in the vagina; one half of the vagina lacks an exit and the other is in communication with the uterus. The problem of "temporary sterilization" without interruption of the regular sexual life would thus be solved. To speak of a normal sexual life when it is a matter of artificially forming a deformity for the purpose of onanistic sexual activity in a blind vaginal sac, can be considered nothing else but an aberration.

(d) *Vagina septa*

Insofar as the removal of a vaginal septum serves to better the capacity for copulation and conception, there is certainly no objection from the standpoint of Pastoral Medicine; yet there is always need of examining whether the thing that is desirable is licit from the standpoint of the individual—that is, is not to be discouraged in consideration of hereditary disease, especially when there is a cumulation of elements of disease. In these cases it is difficult to establish rules of general obligating value.

6. OPERATIONS FOR THE PURPOSE OF SEX TRANSFORMATION

a. Pathological processes

In a formerly healthy woman morbid disturbances of the endocrine system can develop, through which the "secondary sexual characteristics" can be completely changed ("masculinization").

This is especially the case when there are definite ovarian tumors (arrhenoblastoma). After the removal of the tumor, there is verified, in the greater number of cases, a complete regression, "refeminization" (Sellheim). In one case of this kind, pregnancy followed by birth was established (Strassmann).

The moral unobjectionability of the operation is, in such cases, beyond doubt.

b. Cases concerning error of sex (Erreur de sexe)

It is essentially more difficult to pronounce judgment upon operations tending to change the sex in cases in which it is to be decided to which of the two sexes the person in question belongs.

Here more than in cases of *vagina artificialis* there is need of an accurate examination of all the circumstances for and against the operation, so that a pretended humanitarianism will not lead one astray or into the abyss. Thus, for example, a surgeon, in order to render possible a "marriage" desired by an individual of a dubious sexual character, undertakes the following operation: A pseudo-hermaphrodite erroneously reared as a girl is made a eunuch by means of castration. Then, through the construction of an artificial vagina, the external, mechanical possibility of having "feminine" —hence perverted—sexual intercourse with men, is given to him.

In another case, the following series of operations was made upon a man who, up to that time was completely normal, but who, because of homosexual influence, thought that he perceived a " change " of his sexual sensations. First; the removal of the normal male genital organs; then the construction of an artificial vagina, and, finally, the transplantation of healthy ovaries from a woman who had an operation of another kind. The unfortunate individual died immediately after the last " well-done " operation for " change of sex " as a result of a very serious form of marasmus.

There are, however, morally acceptable operations by means of which an *erreur de sexe* is corrected and a person is externally re-established in the sex to which he belongs by reason of the germinal glands and the general disposition of the organism.

All other operations of the above kind can only be considered as surgical aberrations, even if praised as sensational triumphs. From the standpoint of Pastoral Medicine this is all worthless and even wicked.

Moreover, the criteria of moral theology have constant value and the judgment of theology does not cede to corruption.

7. TRANSPLANTATION OF THE GONADS ("REJUVENATION")

a. Medical questions

No less problematic than those mentioned above are operations for transplantation of the gonads. Their moral liceity becomes all the more suspicious inasmuch as the element of purely sexual " reactivation " appears in the foreground.

There is added the injustice committed against another human being, when, on the occasion of operations of another kind, healthy gonads are taken for purposes of hormone therapy and used for persons affected with grave psycho-physical disturbances.

Absolutely doubtful—even from the juridical standpoint—are the transactions concerning the cession of gonads, etc.

This does not mean that operations of this kind are necessarily morally illicit in all cases. But too much care cannot be given in discerning, case by case, when such an operation is permissible. In no case can there be a presumption of general liceity.

The same goes for operations of another kind tending toward " rejuvenation " (better, hormonal reactivation). It is difficult to raise objections against the purely hormonal cures.

The struggle against the premature phenomena of old age and deterioration can at times become necessary for a person who is expected to maintain a family or who holds a position of responsibility. Certain ailments—as, for example, that of the prostate—can earnestly suggest an application of reactivating methods in order to avoid radical operations.

Methods: Steinach introduced the method of ligation of the *vas deferens* (vasoligature). Doppler recommended cauterization with phenol of the sympathetic vasomotory fibers of the spermatic cord. The transplantation of organs has been performed by many. Voronoff recommended the use of gonads from anthropoid apes.

Among the non-operative methods the following are to be noted: diathermy and short waves, hormone treatment and psychotherapy.

b. Judgment of Pastoral Medicine

When a process of reactivation is necessary and justified, only the application of morally unobjectionable methods need be brought into consideration. From this standpoint, the methods of organic transplantation, especially that of Voronoff, cause objections to be raised.

Any reactivation which is brought on exclusively for the purpose of increasing the sexual libido, even for considerations of a medical character, is to be rejected.

The artificial incitement of the libido in old people is not seldom followed by a much more rapid breakdown.

Cases have been known in which acute mental disturbance followed the operation according to Voronoff.

From the moral and theological standpoint, objection can be made especially against the transplantation of human gonads, as in general against the transplantation of internal organs; for the transplantation itself cannot be fulfilled without a *mutilatio gravis* of another individual. Moreover, the desired effect can be obtained through indifferent methods (hormone therapy, etc.). The usually short-lasting effect is not in proportion to the permanent damage inflicted upon another person.

8. OPERATIONS IN CASES OF STERILITY

In consideration of its importance, sterility is to be studied more deeply in connection with other questions. Here we will examine only the moral liceity of the most important operations in the treatment of sterility. Basically, the general rule holds that operations which serve to favor natural reproduction have in their favor the presumption of liceity. In the individual case a separate examination of each operation is to be made to determine whether the operation is objectionable or illicit from other standpoints. An operation is at least questionable when the danger it effects is not proportionate to its prospects of success (for example, plastic operations on oviducts obstructed through inflammation—so-called salpingostomatoplasty—or implantation of the ovary in the uterus according to Tuffier, etc.).

The objection against diagnostic insufflation (in certain circumstances, also therapeutic) of the oviducts (perturbation) could be considered overcome with the technical advance of the method. This is not so, in the same measure, with regard to injection of contrast means for roentgenological control (hysterosalpingography). Artificial fecundation (*fecundatio artificialis*), because of the importance and meaning of the problem, must be treated separately in relation to other problems. In the treatment of sterility, the doctor must consider himself solely as the *minister naturae* and must reject any method which is *contra naturam*.

The condemnation of *fecundatio artificialis* by the Holy Office on March 24, 1897, does not refer to those methods which limit themselves to aiding nature (*quae naturam aliquo modo adiuvant,* Antonelli).

The principle of *adiuvatio naturae* applies *mutatis mutandis* for all the methods of treating sterility.

9. MUTILATING OPERATIONS

The following are considered as operations mutilating the organs of reproduction:

(1) Removal of the gonads (castration);

(2) Interruption or exclusion of the organs for the conduction of the germinative cells (sterilization);

(3) Removal of other principal and subsidiary organs of reproduction (removal of the uterus).

Since, because of their importance, sterilization and castration require special consideration, we will here consider only the latter group of operations.

Since the extirpation of the external genital organs—of the *membrum virile* (penis) and vulva or vagina—comes into consideration only relatively seldom and only in cases of serious and malignant diseases (carcinoma), and since the removal of the ovaries and testicles is to be considered in the chapter on castration, and operations on the oviducts and spermatic cord in the chapter on sterilization, here there is nothing else to consider but the most important operations for the removal of the uterus (hysterectomy).

a. Methods

The methods of hysterectomy are classified as vaginal and abdominal according as they are applied in the vaginal way or by means of laparotomy. In both cases, we distinguish between conservative and radical methods according as only the uterus is removed or also the annexed organs (oviducts, ovaries). In the extended radical methods (Wertheim, Schauta), even the connective tissues with their lympathic ganglia are removed. Even the conservative methods (with the exception of the simple enucleation of myoma) per se produce sterilization and the radical operations castration. In the more advanced radical methods (for the purpose of eradicating malignant tumors), a great part of the vagina is removed and thus the capacity for *copula naturalis* is for the most part eliminated, and in some cases completely destroyed.

Among the conservative methods, the simple methods of *defundatio uteri*, of supravaginal amputation, leave the sexual capacity of the woman, prescinding from the effect of sterilization, intact. The sexual capacity is more deeply changed by a radical operation of extirpation of the connected parts and most deeply affected by the extended radical operations which involve also a considerable shortening and atrophy of the vagina.

b. Judgment of Pastoral Medicine

For the medico-pastoral judgment, two standpoints are important:

(1) The question of *abusus*;

(2) The question of "marriage capacity" of the *mulier excisa.*

K

(1) According to the principle *abusus non tollit usum*, the securing of necessary therapeutic ends is permissible despite the possibility of abuse.

It is therefore important to recognize the possibilities of abuse which consist in this, that hysterectomy is at times performed out of motives which are not justly proportionate to the importance of the operation, but is executed solely for the effect of sterilization (Surblèd).

(2) The question of the marriage capacity of the *mulier excisa* is one of the most difficult and most discussed questions of Pastoral Medicine and Canon Law. This was the reason for treating it in a special manner in relation to the question of impotency (cf. *Theory of impotency*).

In reference to the various surgical methods, it can here be stated that, in regard to the conservative methods of hysterectomy and especially the conservation of the *portio vaginalis uteri*, there can be no doubt concerning the capacity for marriage. One cannot say this in general for radical operations; when there is secondary consecutive atrophy of the vagina, the matrimonial capacity can be doubtful and, in determined circumstances, completely abolished. After extended radical operations, the marriage capacity is almost always abolished.

By way of addition, we will consider here the question of surgery in the case of concurrence of myoma—or carcinoma in pregnancy.

In case of myoma, there is in general no reason for an operation during pregnancy; when this occurs, it can only be a case of a conservative operation, above all, when the myoma threatens to be a hindrance to birth. Even then it is more convenient to wait for the termination of pregnancy at the time of birth and then to operate by means of the Caesarean section in a manner no more nor less radical than necessary. Only when there is danger of suppuration of myoma, deviation of the bladder, can an immediate operation be necessary. It must be remembered that even a conservative therapy (enucleation) can effect abortion. If such an operation cannot be deferred, the resulting abortion is an *abortus indirectus*.

The situation is different in case of a malignant tumor (carcinoma, sarcoma). Here the life of the woman is at stake. The responsibility of waiting till the child is viable can be assumed only in cases in which an operation is not possible or in cases in which there is no possibility of a cure for the mother. Then it is important to save at least the life of the child. In cases recognized in time as operable, the operation should not be delayed for a long period.

In cases of this kind, there arises the question—of vast importance to Pastoral Medicine—whether, when a radical operation on the cancerous pregnant uterus is inevitable, it is a matter of an *abortus directus* and hence illicit, or rather of an *abortus indirectus*.

This question has not yet been decided in a definite manner. There are two opinions on the point, both of which can be defended by probable reasons.

According to the opinion of Vermeersch, it is merely a case of *occisio indirecta*: the death of the fetus is not intended, but only tolerated as an inevitable concomitant effect of the operation.

According to the opinion of Gemelli, it is a case of *occisio directa*. The death of the fetus does not arise as a mere secondary effect but immediately and surely (*aeque certe et immediate*) as the effect of the operation as well as of the removal of the tumor.

The opinion of Gemelli corresponds more to the system of tutiorism and that of Vermeesch more to that of equiprobabilism. As long as a doubt exists, one is free to follow the system corresponding to the conviction of one's own conscience. In this question the particular opinion of the author corresponds to that held by Vermeersch.

10. STERILIZATION

a. Concept

By sterilization is generally meant the execution of an operation and the adoption of therapeutic methods by means of which the capacity to procreate and conceive is removed.

According to this definition, the idea of sterilization must also entail removal of the gonads (testicles, ovaries).

It has become common, especially among German authors, to distinguish between sterilization and castration. By sterilization, in the strict sense, is intended solely those operations by which the gonads remain intact. From a strictly logical viewpoint, sterilization presents a more extensive idea, which also includes that of castration. Sterilization has assumed a special importance as a measure "for the prevention of hereditarily tainted progeny," and has importance, too, as a legal obligatory measure.

Here we speak only of sterilization as an operation and precisely as a mutilating operation. The problem of eugenic sterilization pertains to pastoral hygiene in connection with the problems of eugenics (hereditary hygiene, doctrine of hereditary health).

b. Methods

(a) *In the male*

Concerning the methods of sterilization of the male, there are no essential differences of opinion. This sterilization consists essentially in the uncovering of the spermatic cord in the tract between the testicles and the external inguinal ring, in the isolation of the *vas deferens*; in the ligation of and cutting of the *vas deferens* with the excision of a small portion of the same (vasoligation, vasectomy).

The great technical simplicity of the operation has largely contributed to extensive abuse.

(b) *In the female*

Much more difficult is the sterilization of the woman; it consists essentially in the interruption of transport of the ovule in its passage between the ovary and the uterus in the region of the oviducts. Access is possible only after the opening of the abdominal cavity, for the most part through laparotomy and eventually even through the vaginal passage. These operations demand, for the most part, general narcosis. In this there is present an element of danger. A difficulty lies in the fact that, despite the suture's being made in a most accurate manner, an aperture easily follows (tuboperitoneal fistula).

Even the smallest aperture can be sufficient for fecundation, and it is for this reason that the most complicated methods have been planned in order to secure the effect of sterilization.

The most simple of all the surgical methods is that of the contusion of the tubes and ligation according to Madlener.

Besides the bloody methods (operative), there are also unbloody methods which are less commonly used.

Temporary sterilization does not tend toward a permanent sterility, but anticipates the possibility of fulfilling at any moment an inverse operation or of restoring the function at any time. Even for this, most diverse methods have been suggested (surgical methods, hormonal, actinic or radioenergetic). A method that fulfills this purpose completely does not exist; it is not known whether the only temporarily desired sterility does not remain irreversible and become permanent.

c. Indications

Even for medical, social and eugenic sterilization, indications have been established as they have been for the *procuratio abortus*.

(a) *Medical indications*

In the so-called medical indications, it must be distinguished whether it is a matter of an operation in which sterilization is an end in itself, for purely prophylactic reasons, to prevent eventual danger to life or health (for example, because of the danger of an eventual pregnancy), or whether the operation is necessary for other reasons (for example, the extirpation of the uterus because of myoma or carcinoma).

The purely prophylactic indication is to be rejected.

(b) *Social indications*

In regard to the social indication, there is nothing to add to what was said regarding the question of abortion. The difference is solely this, that here it is not a matter of an *occisio hominis*. Sterilization is to be rejected as a means of eliminating terrible social conditions.

(c) *Eugenic sterilization*

The eugenic indication has been formulated in the dispositions of law concerning sterilization which have been promulgated in various countries. It was made the object of special norms of German law of July 14, 1933, for the prevention of hereditarily diseased progeny. According to this law, those who are affected by hereditary diseases can be made sterile through a surgical operation. The following are enumerated as hereditary diseases:

(1) Congenital dementia;
(2) Schizophrenia;
(3) Circular dementia (manic-depressive);
(4) Hereditary epilepsy;
(5) Hereditary chorea (Huntington's chorea);

(6) Hereditary blindness;
(7) Hereditary deafness;
(8) Severe hereditary bodily deformities;
(9) Severe alcoholism.

A detailed criticism of the indication is superfluous. In a special manner, the judgment of the eugenic indication was pronounced by history with the condemnation of the German law on sterilization.

d. Dangers

Sterilization, especially in the male, has been considered a very simple technical operation and absolutely devoid of danger.

The first affirmation is certain, but not so the second. The solid plexus of veins of the spermatic cord (*plexus pampiniformis*) predisposes one to thrombosis and embolism, and these always imply danger to life.

The vasoligation can have a so-called " Steinach effect." This can, in certain circumstances, condition an increase of the sexual libido, an acceleration through the decrease of inhibitions, in virtue of artificial infecundity. Because of this, sterilized persons are dangerous propagators of sexual diseases (Stumpfl).

The mental consequences must also, together with the physical and moral consequences already mentioned, be given serious consideration. Despite its apparent insignificance, the operation has an importance that is to be highly estimated.

The individual becomes as it were separated from his " genealogical tree." This fact often produces very notable mental reactions; the change can be very serious, especially in mentally labile subjects (psychopaths).

Much more serious are the dangers and consequences of sterility in the female sex. The general mortality following operations of laparotomy cannot be reduced below a certain minimum, especially in constitutionally weak women. There is added the dangers of narcosis. These elements of danger increase when the execution of the operation is forced, as happens when sterilization is legally imposed.

The forced application of narcosis especially constitutes a serious shock for patients who, for the most part, are already excited and agitated. Even the treatment that follows is full of complications and dangers.

Cases of death through excitation or suicide are known to have taken place after sterilization.

e. Judgment of Pastoral Medicine

(a) *Direct and indirect sterilization*

Even in sterilization, the distinction between direct and indirect sterilization is of decisive importance.

An indirect and hence licit sterilization is present when the effect as such (provocation of infecundity) is not intended but merely takes place per accidens (even if foreseen) as a consequence of the directly intended end.

Examples of indirect sterilization: removal of severely diseased ovaries or tubes (tumors, chronic pyosalpingitis); removal of the diseased uterus (hysterectomy), etc.

In several cases, it is difficult to judge whether it is a matter of direct or indirect sterilization, as in the operation of *interpositio uteri*—which is a method used to eliminate sinking and prolapse—in which the uterus becomes interposed between the bladder and the interior wall of the vagina. This artificial change of position is incompatible with future pregnancy. In order to avoid the danger that it presents, the operation must be accompanied by sterilization of the tubes. This " prophylactic " sterilization can be considered indirect only when, in a concrete case, the *interpositio* is considered the only possible method. Even then it remains questionable whether there are not probably more reasons *against* classifying it as indirect sterilization.

Moreover, in order to attain the therapeutic effect of the operation, sterilization is not in se necessary. This is not a consequence of the therapeutic operation, but is the result of a secondary action, the sole and independent object of which is sterilization.

Even if this is done for prophylactic reasons—that is, to avoid a serious danger—it must be considered direct sterilization.

In the case of *interpositio uteri*, it can only be recommended that this operation be exclusively reserved for patients who have passed the climacteric age.

(b) *Reasons for the illiceity of direct sterilization*

The essential reason for the illiceity of direct sterilization lies in its character of *mutilatio gravis*.

The encyclical "Casti Connubii," with particular reference to sterilization imposed by law, states that when there is no guilt and, hence, no reason for corporal punishment, it is not licit to violate the integrity of the body.

The individual has no other right of disposition over the members of his body than that of using them in a manner corresponding to their natural end. Hence it is not licit to destroy, mutilate or render them incapable of fulfilling their natural function, except when it is necessary for the welfare of the entire body.

The moral illiceity of sterilization arises also from another standpoint. Since its object is to impede the effects of sexual intercourse, the meaning of sexual life is attacked by this operation.

In this the moral basis of the community life is shaken.

Finally, through such an operation, man assumes an absolute dominion which is not due him, a dominion which extends to the existence of the destroyed things (Rauch).

In this, there is a rebellion against the order of life created by God. (*Non serviam.*) Man forgets the definite limits of his nature as a creature. He is not lord of life and death.

f. Doctrinal decisions of the Church

Concerning the question of sterilization for eugenic reasons, the ecclesiastical magisterium has taken her authoritative position in the encyclical "Casti Connubii" (N. 68-71).

In it, she definitely rejects *perniciosus ille usus* which attacks the natural right of man to matrimony and progeny. Especially severe is her judgment against legal (obligatory) sterilization.

"Quin imo naturali illa facultate, ex lege, eos, vel invitos, medicorum opera privari volunt; neque id ad cruentam sceleris commissi poenam publica auctoritate repetendam, vel ad futuram reorum crimina praecavenda sed contra omne ius et fas ea magistratibus civilibus arrogata facultate, quam numquam habuerunt nec legitime habere possunt."

("Yes, they go so far as to deprive them by law, even against their will, of their natural faculty through medical operation, not as punishment inflicted by public authority for crime committed, nor to prevent future crimes, but against every right and justice by attributing to civil magistrates that which they can never have nor ever legitimately possess.")

Despite the serious words, *contra omne ius et fas*, the doctrinal importance of the encyclical was temporarily underestimated even by learned Catholics. It was considered as merely the taking of a "reforming" position, which limited itself to the erection of a "barrier" against abuses, and not as a decision of principle, universally obliging and definite, with official authority.

The decision of the Holy Office of March 21, 1931, clarified this situation. The Holy Office, to the question of what things must be held in regard to the eugenic theory and the measures proposed by it—which, under the pretext of bringing about the betterment of the progeny, disregards the natural and divine law and the positive law of the Church as well as the personal right of the individual to contract marriage—answered that the theory is to be absolutely and completely rejected: "Eam esse omnino improbandam et habendam pro falsa et damnata, ut in Encyclicis Litteris de matrimonio christiano 'Casti Connubii' datis sub die 31 Decembris 1930."

g. The conflict and its solution

As in the question of the *procuratio abortus*, it seems that even here there is an apparent conflict between the doctrine of the Church and the postulates of science.

The opinion that there exists an insuperable opposition tended to find credit even in Catholic circles. Thus there arose a serious dilemma. One must acknowledge the moral illiceity of sterilization; moreover, it must be admitted that there is not here a matter of taking a position which is merely provisional or purely disciplinary on the part of the Church, but of taking a definite and universally binding position of principle. Nevertheless, people have believed they could remain loyal to the Church's teaching and still hold that sterilization, from the viewpoint of science, represents a postulate that is not only justified, but directly necessary and even inevitable.

Were this outlook correct, sterilization from the moral standpoint would have to be rejected and acknowledged instead from the standpoint of science. Prescinding from the conflicts of conscience which would arise, we find ourselves faced with a "double truth."

On the contrary, scientific Catholic doctrine holds firmly to the principle that there can be no opposition between natural and supernatural knowledge.

K*

It seems no longer necessary to explain in detail the scientific arguments against sterilization, especially since the essential matter is to be treated in the chapter concerning eugenics in our work on pastoral hygiene.

These questions have, however, lost their former importance, since time has pronounced its judgment on sterilization. Those who have not believed the serious opposing reasons given by scientific criticism had to learn by painful experience that even in this question the viewpoint of Catholic science continues to be correct.

The following is a summary of the most important opposing reasons:

(1) The general heredo-biologic basis, as well as the knowledge acquired in the field of heredo-pathology and in that of heredo-prognosis, does not absolutely constitute a basis upon which negative (destructive) measures of eugenics can be sustained.

(2) The basis which heredo-biology finds in the mathematical statistics of variations speaks decisively against the possibility of the elimination of hereditary diseases through sterilization.

(3) The probability of success in regard to sterilization is to be judged, even from other reasons, as completely unfavorable.

(4) Practical experience, moral, sanitary and social elements speak unconditionally against sterilization.

(5) In extensive practice there is the danger of exterminating valuable characteristics tending toward improvement while restricted practice is even more certain of its failure by its inefficiency.

Thus the profound study of these problems leads even here to the point that science in no way postulates a stand contrary to that of moral theology, but, on the contrary, leads to complete agreement with moral theology. Moreover, the encyclical "Casti Connubii" itself represents the most complete positive eugenics. A people that follows these doctrines will prosper and be healthy and will have no need of destructive operations. If these doctrines are disregarded, no destructive eugenics will ever be able to save people from decadence.

11. CASTRATION

a. Concept

By castration is meant the removal or destruction of the gonads.

This can be effected through operation or through roentgen rays or other actinic methods.

Castration in the male is commonly brought about by means of surgery (emasculation). We can speak, in a special way, of "mutilation" when not only the testicles but the entire external genital organ (so-called "grand seal" of Skopzen) is removed. It is one of the barbaric atrocities still committed today in wartime.

b. Sphere of application

Castration is especially considered under two standpoints:

(a) *As "therapeutic castration" for curative ends*

In the case of an anomaly of the sexual instinct, it is at times recommended and practiced in order to liberate the patient from pathological tendencies or from morbid intensity of the sex instinct.

(b) *As "criminal castration" for preventive ends in cases of serious and habitual sexual delinquency*

In practice it is not always possible to precisely trace the limits which separate these two standpoints, since the limit between disease and delinquency is not absolutely exact. Of mere historical interest is the *castratio euphonica*, the use of castration for the purpose of conserving in men a soprano voice.

The sphere of application cited refers exclusively to men. With women, castration finds application exclusively on therapeutic indication, through surgery or by actinic methods: in case of metropathic hemorrhage, myoma and ovarian tumors. The castration once practiced in cases of menstrual epilepsy has been abandoned.

c. Nature of its effects

In contrast to simple sterilization, in castration even the function of the gonads is destroyed: both the external secretion of the germinal products and the entire endocrine gland activity. The results deeply affect the entire organism. If castration takes place before sexual maturity (prepuberal castration), the transformation of the organism characteristic of puberty does not take place and the secondary sex characteristics do not attain their development.

If castration takes place after sexual maturity has developed (postpuberal castration), the secondary sexual characteristics undergo a greater involution according to the nearness to puberty at the time of the operation. When castration takes place at an advanced age, not only can the sexual instinct be completely conserved, but even the capacity of erection; and, in certain circumstances, the *libido sexualis* can become stronger. A disproportion between libido and potency can lead to strong tensions and thus to definite sexual deviations.

d. Critique of the indications

(a) *Therapeutic indication*

There is no need to waste words trying to justify the removal of gonads when these are diseased and their removal is indicated. Moreover, therapeutic castration has been advised and used to liberate persons from the pathological anomaly of instinct. Among these anomalies are the following: excessive ipsation (improperly called onanism), homosexuality, dangerous tendency toward sexual criminal action. In these latter cases, it can be difficult to trace the limits that separate the therapeutic indication from the prophylactic or criminological. Indisputable is the therapeutic indication in case of organic diseases: tuberculosis and carcinoma of the testicles.

The success of therapeutic castration in sexual anomaly does not permit a general recommendation. It cannot be otherwise, if what we have said concerning its effects is so.

Only in exceptional cases has success justified the therapeutic operation and this when, because of it, a patient has become useful in life and society. In such cases, the operation has been capable of liberating the patient from a serious depression and even from desperation. However, in the majority of cases, no favorable effect can be established. On the contrary, the incongruity between the libido and potency can increase sexual tension and this can cause serious mental depression and suicide.

Hence, even in regard to the therapeutic indication, it is necessary to use the utmost prudence and restraint.

(b) *Criminological indication*

In certain states, castration as a punishment or as a means of precaution has been given a legal basis. In Germany, it was regulated by the "law against habitual and dangerous delinquents and upon the discipline of precaution and betterment," of December 24, 1933. Emasculation could be performed on habitual sexual delinquents as a complement to legal punishment.

It was declared a measure of social protection and not an additional punishment. It was imposed in the following cases:

(1) Crimes of forcing one to immorality, of rape, immorality with children and violence (#176-178, German Penal Code).

(2) Crimes and delinquency of immoral actions committed in public (exhibitionism), injuries inflicted on the body for the purpose of exciting or satisfying the sexual instinct (#183, 223-226).

(3) Crime of homicide or mortal injury committed for the purpose of exciting or satisfying the sexual instinct—lustful murder (#211-216, Penal Code).

(c) *Prospects of success*

If the prospects of success for therapeutic castration have to be judged as unfavorable in general, much more can this be said in regard to criminological castration. Theoretically it would be favorable in " precocious castration." That the prospects of success are always greater in "late castration" is clear from the nature of the matter. Precisely for youths who commit sexual crimes it is difficult to justify. In these cases, there are other means of helping them. Castration is neither necessary nor useful for them. But in individuals of advanced age it offers new hope of success; however, at times it involves a greater danger of sexual deviation, and hence, is inefficacious and harmful.

(d) *Experiences*

The experiences which have so far been had with castration are very contradictory and, as a whole, unfavorable. In certain cases, it has been able to free, without danger, some patients from diseases of the instinct, who otherwise would have had to go into permanent reclusion. Controversial is the question of their capacity for work, especially with regard to the effects of character changes.

Numerous sexual delinquents who had been castrated have fallen back into their crimes.

The fact must not be overlooked that a certain percentage of those operated on have subjectively felt that castration was a "liberation" and "benefit." Whether and how much value these statements have is a question that at the present time cannot be decided. In summing up the matter, it can be said that the result of the criticism is predominantly very unfavorable.

e. The castratio euphonica

In the past, when singers allowed themselves to be castrated in order to conserve their soprano voice, the Church was bitterly reproached, since it was believed that a proof of contradiction could be found in her negative stand against sterilization. It was thus argued: While the Church has severely condemned sterilization, she has approved, if not directly favored, castration, which is much more serious.

Here, the fact is overlooked that in the past singers and their parents allowed castration in order that a living might be earned, and they desired castration as an advantage. At times, castration became a general abuse, partly because the castrated were taking part in sexual commerce without consequences.

The Church approved neither this use nor this abuse, even if she was powerless in the face of it. Every time she has taken an official stand on castration she has always condemned it.

f. Moral and theological judgment

The most ancient Councils have objected to castration and have imposed severe penalties for it. We find the same in the "Canones Apostolorum" (21, 24). The Fathers of the Church unanimously opposed castration. The papal Constitutions have declared the "irregularity of eunuchs." Clement XIV and Benedict XIV definitely expressed themselves against the use of castrated singers.

Among ninety theological authors, only four have held the liceity of castration (Arrupe). St. Alphonsus Liguori holds strictly to the illiceity of castration, even if he does concede a certain probability to the opposite opinion.

The defenders of euphonic castration do not penetrate the essence of the question. Usefulness can never eliminate the intrinsic perversity of the action. Even if the Church had to bear an evil proper to the times, which she could not absolutely remove by one blow, yet she never approved it, and even in this question she has never pronounced anything but a *non licet*. Insofar as it is a matter of purely therapeutic castration, it is justified for a curative end as long as a *causa iusta et gravis* is present: A *mutilatio gravis* can only be permitted when it is necessary for health and life. In case of cancer, tuberculosis of the testicles, etc., castration is therefore licit.

It is illicit when used as a means against sexual incontinency, and more so when used as a means of preventing conception or for economic reasons (singers, etc.). In regard to criminological castration, according to the doctrine of St. Thomas, it can appear at least probable that the state, which can punish a guilty person with death, has the right to inflict corporal punishment even on individual members of the body. Life is without doubt a higher good than sexual capacity. St. Thomas defends death punishment for delinquents who are dangerous to the community.

Huerth points out, however, that St. Thomas presupposes here always guilt. The state could never lay claim to a *dominium radicale in substantiam hominis, in totum et eius partes*. Not even the individual person has this right over his members. In regard to capital punishment, we refer to what has been stated in general under the heading *Limitations of the right to life*.

In regard to castration as a punishment we cannot remain silent as to the fact that serious consideration could arise.

As a measure of protection and security for society, it has nothing but a very problematic value. As a punishment, it is not so much the expression of a justified principle of compensation and expiation but, rather, a principle of bodily reprisal and vengeance (law of retaliation).

The inclusion of castration in law is to be deplored, since it is a return to an epoch which was overcome by Christianity.

g. Judgment of Canon Law

Just as numerous councils and Popes have condemned castration from the moral standpoint, so Pope Sixtus V, in the Constitution "Cum frequenter," condemned it especially from the standpoint of ecclesiastical law.

This condemnation was pronounced principally in view of the great number of marriages with castrated persons from whom no progeny could be expected.

Castration was among other things condemned with *excommunicato latae sententiae*, and as a result incurs an "irregularity."

The CIC has not expressly threatened penal sanctions against either sterilization or castration.

As canonical effects, they merely produce:

(1) Irregularity (*ex delicto gem.*, canons 985, 50; *ex defectu gem.*, canons 984, 20);

(2) The *impedimentum impotentiae*.

The question of the matrimonial capacity of the castrated and the sterilized is to be studied in correlation with the subject of impotency.

4. Mental Life—Normal and Abnormal

A. FUNDAMENTAL QUESTIONS OF MEDICAL PSYCHOLOGY

An introduction of the problems of medical psychology is fundamental as a requisite for the study of the important questions of psychopathology and psychotherapy.

1. CONCEPT

a. Medical psychology

By medical psychology is understood the sum of all the notions and problems related to the sphere of human mental life, the knowledge of which is important for an understanding of physical and mental pathological states.

Medical psychology is characterized merely by the peculiarity of its object and not by that of its observations. The concept of medical psychology can never be understood as if there were a special psychology based on medical notions whose notions and results were essentially and necessarily different from those of "philosophical psychology." The justification of a psychology, philosophically and metaphysically based, was, up to the present time, opposed by the trend of "biologism."

As long as it is hoped that a psychology may be formed which is firmly constructed on natural science and which will demonstrate only the "fundamental mechanisms" (continuously repeating themselves), to which the innumerable phenomena could be reduced, the desired insight into the "true and proper soul" must necessarily remain precluded. The psychology with a purely naturalistic basis, necessarily bound to the negation of the concept of an immaterial soul, cannot but lead to a " psychology without a soul."

Contrary to this, a stronger tendency toward a philosophical concept of psychology is clearly seen at the present time.

b. Naturalistic and philosophical psychology

The various tendencies followed by psychology can essentially be reduced to two principal ones:

(1) The naturalistic tendency is based on the hypothesis that the phenomena of human mental life are not essentially different from physical phenomena. According to this, by " soul " is to be understood merely the compendium of the specialized functions of physical organs. Since these functions are acknowledged as " superior," the difference is merely one of " degree " and not of essence. From this it follows that even between the mental life of man and that of higher animals and inferior organisms, there is only a difference of degree and not of essence. This " monistic " concept is necessarily also " evolutionistic." It supposes a continuous and still-enduring evolution of inanimate nature toward living nature, progressing from lower organisms to the highest. This concept assigns to psychology its place among the natural sciences. The investigation of human mental life must proceed from naturalistic data (positivism) and is possible only through naturalistic methods. According to the research methods adapted by it, we distinguish the empirical, experimental and anthropological (ethno-psychological) trend.

(2) The philosophical trend is based on the viewpoint that the questions of human mental life cannot be resolved by purely naturalistic methods. It assigns to psychology its place among the philosophical sciences (Dilthey, Jaspers). Even if acknowledgment of the immaterial nature of the soul is not necessarily found in this trend, yet, logically considered, it necessarily leads to metaphysical psychology.

c. Metaphysical psychology

Metaphysical psychology starts with the idea that the human soul is essentially different from the body and that it belongs to an immaterial (spiritual) sphere. The human soul is distinguished in essence and not merely in degree from the lower degrees of mental life in the animal and vegetative kingdom. This concept alone is logically compatible with the idea of creation (creationism). Evolution is incompatible with it. However, the idea of a development conforming to a plan and a hierarchical order is not.

Thus, this concept can be designated the "metaphysical" concept. Less correct is the designation of "philosophical psychology." That it assigns to psychology its place among the philosophical sciences is an evident matter.

d. Monistic and dualistic psychology—Unity of body and soul

Monistic psychology denies any essential difference between body and soul. Philosophico-metaphysical psychology is necessarily dualistic insofar as it not only admits such an essential difference but demands it as an absolute postulate. In this sense, the dualism is incontestable.

However, there is a dualistic concept which opens an impassable abyss between the material and spiritual being. It makes the question of how the action of the soul on the body and that of the body on the soul is possible, insoluble. This extreme dualism cannot be held and leads either to a unilateral spiritualism, a supernaturalism and underevaluation of the physical, or into materialism. In any case, extreme dualism is not able to overcome materialism.

On the other hand, the concept always held by Catholic philosophy teaches that the immaterial soul is, during life, united to the material body in an indissoluble, substantial unity.

To illustrate this, the allegorical figure of the "nuptials" is used. The Scholastic concept of unity of body and soul is a substantial concept and has an analogical relation to that of the "hypostatic union": that is, the union between the divine and human nature of Jesus Christ. Cf. Symbolum Athanasianum: ". . . perfectus homo: ex anima rationali et humana carne subsistens. . . . Nam sicut anima rationalis et caro unus est homo: ita Deus et homo unus est Christus."

What has been understood in medical literature during the last decade by the "psychic-physical unity" is still very different from this Scholastic concept. The concept of "unity of essence" expressed here approaches that of "identity" and hence has the roots of monism. Hence, despite assurances to the contrary, it cannot overcome materialism.

The doctrine of the unity of body and soul correctly understood shows the importance that the physical natural processes have for the proper course of mental activity. Hence the importance that biological and medical (physiological and pathological) notions have for psychology must be realized.

Also, the problem of the position of psychology in the system of the sciences is thus solved: Psychology belongs essentially to the philosophical sciences, yet has deep roots in the sphere of the natural sciences.

e. The concept of soul

(a) *Scholastic definition*

For Pastoral Medicine only one definition of the soul is possible and has cognitive value for it: that is the definition of Scholastic philosophy. This definition has been approved by the Church and has been firmly held since ancient times. It alone manifests its worth in the face of all the new questions, while all the attempts to use other conceptual determinations have led to insoluble internal contradictions or have destroyed the concept of the soul. According to this definition, the soul is the internal cause of life and the formal principle ("entelechy," Aristotle) of an organic, physical living being: *anima forma corporis*. The Scholastic distinguishes, according to the degree of organic life, between *anima vegetativa*, *anima sensitiva* and *anima rationalis*. The vegetative soul, the vital principle of plants, manifests itself in the vital functions of nutrition and production. The animal soul, the vital principle of animals, manifests itself in perception and movement. In this way, no clear and insuperable distinction is expressed between plants and animals. Still less is this difference to be understood in the sense of reciprocal exclusiveness, but rather the higher degree includes the inferior and simply surpasses it. The possession of the *anima rationalis* presupposes, therefore, the functions of the *anima vegetativa* and *anima sensitiva*. The *anima rationalis* is exclusively united to the human nature. It includes the inferior degrees of the soul in the sense of the unity and indivisibility of the human soul.

(b) *Attributes of the human soul*

The human soul is an immaterial substance, that is, a spiritual substance. The human soul is not pure spirit. It has need of union with the body in the essential unity of human nature, in that " totality which is man."

As a spiritual substance, the soul is simple, indivisible, incorporeal and devoid of spatial extension. It is, of its nature, necessarily immortal.

Spiritualistic dualism is pleased to admit and postulate the immortality of the soul. From the Scholastic definition it is understandable why the Church teaches the resurrection of the body.

Reason and free will belong to the rational soul as necessary attributes. The question of free will cannot be treated within the limits of this study.[1] It remains in essence, without detriment to all the difficulties inherent in the problem: motives, predispositions, influences and inhibitions regarding the formation of the will. On the basis of these properties, the human soul is capable of thinking, knowing and willing rationally. It is capable of consciousness. Through the ego-consciousness it becomes the carrier of the *persona*, a spiritual entity enclosed in se. The " personality " is necessarily bound to the concept of indivisible unity (*individuum*) and to the fact of the unicity and "indivisible unity " of the individual.

Personality is defined as the unfolding of the possibilities contained within the person (Allers). The two concepts have the relation of act and potency to each other.

According to the doctrine of the Church, the soul of every man is created immediately and infused into the body by a special creative act of God (creationism). Thus the doctrine that the soul is transmitted in procreation, together with the "hereditary mass " of the parents (traducianism) or (generationism), is rejected.

(c) *Other attempts toward a definition*

Those opposed to the Scholastic concept of the soul are content to essentially deny it without substituting for it another useful concept.

This is clearly seen from the attempts to define it in different ways. According to Wundt, the soul is only a "subsidiary concept" to

[1] The explanation of this problem remains reserved for a volume on General Pastoral Medicine.

which the phenomena are traced and referred. The concept of a rational soul is rejected by him as a concept "which has its roots in the need of mythology and metaphysics." In the place of substantiality, he places the concept of "actuality" and designates the immediate reality of the processes as the essence of the soul.

Kretschmer defines the soul as "direct experience," the world as "experience," "the sum of all things under definite viewpoints." According to Driesch, the soul is a "special kingdom of being which we conceive as a mediate object that acts as if it subsists independently per se."

These definitions, which in reality are not such, can suffice as examples of many other attempts.

They clearly show the difficulty that arises when the metaphysical concept of the soul is abandoned, and in the long run, they prove themselves insufficient.

A trend which can be considered "agnostic," and which for a long time was widely diffused, especially in psychiatry, realizing this difficulty which it could not solve, attempted to avoid in general the question of the essence of the soul.

According to Krafft-Ebing, psychiatry as a science of nature has to abstain from taking any stand in the controversy concerning the essence of the soul. It leaves this investigation to metaphysics and theology. This attitude does not imply acknowledgment of the "primacy of metaphysics," but merely complete and explicit disinterestedness (agnosticism). Even the trend of solipsism refused to reflect upon the essence of the soul. It suffices for it to establish that, within our experience, the world is divided into the two zones of the "ego" and the "non-ego" (external world).

In contrast to this subjective concept, objective materialism starts only from the outside world and teaches that man, without sense organs, could not develop any mental life. The soul would be nothing more than a function of the sense organs and the brain. Even behaviorism must be considered materialistic. It considers human mental life as merely the sum of modes of behavior. It directly denies conscience as a fundamental fact and acknowledges only the relation of stimulus-reaction.

The most recent attempts toward definition manifest a tendency to come closer to the metaphysical or Scholastic concept of the soul. The more they depart from it, the more they are affected by internal contradiction, weakness and obscurity.

Moreover, as long as these are not completely removed, these conceptual difficulties cannot but exercise their harmful effects on psychopathology, psychiatry and psychotherapy. Unless there is a complete return to the Scholastic concept of the soul, to metaphysics, psychotherapy will remain sterile.

Even a " new psychiatry " will open new ways when it returns to the ancient notions concerning the question of the soul.

2. THE BODY-SOUL PROBLEM

a. Body, soul, and spirit

In recent times, the doctrine of the " tripartition " of the human nature into body, soul and spirit (R. Steiner, Ludwig Klages) has again gained ground. This doctrine goes back partly to the distinctions adopted by Aristotle and partly to those of the old Gnostic heresies (*trichotomismus*). This is to be rejected especially, since it destroys the unity and indivisibility of the human soul and places the " spirit " in contraposition to the " soul "; from this arises an erroneous concept.

Klages, in speaking of the " spirit " as an " antagonist " of the soul, tends more toward intellectualism. It is, therefore, a matter of an untenable use of terms of precise meaning which, however, effect conceptual confusion. Spirit and soul constitute an indivisible unity (" spiritual soul "). One can, with Mager, admit of a distinction only in the sense that, as St. Thomas asserted, the soul is capable of two modes of existence and of two modes of activity, inasmuch as the soul gives life to the body, and inasmuch as it can exist even independently of it. Under the first viewpoint, it is called soul, and under the second it is called spirit. But both constitute substantially one unity, the spiritual (immaterial) soul.

The definition of C. G. Jung in " Seelenbilde " between the male *animus* and the female *anima* is based upon important knowledge concerning the psychology of sex. However, this distinction is not essential for the concept of the soul as such.

b. Body-soul relationship

(a) *Reciprocal relations*

For extreme dualism, the question of the reciprocal relation between body and soul is absolutely insoluble (body-soul problem).

The "psycho-physical relations" become inconceivable. If body and soul are considered as two essentially different substances, without overcoming this dualism by means of the representation of the unity of substance and action, it is impossible to explain a causal action of the soul upon the body and vice versa, inasmuch as the former belongs to a sphere completely different from the latter. The difficulty does not lie in the fact that body and soul are both considered substances, but in neglecting to consider the binding of both into a substantial unity. This unity is something more than a mere "unity of action," and even more than an identical "unity of essence." Without this unity, the relationship can never be satisfactorily explained, as in the realm of the order of being, the relation between God and the world, between the natural and supernatural will never be satisfactorily explained without the "principle of analogy," but will always be partial in the sense of transcendence or immanence. It would be better to speak of reciprocal relation rather than reciprocal action. The most important of these are:

(1) The psychic-spiritual life is united to the existence of a physical substratum (brain, central nervous system, vegetative nervous system, etc.).

(2) The undisturbed progress of the functions of this substratum is an indispensable requisite for the development of a healthy mental life. The disturbance of these functions causes many disturbances of mental life (mental diseases). However, there are also mental disturbances which are of a purely mental origin and which cause their effects to be felt even in the physical realm.

(3) The physical substratum of heredity ("germinal plasm") and its particular nature exercise a vast influence on the development of mental life. In certain circumstances, the development of the normal mental life can be impeded by pathological alterations of the germinal plasm. On the other hand, good dispositions are ruined through psychic influences and vice versa; serious hereditary defects are at times overcome by spiritual influences.

(4) The process of the "internal secretion" can exercise a very notable influence on the processes of mental life and even deeply transform them. Vice versa, this process can be greatly influenced by mental processes.

(5) There are physical changes that are caused exclusively by mental processes (blush, pallor, cold sweat, etc.)—partly through

physiological occurrence—partly through pathological occurrence (so-called "psychogenic" morbid syndromes; "organic neurosis").

On the other hand, there are mental changes which are provoked solely by purely physical states of a physiological and pathological nature. Examples of this kind are: the effect of female genital functions (menstruation, pregnancy, puerperium, etc.) upon the psyche; the change that is verified in the mental life of sterile women, tubercular women, women with stomach ailments, and deformed women (so-called cripple-psyche), etc. Thus, not only does the soul affect the body, but the body also affects the soul. What is more, in order to function thoroughly and normally, the soul has need of the body and its orderly functions. It can equalize certain disturbances and this, for the most part, by a greater consumption of energy. This fact shows the importance that definite care of the body and its health has even for the soul. A premature consuming of bodily strength will necessarily reduce the possibility of action on the part of the soul. Thus there arises not only the right, but also the moral obligation of taking care of the body in an orderly manner. In the same way, an exaggerated and one-sided care of the body (cult of the body), which is not ordained for this purpose or is directly contrary to it, is to be rejected.

(b) Explanation of the body-soul relationship

According to the explanation which was given above concerning the relation between the body, soul and spirit (anima and spiritus), the immaterial soul does not have a complete monopoly on the body. Its spiritual component (spiritus) rises above the physical sphere, while the component designated as anima enters, in a strict sense, into intimate relation with the body. In this last sphere are manifested the mutual relations which have been previously mentioned.

Inasmuch as the spiritual soul rises above the limits of the body, it cannot be affected by disease. But inasmuch as it is united to the body, as spiritus, it no longer functions in an orderly way, or it may not function at all when physical disturbances play havoc with the equilibrium of its spiritual component.

Up to this point, the proposition advanced at times from the materialistic standpoint that, properly speaking, there are no diseases of the spiritus, but only diseases of the brain, is to the point. Hence, this relation is indicated more exactly by the expression "mental disturbance" rather than by the expression "mental disease." More exact, still, would be the expression "impediment of the soul," since the soul is actually not affected by disturbances but merely impeded in its action because of a disturbance in the physical realm. The designation "mental impediment" is established to indicate an entirely specific form of impediment.

(c) *Other attempts toward an explanation*

The difficulties which the "problem of body and soul" present arise only from the dualistic conception, from the denial of the unitary action of body and soul. The dualistic teaching of Descartes supposed a reciprocal causal action. In order not to be misunderstood, we speak merely of mutual relations between body and soul. Descartes distinguished between soul and body, spirit and matter, and held that they cannot directly act upon each other.

The doctrine of occasionalism (Malebranche) held that God Himself on the occasion of a material process provokes the corresponding spiritual process.

Spinoza conceived extension and thought (matter and spirit) as attributes of the one universal substance. He thus stood in the realm of monism. As a result, he held an unconditional parallelism between material and spiritual occurrences.

The doctrine of psycho-physical parallelism was founded by Fechner and reduced to a system by Wundt. Wundt sought to solve the difficulties by his "actuality doctrine." According to Wundt, it is never a matter of different objects of experience, but rather of different points of view regarding the one and same experience.

Psycho-physical parallelism seeks to substitute the simple parallelism of physical and mental processes for causal correspondence and co-ordination. It has dominated for a long time the experimental trend of psychology.

Related to psycho-physical parallelism, but tending rather to the concept of totality, is the representation of "coincidental correspondence" (Auersperg). In recent times, the attempts at explanation tend toward the meaning of the "doctrine of totality," which moves toward affirming the unity of body and soul. Since it recognizes in the soul the informing and constructive principle (entelechy), this conception tends anew toward the Thomistic-Aristotelian view.

As long as the unity of body and soul is intended solely in the sense of identity, it is nothing more than camouflaged materialism.

c. Anatomical and physiological basis

The central nervous system (brain and *medulla spinalis*—spinal cord) is the material substratum of the psychic processes. It is supplemented by the peripheral and autonomic (vegetative) nervous system. The former consists of sensitive (centripetal) and motor (centrifugal) paths of conduction; the latter consists in the sympathetic and parasympathetic nervous system (vagus). The sense organs further belong to the complete nervous system. The " oldest " of these, the organ of smell and the eye, proceed directly from parts of the brain (olfactory lobule, optic vesicle). They are to be considered embryologically as parts of the brain shifted to the surface of the body.

The notable development of the cerebral hemispheres in comparison with that of the basal parts (*Hirnstamm,* brain stem, *medulla oblongata*) is in man more strongly accentuated than in any other living being (so-called cerebralization).

Neither the cerebrum, nor any part of the encephalon, nor central nervous system can be considered as the true and proper " carrier " of the soul; much less can it be considered the "generator " of mental functions. Rather, the nervous system in its entirety merely constitutes the instrument of the soul, an instrument by means of which it governs the body (instrumentalism).

Only this concept will render account of the facts. It fully explains why the action of the spiritual soul must necessarily be disturbed when some part of the structure or some function of the nervous system is disturbed or destroyed.

The effect of such disturbances must necessarily be diverse according to the degree and point of disturbance. From the research concerning functional disturbances, according to the place in which they take place (so-called symptoms of defective function), results the diverse importance which the different sections of the nervous system have for the psychic life.

We can speak of a hierarchical order in the structure and function of the nervous system. According to the predominant opinion, the gray matter of the cerebral hemisphere holds the greatest place inasmuch as it is the organ of conscious spiritual activities. From a purely vital standpoint, the so-called brain axis and the centers joined to it appear to be of greatest importance to life. It is designated as "phylogenetically" the oldest part of the brain—that is to say, it can be found in some of the most primitive plans of structure.

This fact is of fundamental importance. This shows that these regions, considered today as the seat of the subconscious and of the vital functions directed by it, are common to man and to living beings which are classified as lower in the scale of life.

The conscious functions related to the cortical substance are called cortical, and those related to the deeper strata are called subcortical. The conductive paths which run from one cortical center to another are called transcortical.

The subconscious is considered the true and proper "support" of the profound personality, the study of which is the object of depth psychology.

As substratum and instrument of the intelligence, of the activities of consciousness and will, the cerebrum gives growth, out of its abundant and intricate composition, to a "new" and most highly developed kind of structure, the remarkable system of "centers," each serving special functions.

In particular, the cortical gray substance as found in man presents specific peculiarities.

Thus the fact that consciousness in its fullness is proper only to man finds its basis in the anatomical substratum. Up to now, we did not know any anatomical basis for the phenomena of the consciousness of the ego and of the personality, and the realization of the contrast between the ego and the external world (non-ego).

Of importance are the two formations connected with the diencephalon: the pineal body (*epiphysis cerebri, corpus pineal, conarium*) and the pituitary body (*hypophysis cerebri*).

The hypophysis plays an important part as an organ of internal secretion—above all, as a "motor" of sexuality. The *tuber cinereum*, which is found near it, at the base of the diencephalon, is considered the "sexual center."

The epiphysis seems to act antagonistically to the hypophysis— that is, it curbs sexuality. For a long time its importance was underestimated by the researchers. Though at one time it was considered the "seat of the soul" (Leibniz, Descartes), evolutionistic researchers have degraded it to the degree of a rudiment of the "pineal eye" of the reptiles. Today there is a tendency to consider it more as a co-ordinating center of the first order, which has great importance —if for nothing else, for its position near the extremity of the brain axis, at the base of the cerebrum, as a "switch station" between the cerebrum itself and the brain axis.

In regard to the vegetative nervous system, it is to be noticed that it is the organ of the "autonomous" vital functions and that its principal task is that of automatically regulating the internal organic functions. This appears in a very clear form in the complicated regulating of cardiac activity but also even of the glands, digestive organs, etc.

The sympathicus and vagus (parasympathicus) have, therefore, "antagonistic" functions but, as a whole, constitute a functional unity.

The antagonism is manifested in determined circumstances, in the secretion of acetylcholine and adrenalin provoked by the excitation of the vagus and sympathicus, as well as in the antithetical reaction to the ions of calcium and potassium.

Vegetative hyperexcitability (vegetative stigmatization), as well as the dysfunction of the vegetative nervous system (*distonia vegetativa*), is of great significance in psychopathology. These correlations show the part that the vegetative nervous system, as a system of "vital nerves," plays in the economy of life.

d. Fundamental phenomena of mental life

Sensations and feelings are indicated as psychic elements and as an antithesis to mental representations. To these belong ideas (spatial, temporal and intensive) and the emotions or movements of the soul (affections, volitive processes, intensive movements of the soul). The faculty to feel, imagine and decide is designated as the mental faculty.

Modern psychology rejects, in great part, the "psychology of the faculties." However, a deeper penetration and study of the Scholastic doctrine of act and potency will teach it to appreciate it anew.

The further connection of the mental processes is designated as consciousness. This connection is divided into simultaneous and successive. There are also degrees of difference in consciousness. We must distinguish between unconsciousness, the absolute lack of mental connections; and subconsciousness of mental contents, in which the mental contents sink under the "threshold" of consciousness.

The state which accompanies the clearer comprehension of mental contents is called attention. The singular process by which such mental contents are brought to a clear comprehension and co-ordinated with other contents is called apperception, whereas by perception is meant the comprehension of the same without the accompanying state of attention.

The uniting of ideas is called association.

From the medico-pastoral standpoint, consciousness and its vast complementary region, the subconscious, are the most important of all the phenomena of mental life.

There are various degrees of consciousness. A mental content which arises from the subconscious must pass the "threshold" of consciousness and vice-versa.

By restriction of consciousness is meant the limitation of one's capacity to various conscious contents at one time. The artificial restriction of consciousness takes place in hypnotic phenomena.

To be exact, we should distinguish between a "concentrative" restriction and a "relaxing" restriction of consciousness, since it is a matter of two different forms of a "restricted" consciousness, according as it refers to an apparent "distraction" of one knowing and concentrating intensely on a problem or to a hysterical or hypnotic crepuscular state.

In the disturbance of consciousness, there is a distinction of various degrees:

(1) Apathy (somnolence);
(2) Loss of consciousness (sopor);
(3) Most profound loss of consciousness (coma).

These disturbances are of absolutely pathological nature and exclude the free determination of the will (responsibility). The fundamental phenomenon for the human mental life is consciousness of oneself (consciousness of the ego).

It is characteristic of behaviorism that it rejects not only the concept of the soul, but even that of consciousness and of subconsciousness.

Consciousness of the ego is the basis of the person or personality. Of greatest importance for the formation of the moral person is consciousness of one's worth, the disturbance of which causes inferiority feelings.

e. The subconscious

Some psychologists distinguish between the subconscious and the unconscious. According to them, the first is to be understood as the region immediately proximate to consciousness, within which region it is possible to have a continuous fluctuation, in various directions, of mental phenomena above the threshold of consciousness; whereas unconsciousness truly and properly represents the deep state normally inaccessible to consciousness. As clear as such a differentiation between subconsciousness and unconsciousness is, we refrain from using it as a basis for our exposition, and instead we use the two terms synonymously.

The subconscious represents, in relation to consciousness as the highest stratum, not only the deepest stratum; but, in comparison to the relatively constricted region of consciousness, it is by far the greater region of mental life. It can be considered the complementary region of consciousness.

We propose this designation, which will illustrate the relation between subconsciousness and consciousness: the subconscious contents enter into consciousness when, as it were, the reservists are called by the district command to fulfill "active service."

There is a vast region into which all the contents of consciousness sink as soon as they disappear from the view of consciousness and retire, above the threshold, into unconsciousness. Its relation with the "phylogenetically old" parts of the brain axis has already been mentioned.

If consciousness is the bearer or support of the person, and if the person is not thinkable without the capacity for consciousness of the ego, so is the subconscious of great significance for the personality.

It is considered as the true and proper bearer or support of the "deep personality" (depth psychology).

The subconscious is the realm of the id, of the natural and instinctive, which Freud distinguishes from the conscious region of the ego. In it are found the obscure regions of the mental life, the dark places which Freud significantly designated by the words: *Acheronta movebo.*

These are the regions in which are documented the fall of human nature, the effect of original sin—the continual unity with all generations in good as well as in evil.

As important as is the research on unconsciousness for depth psychology, it would be dangerous to consider unconsciousness strictly as the human soul.

While psychoanalysis sees exclusively in the unconsciousness the realm of the repressed dark parts of human mental life, the analytical psychology of Jung (also recently called complex psychology) has examined the positive aspect of the subconscious and has systematically developed the doctrine of the collective unconscious.

To the essential elements of the collective unconscious belong the archtypes, myths, hereditary patrimony of past civilizations. Thus the function of the subconscious, so important for life, is clarified in a special manner. The archtypes are not derived from the personal experiences of the individual but constitute a sediment or deposit and hence are a typical, basic form of a constantly recurring mental experience which has its origin in the condensation of innumerable processes similar one to another. In the primitives, we find an immediate mystical participation.

According to Jung, the subconscious is divided into a personal and collective part (personal unconsciousness and collective unconsciousness).

Only in the comprehensive study of consciousness and the subconscious, which complement each other, will a psychology result which takes into account the psychic totality.

The subconscious of the individual is without doubt closely connected, in a way not yet resolved, with the subconscious of others, as a "consciousness of the community."

In this community, consciousness both as a successive component and a simultaneous component can be distinguished. It must, however, not be overlooked that there is no such thing as a "collective soul"—in the substantial sense. But, rather, the soul of every individual person is per se directly created (cf. above, concerning creationism).

With this reservation we can acknowledge the phenomena of a community consciousness.

The important part which subconscious processes represent in mass psychology is especially revealed in mass suggestion. The aggregation of these processes leads to an increase of the potency (not to a simple summation) of mental dynamics. The elementary form of this is especially manifested in the outbreak of collective fear (panic), mass hysteria, and mass psychosis.

In the strong predominance of the so-called prelogical elements, the mass psyche is, in a certain sense, close to the psychic life of primitive man (prelogical, magical) and infantile mental life.[1]

Collective elements are always present in the subconscious. They contribute not a little to the configuration of a "type." At the same time, they exercise an essentially determining action upon personality and character. In certain circumstances, they can even rise above the threshold of consciousness, i.e., become conscious.

The subconscious plays an important part in the theory of psychoanalysis concerning the origin of neurosis; and of special cognitive value is the theory of the repression of certain mental contents (complexes) and the theory connected with this, of "abreaction of repressed effects" by means of the conscious revoking of the same (psychocatharsis).

"Frustrations" or "deficient actions" (Fehlleistungen) constitute an important access to the research or study of the subconscious. Psychoanalysis has justly seen that frustrations are very instructive. Equivocations in word or action, mistakes and the like are often based upon hyponoic and hypobulic mechanisms and are not to be considered as merely casual phenomena.[2]

A further mode of access to the subconscious and one that is very important is the study of the "dream life." Dreams consist of representative images (mnemonic images, phantasmic illusions, at times even of the nature of hallucination; cf. below, under *Psychopathology*).

These surely do not rise casually from the subconscious. The seeming irregularity of dream images obeys definite laws. Thus representative images undergo a characteristic deformation (condensation, disarrangement). Their interpretation can be facilitated by means of a knowledge of certain typical symbols. One must be careful to avoid the error of merely seeking sex symbols in dream images, without, however, underestimating its importance.

The archaic, primitive and infantile character of dream images

---

[1] The evolutionist hypothesis of a "prelogical" stage of man in the state of "primitivity" can well be the phantasy of Levy—Bruhlism. One cannot imagine a man without logico-rational thinking; he could not be thought of as man.

[2] "Hyponoic"—under the threshold of conscious thought. "Hypobulic"—under the threshold of conscious volition.

confirms what has been said concerning the collective character (successive and simultaneous) of the subconscious. Often the dream has the character of wish fulfillment ("wish-dream").

Worthy of consideration is the psychoanalytic theory of the "dream censor." The fact is true that dreams of explicitly immoral content, which contradict the moral character of the personality, provoke perceptible resistance in the subconscious.

It is the task of depth psychology to give the proper interpretation to this important phenomena: to interpret it as a confirmation of conscience and the moral nucleus of the personality, which reaches to the deepest realms of personality and has its roots in it.

f. Development of mental life

When we speak of the development of mental life, development within the individual life is meant.

The study of animal psychology has not furnished any proof of a development of the human soul from that of the animals, in the sense of a difference merely of degree.

The phenomena which seem to strengthen this hypothesis find their explanation more in the fact that the acquisition of the rational soul presupposes the inferior mental degrees of the vegetative and sensitive soul. On the contrary, it is significant that with the increase of rationalization there is a loss—or at least a notable retrogression—of those mental mechanisms functioning automatically and inevitably which animals possess and which we call instinct.

We must distinguish between instinct and impulse (Trieb). The concept of impulse pertains for the most part, but not exclusively, to biology, inasmuch as it treats with the tendency toward self-affirmation (self-conservation, conservation of the species, expressed in the nutritive and sexual impulse). Besides these basic impulses, we can still distinguish the movement and activity impulse, which presents itself in the child as the play impulse.

The impulse presses toward normal satisfaction, in which certain tensions tend toward "unloading" and the lack of tension tends toward "loading." Non-satisfaction is accompanied by feelings of displeasure, and satisfaction with feelings of pleasure.

The study of instinctive and impulsive reactions, especially in persons who are not developed, is important. These reactions must be held strictly distinct from purely automatic reflexes.

The concept of reflex pertains to physiology. Essential to the reflex is the abbreviated path of conduction (reflex path), which does not touch the superior centers.

The theory of the conditioned reflex, founded by Pavlov, and formed into a system by Bechterew (reflexology) attributes all mental phenomena to mere reflexes.

Characteristic of the American trend of behaviorism is the study of the modes of reaction (modes of comportment or behavior), which conceives all vital functions as mere forced reactions, similar to reflexes.

Even the moral conduct of man represents, according to Watson, nothing else but such a reaction (so-called modes of behavior); hence we can speak directly of experimental ethics. He makes use extensively of the experimental methods of tests.

Of fundamental importance for the research on the development of mental life is the study of the child's and the adolescent's mental life. Even infantile mental life can be especially instructive in the comprehension of psycho-pathological phenomena in adults.

Certain test methods, critically evaluated, can be of great help. Of the modern test-methods of psychology, the following are of particular importance: The Rorshach test, the Wartegg test and the Szondi test, which for the most part are used for adults. The indications thus obtained can be reported in a diagram and can make known the "profile of development" ("psychogram") (Rossolimo, Buehler). This diagram will demonstrate whether the development is to be considered normal and harmonious, whether it is uniform or partly arrested.

Important diagnostic conclusions can be drawn which will be of great use in pedagogical counseling and, in abnormal cases, for early therapeutic pedagogy. When the method is removed from any behavioristic application and is based on Scholastic psychological doctrine, it can surely bring valuable results both for theory and for practice.

Of particular interest is the study of the development of language, and also the research on the different mental development of the sexes (psychology of sex). In this latter, there is consideration of the importance that the differences between the sexes have upon mental behavior.

By the psychology of sex is understood the research on the relationship of mental life to sexual phenomena (normal and pathological). Important for the psychology of the sexes are the differences, conditioned by sex, in the so-called mental rhythm and the influences exercised upon this by constitution and heredity.

In the mental development of the child and adolescent, especially in the period of maturity (puberty), of great importance are the subordination of the impulses to reason and the development of inhibitions. This is so in a particular manner for the normal development of sexual life.

Even before psychoanalysis, it was acknowledged that the development of the sex impulse does not first appear merely in puberty, but in the prepuberal phase which reaches back, more or less, into infancy.

A precociously conscious sexuality is a sign of abnormally precocious maturity, which is often the expression of a psychopathic personality.

Psychoanalysis has justly seen that sexuality unconsciously announces itself in certain manifestations of early infancy. A kernel of truth is found, therefore, in many at-first-surprising doctrines—as, for example, that of the "polymorphic-perverse" sexuality of the suckling. The unilateral superevaluation of such data can lead to the danger of pansexualism. Apart from the sexual interpretation, the data often permit a deeper interpretation.

Thus, the oedipius complex is, without doubt, to be considered a primordial complex common to all men. Its deepest interpretation, however, has its roots in the fall of humanity as a result of original sin: the rebellion against God, our Father, that is, the symbolical "killing" of the father in order to obtain possession of "mother" nature, with the desire of being the exclusive sovereign over it (*Eritis sicut Deus* . . .). Without the doctrine of original sin, all these things cannot be understood in their entirety. Only in the light of this doctrine do they acquire their true meaning.

Only in puberty is the adolescent wont to become more conscious of sexuality: he begins generally to interpret its meaning only when he has acquired complete mental and moral spiritual maturity. To form, at the right time, the proper foundation is the very important task of education and, in particular, of sexual education. This task cannot be fulfilled with an "instruction" in a rationalistic sense, nor through coeducation, but only by a respectful initiation upon the basis of a religious and moral education and by the formation of conscience.

According to psychoanalysis, a role in mental development is played by infantile sexual experience, especially sexual trauma. As viewed by "individual psychology," which particularly emphasizes the influences of environment, that role entails social experience: the origin of an "inferiority feeling" through social non-adaptability, through renunciation and the discouragement which results; the need of being considered, which has been injured, seeks in every way possible to overcome the inferiority complex by means of compensation in another sphere (overcompensation). Without doubt, even this concept is based on a true notion, even though a partial truth.

Likewise, a partial truth is at the base of the opinion that the psychic life of man is largely determined by hereditary disposition. Not even the importance of this should be underestimated. Its over-evaluation leads to a biologico-hereditary determinism, just as the overevaluation of the social and environmental factors lead to social determinism. The extreme biologico-hereditary determinism denies every possibility of education. Some more modern trends of psychology (Jung, Klages) have become orientated toward a "doctrine of totality"; such a doctrine can become accessible only through a truly universalistic cognition which takes into account, above all, the fact of fallen human nature.

In the spirit of this universalistic concept, it is deplorable that to the most important aspect of mental development, that is, the development of religious and moral life, not even a small part of the work of research has been to the present time dedicated, as, for example, has been dedicated to sexual development or to the social development.

g. Social psychology

(a) *Psychology of the people*

The study of mental development cannot be limited to individual development; it must also extend to the biological, spiritual and social community; with the reservation, however, that in the interpretation of facts the danger of a purely evolutionist criterion be avoided. Here sociology and ethnology, especially when these embrace even the religious life of people (psychology of religion), can assume a great importance.

From research concerning the mental life of community formations results important knowledge even for psychopathology. Certain forms of mental illness are characterized by loss of complicated mental faculties, the effects of culture and civilization. The course of mental life becomes always more unilateral, typical and archaic. This takes place in a manner especially evident in certain forms of schizophrenia, as also in imbecility and in certain manifestations of hysteria.

Inasmuch as the hereditary predisposition exercises a strong influence upon the mental development of the individual, it is justified to speak of racial psychology.

The fundamental phenomena of mental life are a general attribute of human nature and are in no way bound up with the race or dependent on it. The differences are based more on culture and tradition, that is, more on spiritual influences than on simple " hereditary mass." Since with the idea or concept of race certain constant characteristics are associated, race must be considered an effective factor in the natural order and, as such, it is to be respected.

(b) Race and constitution

Race and constitution belong to the corporeal foundations of the mental life.

The concept of constitution contains an individual component and a superindividual component. It must be distinguished from the disposition or propensity of an individual to react to external influences, especially to those which determine diseases, a disposition which is found in the individual in a determined phase of life.

The concept of constitution cannot be reduced to the totality of hereditary predispositions and tendencies of development. Otherwise, it could not be distinguished from that of " race." In practice, the concept of constitution is applied in the sense of a doctrine of types. According to Kretschmer, certain types of mental disposition, both in the normal as well as in the pathological sense, correspond to determined types of physical constitution. According to this theory, the structure of the body has a decisive influence upon the formation and the course of mental life.

After what we have said in the beginning concerning the

Scholastic concept of unity of body and soul, it is not surprising that we attribute even to this theory a fragment of truth. But even this theory can be exaggerated and vitiated to the point of serious error.

h. System of human types

The theory of types is based upon the knowledge particularly established by Sigaud, Stiller and Matthes.

Sigaud distinguished a respiratory type, a digestive type, a muscular type and a cerebral type according as a determined organic system seemed to have a definite preponderance.

Matthes and Stiller have especially represented the asthenic type in his physical and mental characteristics.

An object of special study are the manifestations of intersexuality in the feminine representatives of this type (Matthes).

Kretschmer compares two fundamental types, the leptosomatic and eurysomatic (pyknic).

In the mental realm, the types corresponding to the leptosomatic are: within the norm, the schizothemic type; on the border of the pathological, that of the schizoid; and beyond this border, the schizophrenic.

The types corresponding to the pyknic types are: within the norm, the cyclothymic; on the border, that of the cycloid; and in the pathological realm, the cyclic insane (manic-depressive).

Besides these types, there are other types, such as the athletic; the dysplastic; and a series of transitional forms from one type to another.

The mental life of the cyclothymic is, according to Kretschmer, characterized by so-called diathetic proportion: it swings between the two opposite poles of serenity and sadness. A corresponding characteristic of the schizothymes is excitability and indifference.

Mania, with its verbosity, flight of ideas and furious excitability, represents the extreme pathological phase of the cyclic insane; the extreme phase of the schizophrenic is manifested in catatonic stupor, with its absolute negativism and its retreat into phantasy, to the exclusion of interest in the external world.

The theory of Kretschmer's types contains many things that are correct but, when exaggerated, it leads to a deterministic conception. In practice its usefulness is affected, since types rarely present themselves as pure but are obliterated by every kind of passing form.

The variable characteristics of all these classes shows how difficult it is not only to establish any typology, but even to distinguish such apparently simple concepts as "normal and pathological." These difficulties seriously affect psychopathology, since on this differentiation at times depends the establishment of responsibility, with all its import. The concept of "diminished responsibility" becomes indispensable in the consideration of limited cases. Moral theology has, without renouncing the doctrine of free will, always acknowledged the "impediments to free will" and has always taken account of the same.

Useful in ways is the distinction applied by Jung and his school —between introvert and extrovert types. In manifest cases they correspond approximately to the schizothemic type and that of the cyclothymic.

Some authors distinguish between "obsessive" and "impulsive" character.

The obsessive person is characterized by exaggerated scrupulosity, inflexibility, tendency toward pedantry, invariable self-control and by his weak sense of duty to mankind.

The impulsive person is characterized by an elementary vitality, lack of self-control, phantasy, passion, levity, irascibility and prodigality.

On the one hand, excessive moral rigor and on the other, a lack of the same.

Monomania, as the pathological form, is to be ascribed to the first type and hysteria to the second type.

Some authors have attempted to assign the leptosomatic-schizophrenic types to the Nordic race, and the eurysomatics-cyclothymic to the Alpine race. Here we must guard against the generalization of observations in se as well as against deducing extreme conclusions from the same.

In any case, these points show how many unsolved questions there are concerning the concepts of race and constitution, and especially how far from being clarified is the question of their relation to mental characteristics.

i. Characterology (Special personal characteristics)

(a) *Temperament*

The old distinction of the "four temperaments" (sanguine, choleric, melancholic and phlegmatic) and their relation to the "four elements" (fire, water, air and earth), with their fundamental peculiarities (warm, cold, dry, humid), has been abandoned by science.

The cognitive value of this classification should not be considered completely exhausted even today. The concept of temperament is to be held distinct from that of "personal rhythm," which is connected with that of psychophysical reaction time and with that of personal equation. These concepts lead to the question of the value of the psychotechnical examination of the qualifications of an individual, especially when it is merely a case of qualifications in regard to mechanical ability. The exaggerated evaluation of tests is prejudicial and is based upon a mechanistic conception. The test underestimates the fact that the most important mental elements of men (internal sentiments, exactitude, fidelity, etc.) can never be revealed or measured by an examination of qualifications which is purely technical. Hence its schematic application can often do nothing more in the individual case than lead to an unjustified judgment.

(b) *Physiognomy—Graphology*

An important auxiliary means in character study is physiognomy. Because of the close union of body and soul, bodily expression makes possible certain conclusions concerning the human soul.

One of the most important means of expression is writing. There is a scientific graphology which is worthy of being seriously considered. This can bring important results when it is associated with intuition. In the hands of incompetent persons, it can become a serious danger. Even here, as in the psychotechnical examination of qualifications, there exists the danger of generalization and exaggeration of partial notions, especially when graphology is used by incompetent persons lacking self-criticism.

(c) *Parapsychology*

The danger of abuse on the part of incompetent persons is

L*

present in great measure, even in so-called parapsychology or *metaphysics*. Under these concepts are contained the heterogeneous mental phenomena which are found in part within the confines of phenomena which can be explained in a natural manner (cf. *Border-land states*).

While scientific research concerning the properties of human character was based, up to the present time, upon a concept of the soul corresponding to the "naturalistic" trend of psychology, parapsychology is, instead, based on heterogeneous elements of being.

3. FUNDAMENTAL QUESTIONS OF MORAL PSYCHOLOGY

Moral psychology treats of the mental presuppositions of the moral life. Hence the fundamental importance of medical psychology for Pastoral Medicine is evident. Moral psychology does not occupy itself merely with normal mental life, but also with pathologically perturbed mental life. It utilizes both the knowledge of normal psychology as well as that of psychopathology.

The object of moral psychology is the formation of conscience and its influence by psychic factors. In particular, the impediments to freedom of the will constitute an important sphere.

It studies the "mental strata": structure and structural types of the soul as the basis for action; the influence of "obscure forces" (Klug); hereditary diseases, acquired inhibitions, complete constitution, influences of eroticism and sexuality and of the gifted predispositions, as well as diabolical influence and, in particular, the signification of the problematic predisposition, of doubts concerning faith (skeptic), morbid hypersensitivity of conscience (scrupulosity) and the conduct of conscience "autonomously" orientated; finally, the influence of hallucinations, illusion and guilt upon mental life and the importance of religious awakening in the overcoming of pathogenic conflicts.

With these tasks outlined by Klug, it confines itself closely within the sphere of psychotherapy.

The methods of moral psychology are the same as those of psychology: the "explicative" experimental causal method of naturalistic psychology and the "intellective" method of philosophical psychology. The procedure of the one is predominantly inductive and that of the other is predominantly deductive. The methods are based on self-observation and experiment. The decision of the conscience is the central act of the moral personality (Munckner).

The Scholastics do not adopt an entirely unanimous attitude in respect to the formation of conscience. According to St. Thomas Aquinas, conscience is principally located in the intellect and assigned to reason. Its activity (synteresis) renders man capable of informing himself on moral principles.

According to St. Bonaventure, conscience is the faculty of the soul from which moral notions are acquired. Synteresis pertains to the faculty of the will; it strives toward good and warns one to abstain from evil.

"Conscience is the function of the entire human personality in which the personally obliging need of moral duty comes to consciousness." (Munckner.)

In pathological cases, a mental disproportion between intelligence and moral dispositions can be manifested (e.g., imbecility: intelligence deficiency, often with existence of moral disposition; vice-versa, so-called "moral imbecility"; deficiency of moral sense with an often surprisingly pronounced intellect).

Moral theology distinguishes between:

(1) Just conscience and erroneous conscience (*conscientia recta* and *conscientia erronea*).

(2) Sure conscience and doubtful conscience (*conscientia certa* and *conscientia dubia*).

(3) Delicate conscience and lax conscience (*conscientia tenera* and *conscientia lapsa*).

The decision of conscience is original and autonomous. Important, as a preliminary phase, is the interior preparation. Free will signifies, in a positive sense, the possibility of self-determination in the choice of motives and in a negative sense, freedom from external coercion and internal constriction.

The decision of conscience is endangered by internal and external influences. To the internal influences belong affection, passion and habit; to the external influences belong violence and fear (*vis* and *metus*).

The Scholastics distinguish, as important impediments, the following: *ignorantia, vis, metus, concupiscentia*.

Character and temperament belong to the individual influences (see above). Here the influences of constitution must also be taken into account. In serious cases, hereditary taint or disease assumes particular importance. Even (exogenous) embryonic lesions caused by certain poisons (alcohol, radiation, syphilis and, at times, even chemical contraceptive means) play an important role. The influence of age (e.g., puberty, climacterium) and the character of sex must likewise be taken into account.

The pathological (psychopathological) influences upon the formation of conscience are manifested in various ways. A group of these morbid deviations are found in the following forms: psychopathy, neuropathy, neurasthenia, hysteria and epilepsy. A second group includes the genuine psychoses (mental diseases or mental disturbances). Among these the endogenous (for the most part, conditioned by heredity) and the exogenous (for example, reactive, infectious or post-infectious) can be distinguished.

Obsessive neurosis and morbid scrupulosity occupy a special place. Besides hereditary disposition, the environmental influence often has a great effect upon the development of moral life.

The reason for innumerable deviations can be found in bad living conditions, together with economic factors involving misery. The dissolution of marriage, the pauperization of the family, etc., often lead to serious disturbances of the moral life. Here is to be noted the increase of extramarital sexual relations, abortions, sexual diseases; alcoholism, prostitution, incest and other sexual aberrations, suicide, etc. That these phenomena lead, for the most part, to a complete decadence of religious life, and are reciprocally conditioned by this, is quite evident. The decadence of the religious life is, therefore, not merely a phenomenon conditioned by society. On the contrary, it must always be remembered that it has had its origin in the higher strata of society in the form of so-called rationalism. So, likewise, a modern symptom especially typical of the extirpation of religion, namely, birth control, has had its origin in these circles and then was imitated by the poorer circles of society, where economic factors prevailed in a secondary manner.

The decadence of religious life has exercised its destructive effects upon society as well as upon the individual. A greater part of the mental suffering of modern man (neurosis; in part also, mental disturbances) is to be attributed to this eradication.

For most of these sick can be repeated the words which Shakespeare has Lady Macbeth's physician speak when she is affected with mental disturbances: "More needs she the divine than the physician."

The importance that a renewal of the religious life can assume in the mental re-establishment of a person is clearly described by I. Klug in the chapter on Rehabilitation in his excellent work on moral psychology entitled "Die Tiefen der Seele."

In such a rehabilitation, the ability to have genuine sorrow and purpose of amendment has a decisive part. Rational introspection and the formation of the will are the natural psychologico-moral requisites. These, however, only render natural sorrow.

The species of supernatural sorrow (attrition and contrition) do not belong to the domain of moral psychology, but to that of theology.

B. FUNDAMENTAL OUTLINE OF PSYCHOPATHOLOGY

I. General view

1. HEALTHY AND DISEASED MENTAL LIFE

a. Concept

A clear distinction between the concepts "healthy" and "diseased" is still not always easy, even in the field of plainly bodily organic ailments. It is much more difficult to trace these limits in the sphere of mental life. The confines here are in many ways indefinite and the degrees of transition are passing. It is not even always possible to make a clear distinction between bodily diseases and mental diseases.

This is understandable because of the mutual relation of body and soul. Even here there is a zone of limitation. Even bodily diseases are to be divided into "organic" and "functional" diseases.

Those diseases are considered organic in which it is possible to show the existence of a substratum anatomically well characterized in virtue of structural modifications, visible either by simple sight or with the aid of a microscope. Where such modifications are lacking, the disturbances are called functional (nervous).

Progress in research has often revealed anatomical modifications which, up to now, were wont to be considered functional. Thus, for example, within a few years, the opinion concerning the nature of muscular rheumatism has been basically changed.

Even in cases of definite mental diseases, drastic modifications of structure, e.g., of the cerebral cortex, have been discovered. For a long time, one of the most serious mental diseases, progressive paralysis, has been recognized as the effect of syphilitic infection, of the neurotropic fixation of the virus *Spirochaeta pallida*. As a result, research concerning the anatomical basis of mental diseases, especially of the more subtle structural modifications of the central nervous system, has made great progress.

It does not seem absurd to think that in time all the diseases which are still called mental diseases will be considered as simple illnesses of the central nervous system. This will correspond to our opinion that the spiritual soul as such cannot become ill, but can become ill only in its substratum and corporeal instrument. In such a sense—and not in the materialistic sense—it will be justified to hold that mental diseases are merely diseases of the brain.

If we consider what we said about the distinction between *anima* and *spiritus*, it seems more exact to speak of psychic disturbances instead of " diseases of the spirit."

The expression " mental disturbance " has become of common use, but it would be better still to speak of a " psychic inhibition," were this term not already used in another sense.

b. Types of deviation from the norm

The deviation of the pathologically disturbed mental life can be represented by the following tendencies:

(1) The state of health and that of sickness are raised as a pair of polar antithetical terms.

(2) Sickness simply consists of the non-existence of an essential characteristic of health. The opposite is contradictory. The lack of mental capacity is called a defect. The defect can be complete or partial, and hence there can be differences of degree. The states of defect can be congenital or acquired.

(3) Sickness can consist in the appearance of something entirely new which disturbs the equilibrium. It is perceived as an element extraneous to the being, introduced from the external.

(4) Sickness is distinguished from health only by an alteration of proportions. The aspect of health is clearly recognizable in all its detail, and its structure is not completely eliminated, but is as if disfigured. The harmony of the parts is disturbed (disarranged).

With this, not all the possibilities are exhausted; and they need not be limited to occurring one at a time. In the case of most mental disturbances, this last form of deviation is recognizable, or at least, participates in some way. It is as if the image of God which is in the soul defends itself as long as possible against the eventuality of becoming completely unrecognizable or directly extinguished by means of external action.

Only one who still sees, even in the soul disfigured by sickness, the true image of God can completely comprehend the essence of the mental disturbance and the resulting harm. Psychiatry without the soul is even worse than psychology without a soul.

c. Mental life of the mentally diseased: Spiritually dead?

The mentally healthy person forms ideas concerning the mental life of the sick of mind that are nearly always false, since, devoid of a specific understanding, he is not able to put himself in the mental situation of the sick.

Relatively uncomplicated is the mental life of the cyclic ill (manic-depressive), whose mentally normal type, the cyclothymic, is usually also of an uncomplicated, harmonious (syntonic) nature.

Much more difficult to comprehend is the mental life of schizophrenics. The subject of catatonic stupor does not manifest any contact with the external world, and to the superficial observer it seems that even his interior world is completely extinguished. In reality, the contrary is the case: The schizophrenic manifests an extraordinarily rich interior life, for the most part altered by phantasy, which he strongly closes to the external world.

But even in defective states—as, for example, that of idiocy or the extreme states of mental debility—it would be erroneous to speak of an absolute spiritual death.

Surprising manifestations of a mental life, sometimes an extraordinarily profound one, in persons apparently mentally "absent," show that those presumed "spiritually dead" are in reality not so, but have only lost the capacity of extending to the external world the manifestations of their psychic life. But this capacity can be manifested very impressionably at certain times, especially at the time of death.

Very interesting cases of this kind are mentioned by H. Harmsen. Professor von Neureiter (Riga) reported in 1935 of an insane girl who could not read. But if a person read a very difficult text to her, she would repeat it without error, even in foreign languages (the girl understood only Latvian).

d. Mental disease and exceptional aptitudes (Genius)

The opportunity to look deeply into the deformed mental life of the mentally ill has, at times, furnished cases of mental disease in persons of exceptional aptitudes (genius).

" Talent " and " genius " are not to be placed on the same plane. Genius is something qualitatively different, while talent, in its various degrees, expresses something solely quantitative. Cases of concurrence of genius and mental disease have long been well known, but only recently have they been deeply studied (Kretschmer, Lange —Eichbaum and others).

Not seldom the predisposition of a genius is found in the confines between health and sickness. Yet the genius does not necessarily stand within the confines of pathological predisposition.

The essence of genius consists in the capacity of knowing being and reality in an essential, direct and complete manner (intuition).

It is not a case in which morbid predispositions are necessarily greater than in the ordinary person.

In order to explain the predispositions of genius, we must start from the natural viewpoint. In order to justly evaluate genius for humanity, it is necessary to utilize moral judgment as well as ethico-metaphysical factors.

In no case do moral principles different from those pertaining to the ordinary person hold for the genius. There is often found in the genius merely spiritual proportions exceeding the norm. There is in him the possibility of surpassing the norm both in a good and evil sense (ambivalence). Actually, many of those who are above normal can become great bearers of light as well as enemies of light. This is evident even in highly talented delinquents, in whom the predisposition for great things is present.

Goethe has given expression to this ambivalence in a famous passage. He could not imagine any crime he could not have committed had his life been less fortunate. Without doubt, in order that exceptional talents may concur, hereditary and environmental factors must be associated in a fortunate manner. But in a case of a "genius of divine grace," the call from God is indispensable. One who refuses this and abuses his talent exercises an action that is more diabolically destructive than constructive: *corruptio optimi pessima.*

In the mental illness of a genius, the tragedy of mental disease manifests itself in a more intensive manner. Syphilis often has a part in the mental disease of personalities with exceptional talent. In certain cases (Nietzsche, Strindberg and others), there has been manifested in the mental disease, without prejudice to other causes, a religious breakdown. Thus is presented the question of the relationship between mental disease and guilt.

2. CAUSAL FACTORS OF MENTAL DISEASE

a. Endogenous and exogenous factors

Among the causal factors of mental disease the endogenous and exogenous factors are to be distinguished.

(a) *Hereditary dispositions*

Among the endogenous factors, hereditary predisposition is generally given first place. The important part that this factor plays is not to be overlooked, especially in schizophrenia, cyclic dementia, epilepsy, psychopathy, alcoholism, inclinations to suicide and crime, and yet this factor is not to be exaggerated. It is not always properly recognized that the hereditary factor does not act in the sense that a hereditary disease is transmitted according to determined laws. What is inherited is not the disease in se but only certain possibilities, often polyvalent, of development: there are hereditary potentialities, but not specific material (genes) of mental diseases.

Thus is explained the fact that a schizophrenic does not necessarily have to be born of a schizophrenic and give birth to a schizophrenic. The conditions are much more variable.

In the line of ascendancy, there are, besides indeterminate psychopaths, also carriers of varied deviations which come under another diagnosis. Even in apparently healthy hereditary lives, negative variants can present themselves, and in diseased lineage the disease can disappear.

The theory of mutations adduced to explain such irregularities is only a working hypothesis—an attempt to explain through reason the deviations of the theoretical-hereditary prognosis on the basis of the laws of Mendel; in the same way the so-called empirical prognosis is an attempt to overcome the practical difficulties which result in the uncritical generalization of hereditary laws held valid in general.

Mendel, in his rules concerning hybridization of plants, did not perceive general valid laws of heredity for the human race.

Selectionistic-hereditary biology with its so-called Mendelism, and no less with its " twins-hypothesis," has met difficulties from which it can recover in only one way: by applying to the problem of heredity the Scholastic concept of potency and act.

If one considers the conclusion which selectionistic-hereditary biology has deduced from its theories for practical application in regard to the mentally diseased and their care, then the fatal import of this theory will be fully appreciated.

(b) *Environmental influences*

Besides hereditary disposition, the factor of environment no doubt plays an important role. If the hereditary factor was formerly overevaluated, so later was environment. Personal destiny is certainly strongly influenced by the factor of hereditary disposition, yet external experience, true elements of fate, influence the appearance of mental disturbances not merely in the sense of releasing them but in determining their essence.

Both factors exercise an effect. At times one of them appears with greater intensity, as for instance, the factor of hereditary disposition in endogenous depressions; the environmental factor in reactive psychoses, which for the most part are provoked by episodal elements (so-called situation psychoses).

(c) *Ethico-metaphysical factors*

Besides the two factors mentioned, the biological and social, the ethico-metaphysical factor has its role in the origin of mental diseases. This is in many ways overlooked or exaggerated. As we indicated earlier, the relation between mental disease and guilt is very important.

b. Personal and collective guilt

The connection with collective human guilt (original sin) does not require any further clarification for the intelligent person. In particular, it must be understood that the *natura vulnerata* is the source from which new taints or diseases will continue to arise. This realization shows how narrow are the confines in which there is a possibility of impeding the new appearance of disease by means of negative selection.

Here we treat in the first place the question of personal guilt. The fact that such connections can also exist has already been treated under the heading *Mental disease and exceptional aptitudes*.

A typical example is that of the "ideas of sin" which arise in certain forms of mental disturbance. In the case of genuine melancholy it is difficult to say to what point they are expressions of personal guilt. Practice teaches most impressively the part played by *abusus sexualis*, in the form of ipsation or *abusus matrimonii*, or in the form of premarital or extramarital relations. Abortion plays an especially devastating role. There does not exist in all mental diseases a connection with personal guilt, yet such can easily destroy the equilibrium of mental life. This happens more easily when the equilibrium is very unstable or when the mental effect which results from the guilt is very serious.

3. DEVELOPMENT OF MENTAL DISEASES

a. Preliminary stages—Prepsychotic personality

It is only in rare cases that a mental disease will appear without some preparation. If this occurs, it is to be asked whether unnoticed profound modifications have not preceded. It is still more doubtful whether such an outcome could arise in a personality which was at first completely sane. This possibility must not be absolutely excluded, especially since there are ethico-metaphysical factors which elude all calculation. To deny such a possibility means denying even the efficacy of such factors.

In general, however, the manifest appearance of disease is pre-

ceded by a latent preparation. In the deepest strata of the personality the breakdown already exists (so-called prepsychotic personality). An apparently moderate external occasion can at times
provoke the catastrophe.

The evaluation of the prepsychotic personality can be of practical
importance; for example, in the canonical matrimonial process,
when it is a matter of judging whether before marriage there existed
a mental disturbance, and to what extent, this factor can cause the
"incapacity to give consent" according to the meaning of canon
1081, CIC.

The close relations which exist between the character of a
psychotic and the psycho-physical constitution, between the character and the temperament of the sick, have already been considered
in the first section. The prepsychotic personality acquires its psychosis, i.e., that psychosis which corresponds to its peculiarity. Its
mental life experiences the transformation from normal to abnormal.

b. Course and nature of psychosis

The course of a psychosis is extremely varied, according as it is a
case of reparable disturbance or of irreparable damage, which leads
to a complete disintegration of personality.

In the latter case, the superior and more differentiated strata of
the personality are destroyed: the sphere of moral feeling, the
consciousness of value, and the social impulses; the capacity to
judge, intelligence and decision.

The purely vital sphere seems to be more resistant than the more
spiritual sphere. In the most profound spheres of dementia, a surprisingly tenacious will to live is often still recognizable, and very
often manifests itself in the instinctive, inordinate desire for nourishment and sexual pleasure.

Many psychoses are characterized by the course of attacks and
remissions (e.g., schizophrenia); in other psychoses, "fits" (for
example, furious excitation, *raptus melancholicus*).

Between individual attacks or "fits" there can exist periods of
more or less absolute calmness and external appearance of complete
normality. The older psychiatry considered these lucid intervals as
periods of passing health. During this, complete insight into the
morbidity of the passing phase can be had (notion of the disease).
According to the newer viewpoint, there is no true health in the

sense that, in the phase of lucidity, the personality is intact and there is present full capacity to act and full responsibility.

One should not overlook the connection between this concept of interval and the theory of the hereditary character of psychosis. Justification will be acknowledged in those cases in which the endogenous character of psychosis is very clear.

But, even in these cases, in regard to capacity to act in the interval, we must distinguish. For actions of decisive importance, as, for example, the contracting of matrimony, the intellectual capacity must be demanded with greater insistence, so that in doubt the ability to give consent must be denied with less scrupulosity than in cases of lesser importance.

4. NEED FOR HOSPITALIZATION—CARE OF THE INSANE

a. General view—Historical view

In consideration of the common good, as well as of the interests of the mentally diseased, it is preferable that the need for institutional care be met more liberally rather than within limits too narrowly drawn. Certainly, when assistance given to the mentally diseased is worthy of human dignity and is of a private nature, it requires great public expense.

With the intention of diminishing these expenses, the tendency, in the not too distant past, has been to remove the mentally diseased as soon as possible from private to public care.

The presumed-favorable results of this maximum limitation of the necessity of hospitalization was a motivation for the "cause" of eugenic sterilization, since sterilization, according to its defenders, will make possible the early transference of patients to public care.

Prescinding from the fact that this problem cannot be decided solely on a financial basis, it has been shown that this consideration is not correct. The expenses for private care are not merely negative, but also cover many things which forced release renders again indispensable.

This is not the place to examine what great sums of money were spent in Germany in the execution of sterilization and the so-called tribunals of hereditary health. Nevertheless, what was foreseen took place—namely, the theory did not stop at sterilization, but went further, to euthanasia of the mentally diseased; they were simply exterminated.

Thus confidence in enclosed or private care of the mentally diseased, slowly formed by the century-long hard work of conscientious doctors, was destroyed by a single stroke. This was the inevitable and foreseen consequence of an illusion which was more dangerous to the community than all the mentally diseased. The history of the care of the mentally diseased shows the long way that had to be traversed in order to arrive at the conditions of the year 1933. In Germany, the Religious Order of Knights founded in Elbing in 1326 the first insane asylum, thus fulfilling a great pioneer task.

Certainly, the treatment of the sick in the so-called insane cages of the Middle Ages was incompatible with human dignity. The insane were treated not as sick, but rather as condemned persons. The care of the mentally diseased of that time consisted of corporal punishment, chains, strait-jacket, "bibs," various types of suspensions forcing the patients to remain in a standing position, boxes or chains of force, gyrating chains, shower baths, emetic cures, treatment with red-hot irons, etc. In the fifteenth century, the insane were considered victims of a diabolical influence and were exorcised or imprisoned. This concept was favored by the "spiritual epidemic" of the time, flagellantism, dancing mania, etc. Only in the sixteenth century did doctors begin to deal with mental diseases according to a definite plan. Witchcraft raged strong up to the eighteenth century.

Pinel is to be considered the father of modern aid to the insane. Before him a pioneering work was fulfilled by St. Vincent de Paul. The General Hospital in Vienna in 1784 had its "tower for the insane," a department for the mentally diseased, and the same was so at St. Luke's hospital in London.

Along with progress in psychiatry, the nineteenth century offered outstanding advances in the care of the insane. This development was manifested by the way that was traversed from "the tower of the insane" to the modern "institute of care and assistance," with all the conquests of hygiene, in which the sick are given more human attention.

Important questions for the future development are those of assistance to psychopaths and therapeutic pedagogy. They are of great importance for the prophylaxis of the necessity of hospitalization.

b. Limits of open and closed assistance

The question of the need for hospitalization and the possibility of open or closed assistance are decisively influenced by the character and course of the sickness, by the intelligence and behavior of the patient as well as his external conditions of life.

When it is guaranteed that the patient can receive good home care and secure vigilance, then the limits can be more widely drawn. But it must not be believed that home treatment is always in the interest of the sick. It seems that clinical treatment in all its extent is usually more advantageous for the patient.

The patient becomes more quiet and sociable in an institution. It is clear that restless patients and those exposed to the danger of suicide always have need of hospital care.

The question of the permanent internment (forced asylum) of asocial and criminal psychopaths—eventually in special colonies (establishments of detention)—will only be mentioned here.

5. LEGAL QUESTIONS

The establishing of a mental disease produces serious consequences of a juridical character. It is therefore one of the tasks of legal medicine which entails the greatest responsibility. The director of souls should recognize the relative dispositions of law.

a. Mental disease and mental debility

Civil law applies the concept of mental disease in the sense of total deficiency of capability to act, and that of mental debility in the sense of limitation of the same capacity. The confirmation implies the declaration of incapacity. Of secondary importance is the question whether the distinction between mental disease and mental weakness is merely a distinction of degree or a qualitative distinction. This question is resolved differently in the legislation of various countries. In any case, the lower degree of disturbance conditions a limited incapacity, and that of the higher degrees a complete incapacity.

b. Responsibility

In penal law an act is not considered criminal, or its perpetrator guilty, when the agent, at the time of action, lacks the use of reason or free decision of the will.

The law for minors, when the minor is responsible, takes into consideration the idea of diminished responsibility. This concept should also be generally included in penal law.

c. Other legal consequences

The capacity to act corresponds to the penal concept of responsibility. The age required for contracting marriage and the capacity to contract marriage conform to the general prescriptions of civil law. In the case of limited contractual capacity, the consent of the legal representative is required in order to contract marriage. Legislation in some countries allows divorce because of mental disease of one of the parties (thus, the German Civil Code BGB: #1569; also, annulment of marriage according to #1333; and further, #51 of the German marriage law of January 1, 1939). During the years 1933-1945 mental diseases were, in Germany, considered matrimonial impediments (eugenic-matrimonial impediments). A law for the protection of the hereditary health of the German people of October 18, 1935 ("law for health in marriage") prohibited marriage in the case of hereditary disease in the sense of the law for the prevention of hereditarily tainted progeny of July 14, 1933.

This latter law prescribed sterilization in case of the following hereditary ailments: congenital mental weakness, schizophrenia, *folie circulaire*, hereditary epilepsy, hereditary St. Vitus dance (Huntington's chorea), hereditary blindness, hereditary deafness, serious bodily deformity, serious alcoholism.

The law against dangerous and habitual delinquents and the means for obtaining security and correction, of November 24, 1933, contains among such means: internment in an institute of cure and assistance, in an asylum for alcoholics or in an institute where the patient is weaned from the defects, or in a work house; reclusion as a measure of security and castration of dangerous moral delinquents.

The laws just cited can serve as examples of a *lex iniqua*. They are contrary to the natural law, the positive law of the Church, and the law of God. The encyclical "Casti Connubii" condemns, as an infraction of natural law, the prohibitions imposed by law through hygienic motives, even in those cases in which marriage is to be discouraged (*Quamquam saepe matrimonium iis dissuadendum est*, n. 69). In cases of mental disease, matrimony is not valid because of incapacity for consent (cf. below).

That the dissolving of marriage because of mental disease following marriage is not possible is evident from the very essence of the Catholic concept of marriage.

6. CANON LAW

The Code of Canon Law treats of many juridical questions concerning mentally diseased and mentally limited persons. In canon 88 it rules on juridical capacity; in canon 2201 it treats responsibility, and in canon 2218 the criterion concerning the measure of punishment is stated.

Canon law distinguishes between adults and minors. The major age (*persona maior*) is attained with the completion of the twenty-first year. Among minors, the Church distinguishes two groups: (a) *impuberes*, i.e., boys before the completion of the fourteenth year and girls before the completion of the twelfth year; (b) *puberes*, sexually mature minors who have completed the fourteenth or twelfth year respectively, but not yet completed the twenty-first year. The infant (*infans*), that is, the *impuber*, before the completion of the seventh year, is incapable of fulfilling juridical acts. A permanently mentally diseased person is equivalent to an infant. These persons are incapable of fulfilling juridical business, and juridical efficacy is lacking in their declarations of the will. Juridically, they are equivalent to infants (less than seven years old). Canon 88, #3 states: *Infanti assimilantur, quotquot usu rationis sunt habitu desituti.*

Imputability is excluded when motives which exclude fault are present. Incapable of crime are the persons who were mentally disturbed at the moment of the act. In persons with a permanent mental disease, irresponsibility is presumed even in case of apparent lucidity. The contrary must be proved. The furiously insane and those infected by fever are irresponsible; also, drunkards and those hypnotized, when the state or condition in which they find themselves has not been voluntarily provoked (thus there is no *voluntarium in causa*) and the use of reason has been completely removed. Even passion can have the same effect.

Responsibility is diminished when motives which diminish fault are present. If a crime is committed in the state of voluntary drunkenness, the agent is guilty insofar as he is responsible for this condition, yet in a lesser degree than in the case of committing the crime with full consciousness. If, however, this condition has been provoked for the purpose of facilitating fulfillment of the act, the agent is fully culpable. In the case of involuntary drunkenness, guilt is diminished even if the use of reason was not completely removed. The same goes for the other states (hypnosis, fever); weakness of mind lessens guilt.[1]

The following norms, among others, prevail in the application or measure of punishment: The punishment must be in proportion to the punishable deed. It must take into consideration not only the importance of the objective infraction of law, but also the subjective element.

Among the subjective elements, the mental state of the delinquent is taken into consideration. The motives that lessen culpability do not always excuse from grave fault (cf. canon 2196); in case they remove the same, they excuse, if not from sin at least from punishment for *foro interno* and *externo*.[2]

The capacity to receive the sacraments is likewise treated in certain canons. Here we merely discuss the capacity to contract marriage, regulated by canon 1081. The incapacity to give consent on the part of the mentally diseased person results from the words: *inter personas iure habiles*.[3]

In the expressed disposition that the declaration of will cannot be substituted for by any earthly force is found the most secure

[1] Canon 2201: #1. Delicti sunt incapaces qui actu carent usu rationis.

#2. Habitualiter amentes licet quandoque lucida intervalla habeant vel in certis quibusdam ratiocinationibus vel actibus sani videantur, delicti tamen incapaces praesumuntur.

#3. Delictum in ebrietate voluntaria commissum aliqua imputabilitate non vacat, sed ea minor est quam cum idem delictum committitur ab eo qui sui plene compos sit, nisi tamen ebrietas apposite ad delictum patrandum vel excusandum quaesita sit; violata autem lege in ebrietate involuntaria, imputabilitas exculpat omnino, sit ebrietas usum rationis adimat ex toto.; minuitur, si ex parte tantum. Idem dicatur de aliis similibus mentis perturbationibus.

#4. Debilitas mentis delicti imputabilitatem minuit, sed non tollit omnino.

[2] Canon 2218: #1. In poenis decernendis servetur aequa proportio cum delicto, habita ratione imputabilitas, . . . quare attendi debent . . . aetas, scientia, institutio, sexus . . . status mentis delinquentis. . . .

#2. Non solum quae ab omni imputabilitate excusant, sed etiam quae a gravi, excusant pariter a qualibet poena tum latae tum ferendae sententiae etiam in foro externo, si pro foro externo excusatio evincatur.

[3] Canon 1081: #1. Matrimonium facit partium consensus inter personas iure habiles legitime manifestatum qui nulla humana potestate suppleri valet.

guarantee that persons incapable of consent are excluded from the possibility of contracting matrimony. A comparison of the dispositions of Canon Law with those of the majority of legal codices of the various states shows how complete are the norms of Canon Law, how solidly based on natural law, and how carefully considered and formed from the standpoint of a healthy eugenics.

7. PASTORAL QUESTIONS

The spiritual care of mentally diseased persons is an especially difficult phase of the spiritual care of the sick. It can be practiced with some hope of success only by a spiritual director who is versed in psychiatry. Even if the clinical-medical part of von Familler's " Pastoral Psychiatry " becomes outmoded, the principles which are there explained in reference to the spiritual assistance of mentally disturbed persons retain their full validity. The task is one of the most difficult imaginable. The spiritual director of the mentally disturbed must not only familiarize himself as much as possible with the clinical situations—knowledge of which is the most important supposition—but must, moreover, take into consideration those phases of mental disturbance which up to now have not been considered by medicine or have been considered in an insufficient manner. He must make his own the universalistic interpretation of Pastoral Medicine.

He must attempt, together with the doctor, to avert the danger of suicide which often menaces those who are mentally ill. He must be able to judge whether and to what point an objective sin (material) can be considered as willed (formal). It is very difficult to decide in certain cases whether absolution can be given, whether the refusal of it can provoke a spiritual disturbance; whether a certain confession is valid and whether or not a sacrament has been received sacrilegiously.

He must give spiritual comfort and administer the sacraments and must be able to judge up to what point the sick are capable of receiving this comfort and to what point they possess the capacity of receiving the sacrament. Moreover, it is indispensable for him to have knowledge of the " lucid interval." Even if this concept, understood in the sense of complete but transitory mental health, should be rejected by medical science, it is completely justified and necessary for pastoral practice. Moreover, even the Code of Canon Law takes it into account.

Special norms for the mentally disturbed are set forth in canon 754. The mentally diseased are not to be baptized as long as the intention to be baptized is lacking in them.

Those who have been mentally ill from birth or infancy can be baptized as infants according to the rite for infants. Otherwise, they can be baptized only during the lucid intervals, if they so desire. In case of danger of death they can be baptized if they have expressed the desire to be baptized. The same goes for those suffering from lethargy and phrenitis.[1]

That Canon Law recognizes capacity for baptism in the lucid interval, results from the necessity of this sacrament for salvation. Hence it is just that the requisites regarding capacity for a voluntary disposition be less rigorous than those for matrimony.

Regarding the capacity for receiving Confirmation, it is required for valid reception of Confirmation, according to canon 783, that the person be already baptized; and for licit reception of Confirmation, that the person to be confirmed be in the state of grace. The conditions under which confirmation of dying infants is permitted can likewise be applied *per analogiam* to the mentally diseased for whom there is no hope of recovery of the use of reason before death.[2]

The capacity for reception of Extreme Unction is regulated according to canons 940-943. If there is any doubt whether a sick person or one in accident has ever regained the use of reason, the sacrament can be administered *sub conditione* (canon 942).

For the sick who, at the time they were still in possession of the use of reason, expressed or at least implicitly expressed the desire, the sacrament can be administered even if they afterwards lost consciousness or the use of reason.[3]

---

[1] Canon 754: #1. Amentes et furiosi ne baptizentur, nisi tales a nativitate vel ante adeptum rationis usum fuerint; et tunc baptizandi sunt ut infantes.

#2. Si autem dilucida habeant intervalla, dum mentis compotes sunt, baptizentur si velint.

#3. Baptizentur quoque, imminente periculo mortis, si antequam insanirent, suscipiendi baptismi desiderium ostenderint.

#4. Qui lethargo aut phrenesi laborat, vigilans tantum et volens baptizetur; at si periculum mortis impendeat, servetur praescriptum #3.

[2] Canon 786: Aquis baptismi non ablutus valide confirmari nequit, praeterea, ut quid licite et fructuose confirmetur, debet esse in statu gratiae constitutus et, si usu rationis polleat, sufficienter instructus.

[3] Canon 943: Infirmis autem qui, cum suae mentis compotes essent, illud saltem implicite petierunt, aut verisimiliter petiissent, etiamsi deinde sensus vel usum rationis amiserint, nihilominus absolute praebeatur.

For the sacrament of Holy Orders, there is presupposed, as is expected, complete physical and mental health. According to canon 984, the following are *irregulares ex defectu*: epileptics, idiots, and the diabolically possessed, whether they are possessed or were possessed.[1]

We have been able, here, to give only general hints regarding the spiritual care of the mentally diseased, especially in regard to spiritual assistance given in institutions. Special hints for the "open" pastoral care of neurotics and psychopaths will be given in their respective places.

All in all, the spiritual assistance of the mentally diseased requires not only a vast knowledge and great prudence and pastoral sagacity, but greater firmness than is required for the care of healthy souls, great courage, energy, strength of soul and, above all, love.

II. A Summary of Pathology—Classification

It is not the purpose of this study to present an introduction to psychiatry. We leave this to the pertinent tracts on the subject. Here, only the necessary fundamental concepts will be presented.

For practical reasons, we present in this summary the following classification of the subject matter:

(A) Psychosis; (B) Neuropathy; (C) Psychopathy

The criterion of classification does not completely correspond to the accustomed scientific system, but is, however, useful for the purpose of this work, since it makes it possible to obtain a complete and quick view of the subject matter. By psychosis we here mean actual mental disease. This expression, in a strict sense, indicates acute disturbances and hence refers only to a part of psychiatry.

By neuropathy is in general meant all the purely functional diseases of the nervous system. Together with the organic nervous diseases (for example, tabes, syringomyelitis, multiple sclerosis, spastic spinal paralysis, neuritis and others), it constitutes the branch of neurology. The term "neuropathy" is used merely as a concept of order.

---

[1] Canon 984: Epileptici, amentes vel a daemone possessi, scil. "qui sunt vel fuerunt."

Psychopathy, as a degenerative predisposition of character, belongs in se neither to psychosis nor to neuropathy and cannot even be called psychoneurosis. It rather represents the sphere suitable for the origin of varied anomalies and thus also of neuropathy and psychosis of every kind.

The choice and description of the diseases here cited are neither complete nor strictly systematic. Only the morbid conditions which are important for pastoral consideration are presented.

Moreover, the system of psychiatry adopted up to the present time need not be considered as something definite. There is every reason to believe that a new psychiatry is in the making, which justifies the greatest hopes.

A. PSYCHOSIS

1. SYMPTOMATOLOGY

a. Fundamental concepts

Of fundamental importance are character changes; changes of disposition (ill-humor); motor reactions, changes in the volitive sphere (inhibition and impediment: excitation, mania); disturbances of consciousness (comprehension and orientation); states of unconsciousness (somnolence, sopor and coma) and darkening of consciousness (confusion, delirium, crepuscular states, restriction of consciousness); formal disturbances of course of thoughts (thought impediments, flight of ideas, confusion); content disturbances (sense deception, illusion and hallucination); illusory ideas (grandiose ideas); obsessive representations; and finally, disturbances of intellectual capacity (memory and capability of judgment) and of ethical concepts.

Sense deception: An external object (stimulus, peripheral sensory excitation) is the basis of illusions and undergoes only a morbid transformation. Hallucinations arise without excitation on the part of a corresponding stimulus of the external world. We distinguish between optic hallucinations (which refer to the sense of sight), deceptions of sight ("visions"), and acoustic hallucinations (deception of hearing, acousma).

The term "visions," used to indicate optic hallucinations, can be misleading, since it is also used to indicate supernatural apparitions. It is inadmissible to indicate by the same word a supernatural and a pathological phenomenon; it would then denote that one intended to identify the two.

The hearing of voices (phoneme) is one of these phenomena. Moreover, there are deceptions of touch (tactile hallucinations) and of motion and position.

Illusory ideas: Fixed illusory ideas are to be distinguished from passing illusory ideas. They are either absurd, fantastic, confused or "systematic." In regard to their contents, they manifest themselves as ideas of persecution or mistreatment, ideas of grandeur, illusion of insignificance and of unworthiness, ideas of guilt and hypochondriac illusion. All the illusory ideas can assume, in predisposed sick persons, a religious coloration (religious illusion). Erotic coloration is also frequent. At times, especially in women, there is found a curious mixture of religious and sexual components. Peculiar are the forms of illusory ideas conditioned by time. Their appearance is favored by certain currents proper to the time (illusion of the devil, of witches). By suggestion, on the part of those already afflicted, delusions can be transferred to others. This "induced insanity" plays an important role in the origin of mass psychosis.

Obsessive representations: Contrary to the case of illusory ideas, in the case of obsessive representations the sick person is aware of his illness, but cannot resist it. These obsessive representations are at times connected with feelings of anxiety (questioning mania, doubting mania, etc.) and obsessive impulses and inhibitions (phobias). Obsessive ideas often oppress the sick person in the form of religious aberrations. For example, at the time of religious elevation, the person is assailed by blasphemous and obscene representations. These purely pathological representations must be distinguished from authentic temptations. Yet, the distinction is at times very difficult to make. In the same way, as it was deplorable in the past to interpret purely pathological obsessive representations as temptations of the devil, so is it dangerous in the present to go in the opposite direction and try to explain all apparitions as mere pathological phenomena.

b. Syndromes

Often the symptoms change during the course of the disease. At times symptoms completely different can be found in the foreground.

It is not possible to form a clinical diagnosis upon a single symptom (for example, illusion of grandeur). We speak of "syndromes of the condition" when certain definite symptoms prevail for a certain time. These symptoms can be ambiguous; that is, a symptom can present itself at the same time in different diseases.

c. Difficulty of diagnosis

Diagnosis is often made difficult because of the ambiguity and indetermination of the symptoms. Well-characterized and determined syndromes are not always presented. Since juridical effects of great import result from a psychiatric diagnosis, it would be very dangerous to classify any "strange character" as "schizophrenic" or to consider that the concept of "mental weakness" includes limited cases of simple stupidity or moral incontinency.

It is also very important in pastoral practice to remember that one cannot be too prudent when it is a matter of presuming a definite mental disturbance.

A definite diagnosis is possible only when based upon absolutely unequivocal symptoms. All others are of restrictive diagnosis and obscure limited cases. These are, however, more frequent in practice than the well-specified forms and cause the greatest difficulty for both the doctor and the spiritual director.

2. MORE FREQUENT PATHOLOGICAL FORMS

a. The group of forms in folie circulaire (circular form of manic-depressive psychosis)

Under the concept of *folie circulaire* are contained all the phases of excitation (manic) as well as the phases of inhibition (depressive) of manic-depressive psychosis. The characteristic symptom is the cyclical alternation of the phases. There are also forms in which one of the phases is manifestly preponderant (mania or melancholy). Whether authentic melancholy belongs here does not seem to be definitely clarified.

In the manic phases, the following elements are manifested: the mania to talk, increased need for movement and sexuality; at times, excessive excitation to the point of delirium and prolonged complete insomnia. In the depressive phase, these symptoms often tend to the opposite extreme.

The causal "co-operation" of a hereditary factor can be considered virtually assured. Nothing more can be said in this regard, even if, according to the extensive estimates, the empirical hereditary prognosis is estimated in 32.5% of the progeny, when only one of the parents is sick and 90-100% when both parents are sick. These estimates require a more reliable examination.

The heredo-biological interpretation admits of no distinction between "light" propensities and "serious" propensities. It is only concerned with the question whether the propensities are present or not, without considering the degree and gravity of the manifestation. From the standpoint of Pastoral Medicine, the depressive phase seems to be more important than the manic phase because of the great danger of suicide. Feelings of anxiety, ideas of insignificance, and sinfulness; and, at times, hypochondriacal illusory ideas.

Fearful hallucinations ("visions" of the devil), presentiments and desires of death also manifest themselves.

At times suicide takes place in a sudden manner (so-called *raptus melancholicus*). The melancholic knows how to hide (dissimulate) his suicidal intentions. Hence he is not to be trusted.

The prospect of recovery from a single attack is favorable. Less favorable is the prospect of a permanent and complete recovery of the entire personality. But the fact that those affected with *folie circulaire* are often persons of great talent and high intellectual caliber must not be overlooked.

b. The group of schizophrenic forms

The group of schizophrenic forms was at one time treated under the generic term of "dementia praecox." To this belong, among others, hebephrenia, catatonia and dementia paranoides. This group includes a number of forms very different in nature. Schizophrenia consists in a disjunction of the personality (splitting), with predominant injury to the affective or emotional life, emotional obtuseness, lack of interest in surrounding things; paralysis of the will; the disease is at times accompanied by illusory ideas, sense deception, etc. The sick person is removed from the external world and is turned within himself (autism). Hence schizophrenia is called the psychosis of introversion. The splitting of his personality is often manifested in the ambivalence of his feelings. He feels, at the same time, love and hatred for the same person or thing. The disease

M

often takes a slow course, with alternative thrusts and remissions. The final outcome is catatonic stupor or dementia (mostly with fantastic illusory ideas, dementia paranoides).

A certain number of cases begin in youth (puberty), so-called hebephrenia and dementia praecox, others much later. The relation with sexual phases is probable.

Cure by means of injection of sex hormones and definitely surprising cure through other means (shock) has been confirmed by experience.

In this regard, we mention in passing other mental disturbances effected by the disturbance of the endocrine equilibrium (myxedema, cretinism).

In reference to heredity, it is indicated, on the basis of an extensive empirical hereditary prognosis, that, when one of the parents is diseased, around 9-10% of the children are affected with schizophrenia, 17·6% are affected by a psychopathy similar to schizophrenia and 22·6% are of other abnormal types. When both parents are affected by the same hereditary disease, 53% of the progeny are schizophrenic and 29% are schizoid psychopaths.

c. Paranoia

Paranoia (genuine) is characterized by the appearance of fixed and systematic illusory ideas. Mistrust makes contact with one's neighbor most difficult. The paranoiac believes himself persecuted and maltreated (ideas of maltreatment); refers all to himself (illusion of reference). He has no idea of his disease: he shows that he is absolutely incapable of seeing the unreality of his illusory ideas. The intelligence can be apparently conserved, yet the faculty of judgment is seriously affected by the system of illusions. Finally, the entire position of the paranoiac in regard to the external world undergoes a complete derangement. Paranoiacs are for the most part extremely dangerous, especially when they hold a responsible position. Paranoia probably has a connection with the group of schizophrenic forms.

d. Deficient states

(a) *Congenital defects*

(1) *Oligophrenia, mental weakness (idiocy, imbecility, debility).*

By mental weakness is meant a state of defect which especially concerns the intellect (oligophrenia). It can be congenital or acquired, complete (idiocy) or partial (imbecility; in less degree, debility). In complete idiocy, there exists from birth an extreme mental inferiority. Speech is deficient or very imperfectly developed; the sick are dirty and often remain so for their entire life; they neither learn to read nor write. Their vitality is often surprisingly intense: indomitable gluttony and sexual appetite (many times, excessive ipsation).

In imbecility we encounter a mental weakness which is mostly congenital: deficient capacity of judgment and lack of the higher ethical ideas. Debility passes over little by little into common stupidity (weak intelligence). This is the reason why it is dangerous to wrongly extend the concept of mental debility to cases of lack of talent. However, we encounter all degrees, from the limits of normality to the almost vegetating existence similar to that of animals.

As has already been stated, despite all it is never justified to consider even the complete idiot as mentally dead.

Heredity appears to be very influential, yet the hereditary process has not yet been clarified. The hereditary prognosis regarding mothers with mental weakness seems unfavorable for the male progeny. In case of well-characterized hereditary mental weakness, the empirical hereditary prognosis for the progeny is calculated to be 33-50%.

A special difficulty lies in the fact that in an individual case it is not always easy to distinguish the congenital forms from those acquired (and hence not hereditary). The weak of mind generally distinguish themselves by their good-naturedness and willingness to be of service. Because of this, it happens that for the most part they are able to adapt themselves well to social life. In subordinate functions they conduct themselves very satisfactorily and are faithful, conscientious and trustworthy. On the other hand, girls of mental debility easily become victims of seduction and often become illegitimate mothers and fall into prostitution.

(2) *Moral dementia.* There is a particular group of imbeciles and mentally weak persons who, unlike the sociable ones, are characterized in a special manner by the fact that the deficiency has affected the ethical realm. At times they completely lack higher ethical ideas and manifest strong criminal impulses. Defect of intel-

ligence does not manifest itself too clearly. In such cases, we speak of moral insanity.

In practice, these cases of genuine moral insanity, i.e., states of defect, are very often difficult to distinguish from cases which, from the symptomatic and characterological viewpoint, seem completely similar, but definitely do not belong to the group of genuine morally insane, but rather to the vast group of psychopaths. Especially when the intellect is not entirely adjusted, yet is developed beyond the average, one is not justified in referring to this as moral insanity. Otherwise there would no longer be a precise determination of the concept and all the cases of unstable and misled youths would be included in this definition. The distinction is of great practical importance in the prognosis of life, since psychopathic youths in time often orientate themselves well in life.

If it is not possible to attain a precise distinction between cases of true mental insanity and those of unstable psychopathy, then, for reasons given, one should speak in general of moral insanity and avoid the term " mental deficiency."

(b) *Acquired mental defects*

In the course of life, an individual can likewise acquire mental deficiencies (exogenous), symptomatically similar to congenital mental debility (endogenous). Here the following can play a causal role: lesions (trauma), toxic and infectious influences, etc.

Not even the distinction between congenital and acquired mental debility is always easy to make. Often, in the first stages of development, it is not possible to distinguish the acquired from the congenital defects. Moreover, not all congenital defects are conditioned by heredity, i.e., are set in the germinative plasma. If they are caused by the trauma of birth, especially in the case of a difficult birth by forced obstetrical operations or by intrauterine infection accompanied by lues, then we are faced with a defect definitely congenital and in no way conditioned by heredity. To the acquired states of defect are also to be added all the forms of secondary loss of the mental faculty, which represent the outcome of most varied organic cerebral diseases: dementia.

Moreover, dementia can develop in later old age as a consequence of arteriosclerotic softening of the brain (*dementia senilis seu arteriosclerotica*), and also as a final state of severe chronic alcoholic intoxication or of syphilitic consecutive states (metalues). To these belong progressive paralysis (dementia paralytica). Dementia can also develop as a consequence of infectious diseases (" brain grip," encephalitis).

It also presents itself as the final course of endogenous mental diseases: dementia paranoides with absurd, illusory ideas in schizophrenia. Absurd illusory ideas, especially the fertile ideas of grandeur, are characteristic of progressive paralysis, the first symptom of which is the mania for unmotivated prodigality, which at times arises suddenly, or the loss of the sense of decency.

e. Acute states of confusion

In relation to dementia as a conclusive and permanent state, is the acute confusion (amentia), a transitory state, often caused by acute infectious diseases (febrile) and intoxication (alcohol, etc.). It is generally associated with disorientation, hallucinations, confused discourse (delirium), clouding of consciousness and, finally, loss of consciousness, which can pass through all degrees (somnolence, sopor and coma).

The phases of acute alcoholic intoxication are a typical example of this. Very similar to these acute states of confusion is apparent acute psychosis brought on by external matters; in the female very often by phases of generation (psychosis of menstruation, pregnancy, puerperium and lactation). The prognosis in regard to permanent cure is, for the most part, absolutely favorable, but attention must be given to the danger of suicide. At times, " closed " treatment in a hospital is required, since the psychosis can often be associated with serious agitation.

Reactive psychoses provoked by an external experience can be situated between the acute psychoses already mentioned and the states of excitation with a psychopathic basis.

" Prison psychosis " is considered by some authors merely an explosion of an unbridled psychopathic nature; by others, more as an expression of simulation (to play the wild man), and finally by others, as an expression of guilt consciousness.

Unjustified is the opinion which states that only a guilty person can be affected by a prison psychosis. Mentally labile natures can be predisposed to it.

f. St. Vitus Dance (Chorea St. Viti)

We differentiate chorea minor (Sydenham), which is of infectious origin (articular rheumatism) and is principally observed in young persons. This does not pertain to our present discussion.

Then there is the tarantism which in the Middle Ages presented itself as a mass psychosis and which is a form of grave hysteria with adults (chorea major), and, finally, the hereditary Chorea Huntington. The latter is a very rare disease which appears mostly in persons of fairly advanced age (30-45 years). This leads to a progressive degeneration of the central nervous system, with contractions in the most varied muscular groups.

In the sick there is manifested at times a surprising unrestraint in pleasure and instinct. A complete dementia can be the outcome of this. The disease can also be treated in the section on *Neuropathy*.

g. Mental disturbances arising from chronic intoxication

(a) *Alcoholism*

Chronic alcoholism, which for the most part develops from a psychopathic-degenerative cause, but also from extraordinarily exhausting efforts (military service in war or in tropical regions), consists in an irresistible inclination toward the consumption of alcoholic drinks. Symptomatic is the loss of the higher ethical standards, apathy (at times associated with weeping sentimentality), brutalization, excitability, diminution of memory, weakening of the will, exaggeration of the sex libido, often with the suppression of potency; jealousy often exaggerated to the point of delirium; neglect of domestic and professional duties, economic decadence and the dissolution of marriage and family life.

Chronic alcoholism brings on, little by little, a degradation in the social realm. Dementia is often the outcome—the end follows a state of complete depravity, and frequently comes by way of heart or lung infirmities or arteriosclerosis (apoplectic attack—apoplexy).

A great number of severe mental diseases arise from chronic alcoholism: delirium tremens (serious motorial agitation, states of anxiety, optical hallucinations, e.g., mice), the classical delirium of the drinker, acute hallucinations (often suicidal attempts, attacks on persons) and the Korsakoff's psychosis (loss of attention, so-called retrograde amnesia, disorientation and confabulation).

Pathological intoxication is the reaction of a mentally abnormal (psychopathic) person to alcohol, often even from surprisingly small amounts of alcohol (alcoholic intolerance). Even in normal people tolerance can be reduced through exhaustion, excitement, etc.

Dipsomania belongs to the group of so-called monomanias, therefore to the states which we attribute to psychopathy. It is a matter here of a mania to drink which is transitory (periodic dipsomania) with regular free intervals. It is possible that it has some affinity with epilepsy.

(b) Narcomania

Strictly related to alcoholism are the other so-called toxic-manias (morphinism, cocainism, hashishism, opiumism, etc.). Here there is often present an exogenous component (seduction, custom, mania to imitate), but in most cases, the endogenous psycopathic predisposition is basic: the subject does not become psychopathic because of the mania, but becomes maniacal in this regard because he is a psychopath. He can, however, become psychotic as a result of this mania.

Of importance is the question of heredity: both in regard to the ascendants and descendants. Regarding the ascendants, what is certain is this, that a considerable proportion of the addicts are hereditarily diseased. However, it does not necessarily follow that, when the ascendants are diseased, a disease of the same nature must present itself—in this case, that of dipsomania; it can also be a matter of abnormal characteristics of another kind.

Thus there are found in alcoholic families cases of psychopathy, mental debility, parasitic trends in obtaining help or assistance, prostitution, epilepsy, hysteria, as well as bodily deformities. It would be absolutely an exaggeration to hold that alcoholism arises almost without exception from a constitutional and hereditary psychopathic basis.

Alcoholism and the other toxic-manias can be very fatal to the descendants or progeny. It has been proved, even without supposing a hereditary factor, that stupefacients act as dysgenic poisons and can cause most serious harm. To the hereditary factor and that of direct injury of the embryo, others of exogenous origin can also be added, such as: sexual diseases, neglect, deficient nourishment and education (environmental damage). These damages can to a certain point be compensated by means of assistance for the drinker and the family.

As unfavorable as the prospects are for the progeny, it must not be forgotten that eminent persons have come from families burdened with such a disease.

The social, moral and pastoral importance of the manias is extraordinarily great. Alcoholism can never be too earnestly considered from the social standpoint. Incalculable is the amount of misery, destruction of marriage and the family, the amount of economic and moral devastation imputable to dipsomania. Alcoholism presents one of the most serious problems of social hygiene.

In the individual case, it is very difficult to establish whether it is a matter of disease or vice. This is a question that can be posited even concerning some other deviations (cf. *Sexual pathology*). Without doubt, the moral responsibility is diminished inasmuch as, in the successive states, there are impediments to freedom of the will.

Not even the psychopathic-degenerative disposition, which is almost never absent, is as such responsible. Yet exculpation must not to be too far extended either from the judicial standpoint or in confession. Even the psychopath is capable of having a notion of what is unjust and—at least in the beginning—of determining his will in conformity to this notion. His free will is not suppressed like that of the insane. He must make his decision at the beginning, and hence the actions which he performs when he gives himself up to the mania must be considered as vices. In the later phases or stages, he is no longer free: then there is nothing but disease. There are also diseases of which the diseased is culpable.

The cure of alcoholics is extremely difficult. From what has been said, it is understood that only in very rare cases is it possible to obtain a permanent cure of alcoholism which has reached its late stages. After apparent success in a " closed " institution (withdrawal: made difficult at the beginning by " phenomena of abstinence "; Antabus cure) frequent falls occur, for the most part immediately after the patient has been dismissed.

The really permanent salvation of the drinker, when verified, is quasi-exclusively possible when it is founded on a religious basis. Thus, in a manner which is often marvelous, a regeneration of the mental life can take place. But alcoholics and toxic-maniacs are only with difficulty accessible to spiritual direction. Cures of this kind often can no longer be considered natural, but can only be explained by direct intervention of supernatural grace, which can effect the full and permanent transformation of man when all other means have failed. For this reason, associations for the cure of alcoholics established on a religious basis are almost the only ones that can obtain permanent success.

B. NEUROPATHY

By neuropathy is here meant all purely functional diseases of the nervous system: hence diseases in which no anatomical basis can be found.

This negative note is the only factor that the heterogenous morbid forms which we have here grouped together solely for purposes of order have in common. We should not express an intrinsic affinity that suggests the concept of a superior order. If we separate the group of neuropathies from those of psychoses, this is not done in the sense that a strict distinction is possible for every case. In se neuropathies are not mental diseases. Yet it is not always easy to trace the confines which separate them from mental diseases. For example, there are also mental disturbances of an epileptic and hysterical nature. Even the confines which separate obsessive neurosis from mental disease can fluctuate. The reason for the difficulty in tracing the confines between psychosis and neuropathy in the sense of this exposition can be found in the fact that both arise from the common basis of the psychopathic-degenerative predisposition, and hence as they have a common root, so they also have ramifications in common. As such, it is difficult to distinguish what part of such a common " bundle of the course of progress " is to be attributed to psychosis and which is to be attributed to neuropathy. Under neuropathy, in the meaning explained above, the following are to be considered:

(1) Neurasthenic diseases;
(2) Neurosis (in strict sense);
(3) Epilepsy.

1. NEURASTHENIC DISEASES

a. Neurasthenia

The concept of neurasthenia (general debility of the nerves, " nervosity ") pertains more to the old terminology. By it was

M*

designated a state of increased excitability and a rapid fatigue of the nervous system. The increased excitability is to be considered the primary phenomena, and the rapid fatigue as the secondary phenomena.

Neurasthenia can be congenital (constitutional) or acquired. In the latter case, it presents itself for the most part as "exhaustion-neurasthenia": as the result of illness, operations, pain, fatigue, bodily and mental overexertion. The degrees of transition, from simple, transitory and slight "nervosity" to more serious forms of constitutional and permanent neurasthenia, are fluctuating. The functional disturbance of the nervous system is lasting.

In the physical sphere, there is often present a notable diminution of muscular power (asthenia).

In the psycho-mental sphere neurasthenia manifests itself in the diminishing of will power and the power of decision (abulia, anenergia); the flexibility of the soul is as if paralyzed (psychasthenia).

There is often a diminution of the power of concentration; excitability to environment, fickleness, fearfulness, anxiety (dreams of anxiety); insomnia.

It is useless and dangerous to combat the habitual insomnia of neurasthenia by soporifics, since habitual use of the same can easily cause an addiction to them. More reasonable are the physico-dietetical cures.

In case of simple insomnia through excessive tiredness, it is best to physically calm the excited nerves. The diminution of the power of concentration often brings about in neurasthenics distraction in prayer, incapability of praying well, incapability of devotion and proper participation in the Mass.

He does not feel the comfort which he has sought and which he feels to be essentially necessary.

Often the incapacity to pray is based upon internal mental resistance. Thus, prayer would often be a most efficacious means of easing the mind even in the already mentioned form of insomnia.

The idea of being excluded from the action of grace can also seriously accentuate the depressive state of the soul. From the pastoral standpoint, such persons are in need of a most comprehensive assistance and comfort.

The neurasthenic has as much need of mental consolation as strength of body by means of healthy and moderate physical exercise, a healthy and natural life, but above all he needs increasing confidence in himself. The mental state becomes better with the acquisition of confidence in his productive capacity.

b. Hypochondria

Hypochondria is a morbid inclination toward anxious self-observation and an exaggerated fear of disease. It is doubtful whether it is to be considered a disease properly so-called. It is rather to be considered a simple symptom—yet a very ambiguous symptom. It can be as much an expression of a simple neurasthenia of exhaustion as of psychopathic predisposition or corresponding neurosis.

It is at times difficult to distinguish it from hysteria with all the possible pathological (psychogenic) syndromes produced by it. At times it is likewise difficult to distinguish the " imaginary " disease from that which is simulated. Of importance, however, is one characteristic: the hypochondriac has fear of the disease, but the hysteric wants it (flight into sickness); the simulator simulates it. Even thoughtless statements made by the doctor can lead to hypochondria (Bumke).

At times, hypochondria can become aggravated to the point of converting into grandiose ideas (illusory ideas). Hypochondriacal, illusory ideas are encountered in various mental diseases (melancholy, paranoia schizophrenia, paralysis). In paranoia these are at times accompanied by ideas of persecution (persecution mania); fear of being poisoned, etc. In this case it is no longer a matter of hypochondria in the sense of a neurosis or of a neurotic symptom, but rather the symptom of a serious psychosis.

Morbid organic sensation (organic neurosis) can give occasion to an increase of self-observation and thus to hypochondria.

A curious form of hypochondria is often found in young medical students who believe they observe in themselves all the diseases they learn to recognize. This hypochondria is found in an analogous form in lay people who are interested in medicine and who have read and heard much on the subject. Fragmentary learning is often more dangerous than useful. Especially dangerous is superficial medical knowledge propagated by means of " medical books " of all kinds. The readers of these are, for doctors, the most difficult patients and by their comportment often impede the success of medical treatment.

After going from one doctor to another, the hypochondriac becomes an easy victim of the charlatan, who adopts every sort of magical and pseudo-mystical curative methods. After a time, the psychic life of the hypochondriac suffers as the result of the excessive attention given to the ego; hypochondriacs end up by inconsiderately restricting themselves (egocentric) to their ego. Everything must "turn around them," and in time even the feeling of shame will disappear and they develop an extraordinary unconstraint in speaking of bodily functions.

From the pastoral standpoint, hypochondriacs are accessible only with difficulty. The danger of suicide is less serious in egocentric hypochondriacs with a strong instinct towards self-preservation, but can be notable in depressive hypochondriacs, in whom hypochondria is but a partial symptom of a melancholy or an illusory psychosis. In this latter case, suicide can also come suddenly and surprisingly.

2. NEUROSIS

a. Preliminary concept

The concept of neurosis is difficult to define. Since the era of psychoanalysis, it has acquired a new content, but to date has not been fully clarified. However, taking consideration of the provisional character of present knowledge, neurosis can be used merely as a "concept of order." We intend to assume the concept of neurosis in the sense of actual psychotherapy and to define it when we treat the latter.

Even the practical distinction between organic neurosis and psychoneurosis appears problematic, since there is no neurosis that does not affect mental life, or which is not primarily determined by the mental element; as, on the other hand, all neuroses can produce even psychogenic-organic sensations.

Psychoanalysis—the research concerning subconscious and unconscious mental conflicts—brought us essentially closer to the understanding of neurosis.

b. Organic neurosis

By organic neurosis is understood functional disturbances which can be associated with abnormal sensations in determined organs (organic sensations) or which affect the function of the same (organic system).

Organic neuroses are based in part on an increased lability of the vegetative nervous system (vegetative neurosis; vegetative dystonia).

Not all morbid organic sensations constitute organic neurosis. They can be of a purely hypochondriacal nature. Moreover, organic neurosis and hypochondria can overlap. The fact that a neurosis provokes determined symptoms in a determined organ is, for the most part, not accidental, but in conformity to certain internal laws through which the subconscious tends to express its conflict (so-called organic language).

(a) *Cardiac neurosis*

The most frequent organic neurosis is that of the heart or cardiac neurosis (more precisely, the neurosis of cardiac and vasomotory nerves). It is associated with states of anxiety, fearful awakening from sleep (*pavor nocturnus*), intense palpitation of the heart (*palpitatio cordis*), feeling of pressure in the cardiac region, the feeling of an interruption of the heartbeat and, at times, the feeling of imminent death. In cardiac neurosis, the latter never reaches the point of a "feeling of oppression," which is characteristic of true angina pectoris. Instead, in the cardiac neurosis, the attacks are never objectively dangerous. They are subjectively very unpleasant, so much so that we speak of a "nervous" angina pectoris. Certain authors even hold that the nervous form can in time possibly degenerate into the organic form. But, up to the present time, no decisive proof for this has been brought forth. The causes of cardiac neurosis have up to the present not been definitely clarified. It can follow as the result of excessive physical strain. Still, it is doubtful whether in this case it is a matter of a neurosis or of a participation of the heart muscle. Pure neurosis often manifests a relation to the sexual life. For example, a sudden appearance of a cardiac neurosis can take place when normal sexual life undergoes a sudden interruption, as in the case of the death of husband or wife. These states, for the most part, pass quickly.

Cardiac neurosis in the case of ipsation and as a result of sexual aberration is frequent. Even grief and pure mental excitement of any kind can lead to cardiac neurosis ("to take something to heart").

Cardiac neurosis is in many cases a typical neurosis of the struggle for life. The characteristic sensation in cardiac neurosis is that of anxiety.

Anxiety represents the fundamental symptom of neurosis in general. The psychological study of this symptom leads to deep metaphysical association with guilt, sin and death. Without clear concepts of the ultimate metaphysical causes, the problem of neurosis can never be completely solved.

(b) *Gastric neurosis*

Gastroneurosis or gastrointestinal neurosis is quite common and, in regard to it, it is often difficult to precisely designate the limits between the purely functional and what is organic (for example, hyperacidity, gastritis, ulcer, cancer). As in all diseases of the stomach, the psyche is often seriously and persistently altered.

In the examples of organic neurosis it must be observed to what degree unconscious auto-lesionistic tendencies (so-called psychic masochism) are present.

Gastroneurosis can be an atypical expression of such tendencies : negation of self-preservation by means of resistance (of apparent organic origin) to the taking of nourishment. Behind the " not being able " is, in reality, an unconscious " not wishing."

(c) *Sexual neurosis*

Knowledge of sexual neurosis, which at times is called *neurasthenia sexualis*, is also of great importance from the pastoral standpoint.

This is manifested in impotency (mental), *eiaculatio praecox*, frequent pollution or spermatorrhea; excessive sexual excitation (*erethismus sexualis, hypererotismus*), mostly associated with a disproportion between libido and potency.

Mutatis mutandis, the same thing can be said concerning sexual neurosis behind which often lie tendencies of auto-lesion and even a negation of the instinct for the preservation of the species.

Even these problems cannot be resolved without going deeply into the metaphysical aspect.

(d) *Exogenous neurosis—Traumatic neurosis*

So-called traumatic neuroses (accident neurosis or hysteria) are here considered only in regard to their external and not their internal relation to organic neuroses. There is reference here to neurotic manifestations of all kinds which develop from a serious and sudden physical or psychic shock (accident, railroad disaster, fall, explosion, grenade- or bomb-burst in time of war, etc.). No doubt, when the shock is very serious, these neuroses can arise even in completely healthy persons. The excessive intensity of the stimulus is then proportionate to the effect. In persons who are mentally labile, these arise even from moderate causes.

Certain war neurotics (the agitated, the tremulous) have cultivated their neurosis as a simple " neurosis of purpose " or " neurosis of desire " (discharge from service, pension). Certain authors deny, in general, the existence of a traumatic neurosis as a disease of a definite type and claim that in every case it is a simple "reaction of scope or purpose," and hence, closely related to simulation; or at least, is a reaction of psychopathic predisposition.

Not even the psychoses of war and those of accident are considered authentic psychoses. Yet the external occurrence can, at least in a disposed personality (prepsychotic personality), activate and render manifest the latent psychosis.

Perhaps the majority of traumatic neuroses can be included under the concept of neurosis of scope or purpose (compensation-neurosis) or of hysteria, and arise from a psychopathic predisposition. However, an indiscriminate generalization in this case, as in the case of a prison psychosis, would be unjust.

c. Compulsive neurosis

(a) *Concept*

Under compulsive neurosis are included a number of psychopathological phenomena in which involuntary representations, impulses and fears concur, which cannot be removed and which disturb the normal course of the processes of consciousness.

According to certain authors, the compulsive is that which corresponds to a definite character type: to the " compulsive character " enclosed within himself. According to this the compulsive neurosis is ascribed to the compulsive type, as hysteria is ascribed to the impulsive type. We have already pointed out the danger arising in such generalizing and in establishing definite types.

(b) *Symptomatology*

We distinguish between compulsive representations, compulsive impulses, compulsive actions and compulsive inhibitions.

To the compulsive representations belong profane, blasphemous and obscene representations during prayer, during the Sacrifice of the Mass, or during meditation.

Such representations are felt to be extraneous and opposed by the will, yet impose themselves so strongly and persistently that they produce interior insecurity. Those affected by these compulsions do not free themselves from the idea that they have sinned although they are aware of the compulsive character of the representations.

Thus, compulsive representations and scrupulosity are closely related. Many compulsive neurotics consider these compulsive representations as diabolical temptations. In the individual case, it can at times be difficult to establish whether it is a case of a purely pathological neurotic representation or of a diabolical temptation.

It is possible that the two elements, the neurotic and the diabolical, can be associated, or that the diabolical influences can find in the neurotic processes a facile point of contact.

Hence it appears more important to direct the medical and pastoral treatment first and exclusively to the morbid and neurotic phase of the process, which is surely, in the majority of cases, the most predominant. If it is successfully overcome, the natural point of contact will be removed from the co-operation of the diabolical influences.

Compulsive impulses are those which lead to the performance of compulsive acts; such can be of a completely banal nature, as, for example, that of knocking on every lamp post. Very often, the same takes place in the religious sphere as, for example, the impulse to sacrilegiously profane the sacred host during Holy Communion, etc.

Obsessive inhibitions (phobias) clearly indicate the connection between obsession and anxiety.

Anxiety is not to be confused with fear; at the base of fear lies an objective danger. Anxiety, however, has its basis within the anxious person. The objective, real cause is lacking. Hence anxiety presents a definite metaphysical characteristic. The less man is influenced by religion, the more he is overcome by anxiety. He who has a strong hold on faith and is conscious of his true relation to God, and is firmly established in a religious mode of life, has overcome metaphysical anxiety. It can no longer harm him.

To the class of compulsive inhibitions belong many forms of stuttering and writers' cramp (mogigraphia). Typical cases of phobias are anxiety at finding oneself alone in a room (claustrophobia, not identical with the "booth anxiety" of the sociable alcoholic); a feeling of fear at the thought of being alone in a large open space (agoraphobia); the morbid dread of filth or contamination (mysophobia), associated with the constant "washing of hands"; the morbid fear of blushing (erythrophobia), and many others.

Finally, there is a fear of fear (phobophobia). The fear of germs belongs partly to the sphere of hypochondria and is partly related to mysophobia; it is manifested in absurd and ridiculous methods of disinfection, after having touched door knobs, banisters, etc.

Some of these phobias are related to sexual life; the fear of filth or contamination and the compulsion to wash are associated with ipsation, or with superevaluation of erotic ideas which are hidden behind the mask of decency (prudery).

In the sphere of mental compulsion also belong the "proof impulse": the impulse to verify whether all the doors are closed, whether the light is out, etc. These present themselves even in mentally normal persons, but can assume an impulsive neurotic character.

These manifest themselves especially in the religious realm; in the excessive preoccupation whether the last confession was validly made, or whether Holy Communion was received unworthily, etc.

The overanxious exactitude becomes interrogative obsession and doubt mania in the realm of faith, and scrupulosity in the realm of morality.

Particular phenomena very similar to obsessive neuroses are, at times, encountered in priests. They can be called celebration neurosis.

Thus, for example, the fear of not finishing particular parts of the Mass, especially the Canon, at the right time; scrupulous behavior in the purifying of the Mass chalice, etc.; the dropping of the ciborium in the administration of Holy Communion, dropping the sacred hosts, or stumbling with the ostensorium in one's hands; fear of not consecrating according to the ritual (*consacristi*), of forgetting a memento (*mementisti*), and of forgetting a fragment of the host (*fragmentisti*).

At times, the fear of celebrating unworthily (*amfortas typus*) is the basis of the consecration anxiety.

These types are merely examples; the enumeration of the various forms of neurosis is almost impossible.

The calm discussion of the neurotic and conquerable character of these forms can, for the most part, be helpful. However, the mere comprehension of the morbid character of an obsessive neurosis, especially in serious cases, is not sufficient of itself in overcoming the neurosis.

(c) *Pastoral questions*

It is certainly a great consolation to the obsessive neurotic when he can be convinced that his neurotic ideas and impulses are not the result of his depravity, but are of a pathological nature.

Certain neurotics, especially the scrupulous, tend to see, in the temptations and impulses which assail them, temptations and impulses of a diabolical nature.

The comprehension of these as simply pathological and not diabolical and extranatural has a tranquilizing effect, and this can be complete when the individual is convinced that there can never be sin when interior consent is not given to the thought and the thought is also a cause of torment for the individual.

There are cases, however, in which one can completely remove the last interior support of the neurotic—namely, faith in his personality and 'confidence in himself—by excusing all manifestations of neurosis as disease. We must be on guard against such a method, because it completely misconceives the essence of neurosis and the purpose of a cure, which consists in a reconstruction of the personality.

Moreover, it should be pointed out that true temptations can exist side by side with obsessive neurotic afflictions. It is true that in the individual case it will be most difficult to distinguish which are which, and it is also understandable how a temptation can attach itself to obsessive representations, at least as a concomitant factor, and cover the same in such a way that it is difficult to separate the individual components of the " bundle."

We must take the same position with regard to the question of obsessions. Hence, as soon as such a suspicion arises, the greatest prudence and precaution is required in the pastoral treatment. In doubtful cases, it will be a matter of duty always to tend toward a purely natural interpretation and to avoid disturbing the patient. The hypothesis of an extranatural co-operation can be admitted only when compelling and convincing reasons, which exclude a purely natural explanation, demand it. Otherwise there is the danger of seeing diabolical possession everywhere.[1]

Thus, just as it is absolutely necessary, even in this realm, to first exhaust all the possibilities of a purely natural explanation, so it is dangerous to go too far in this direction and to apply the factor of "disease" exclusively and with exaggeration.

One runs the risk, with this conception, of weakening or abandoning completely the concept of fault (sin) in favor of the extensively interpreted concept of disease.

Partiality and exaggeration in this direction must also be avoided.

d. Hysteria

(a) Concept

Among the neuroses, hysteria assumes the most varied forms. Its name, from *hystera* (the uterus) alludes to the fact that at one time it was attributed exclusively to the female sex and was associated with the genital functions. Its essence has not yet been completely explained and the definitions of it which have been given have differed from each other.

If hysteria is defined in the widest sense as the capacity for provoking purely psychogenic somatic sypmtoms, then hysteria is a completely general phenomenon, at least with regard to persons of a labile nervous system. It can be said, then, that basically every individual is capable of hysteria (Kretschmer) and that it is a matter of greater or less intensity of the stimulus.

Severe external actions can produce hysteria even in persons of healthy nerves (fright-hysteria). In this sense, hysteria would be the psychogenic disposition of reaction. The reaction consists in the arising of morbid somatic symptoms of a purely functional nature, in which any anatomical (organic) basis is lacking.

---

[1] " Now the world is so full of such ghosts that no one knows how to avoid them " (Goethe, " Faust," II).

The somatic pathological form is, in this case, exclusively of psychogenic origin.

When hysteria is considered in such a wide sense, then it coincides with that of neurosis.

Another concept restricts the concept of hysteria to anomalies of the affective life. These provoke an abnormal mode of reaction (hysterical reactions) to external influences, especially those of a disagreeable nature, before which man does not feel adequate. His subconscious provokes morbid symptoms ("escape in sickness," purpose or defense neurosis), for example, fainting, attacks of all sorts, paralysis, loss of sensory functions, incapacity for movement or tumultuous movement.

"The emotion is transformed into a somatic symptom distinct from that which takes place under ordinary conditions" (Breuer). Once such abnormal mechanisms become fixed, the hysterical person can easily reactivate these in a psychogenic way. In this way, even purely somatic processes can be psychogenically "covered."

The concept will be taken in the strictest sense when it is limited to cases with explicit character changes (hysterical character). The concept of hysterical character is not to be put on the same plane as the concept of "impulsive character" (cf. above).

The following can be considered hysterical changes of character or disposition: the pathological need of being of some worth, associated with an egocentric attitude; the need of making an impression upon others, of making oneself interesting, of arousing sympathy, etc. Characteristic hysterical mendacity (*pseudologia phantastica*) develops from this fundamental behavior.

Hysteric patients are, in great part, disposed to pseudology, because of the unreliability of their memory.

Thus, we are to distinguish between hysterical phenomena and hysterical character.

(b) *Symptomatology*

The manifestations of hysteria are of extraordinarily varied forms. There is scarcely a phenomenon that could not be brought forth as a hysterical symptom. At times, such phenomena are easily recognized as hysterical, and at other times it is difficult to identify them.

The classical forms of the "great hysterical attack" (*arc du cercle, attitudes passionelles*), described by Charcot, have become rare. Hysteria is inexhaustible in the creation of novelties.

The hysterical attack is often distinguished from the non-hysterical attack merely from the fact that the former never takes place without the presence of a spectator and always with a certain theatricality and with such prudence that nothing serious could ever happen.

On the other hand, the epileptic attack takes place improvisedly, without regard for environment, with violence so cruel that it often leads to very serious injuries (biting of tongue, fracture of the skull). On the contrary, even the suicidal attempts of hysterics are practically always executed with corresponding "precautions," so much so that the attempt (contrary to the intention of the agent) leads to death only when made in an improvised manner. In such cases we speak of the "demonstrative character" of a suicidal act.

Well known is the paralysis of hysterics; paralysis of the extremity, at times partial paralysis and at other times complete, which can last for years; sudden loss of speech, of sight or hearing (hysterical blindness and deafness).

In cases of hysterical mania for desiring to make oneself interesting, we must be definitely skeptical of the "miraculous cures" which these hysterics like to relate.

Generally speaking, hysteria is found in greater frequency in the female than in the male sex. Symptoms which have a connection with the genital organs (ovaries—Charcot), or at the base of which are found deeper sexual complexes, and corresponding neuroses with particularly erotic coloration, hint at hysteria.

At times erotic symptoms have a religiously colored gloss, and —vice-versa—the religiosity of hysterics contains a certain erotic coloration.

(c) *Judgment concerning hysteria*

Hysteria remains an unsolved problem. Yet we must at least indicate some viewpoints on the basis of which we can take a position.

Two contrasting opinions can be established in the judgment of hysteria: some consider hysteria exclusively as a disease, a serious disease in which it is controverted whether the disease is of an endogenous nature, depending on predisposition or fate, or whether it is of exogenous origin.

At present the tendency to consider it a disposition prevails. Without doubt, the psychopathic predisposition represents the general basis upon which even exogenous elements can become active.

The contrary opinion does not consider hysteria in general as a disease, but merely as a moral problem. Hence hysteric patients are to be considered neither sick, nor worthy of compassion, but solely as culpable of their negative peculiarity. Without doubt, in no other neurosis does the moral problem play such an important part as in hysteria. The formation of the "hysterical character" is almost never fulfilled without the co-operation of personal fault. Thus, even when psychotherapy is successful, it is because it has succeeded in overcoming egocentricity and has brought about the complete reconstruction of the moral person. Therefore, psychotherapy in the wide sense signifies "conversion."

On the other hand, the fact that hysteric patients suffer intensely must not be overlooked. They suffer more than can be imagined by the healthy person and are truly "not understood" except by an understanding spiritual adviser or doctor, to whom the hysterics cling with all their strength.

A strong personality is required on the part of the latter in order to gradually lift the hysteric subject from his state and not be dragged down by him.

Thus understood, hysteric patients are actually seriously sick and suffer, at least subjectively, more than those who are organically sick.

Hence the question "sickness or moral problem?" posited in this form leads to a unilateral judgment. It is not proper to underestimate or overlook either aspect of the problem. Only thus can a just solution to the problem of hysteria be found.

The need for close collaboration between the spiritual adviser and doctor appears especially evident in this form of neurosis.

3. EPILEPSY

a. Symptomatology

Epilepsy is characterized by sudden attacks characterized by loss of consciousness, violent falls, convulsions (clonic contractions and tonic rigidity), frothing at the mouth, cramping of the jaw (stridor dentium), at times, lesions (biting of the tongue). Besides so-called major epilepsy, there is also minor epilepsy, with only a partial loss of consciousness ("absence," *petit mal*; so-called "equivalent").

We distinguish between a symptomatic epilepsy, arising from other diseases (tumors, cicatrices of the meninges and the gray matter, callosity partly with a traumatic and partly a luetic basis) and a "genuine" epilepsy, which lacks any organic basis and which must therefore be considered a functional neurosis.

However, according to more recent viewpoints (Wagner—Jauregg), this distinction appears at least questionable.

Cases of "genuine" epilepsy are to be included among those concerning which we do not yet know the cause but which, nevertheless, have an external cause.

Important possibilities for the distinction between endogenous and exogenous forms of epilepsy have been furnished by encephalography.

The nature of epilepsy has not yet been clarified. The old authors saw in the disease something sinister, diabolical and the expression of a certain association of the disease with a higher world (*morbus sacer*).

A more modern but defeated trend wanted to bring epilepsy, as a purely functional neurosis, into close association with hysteria (hystero-epilepsy). Such a relation is, however, unlikely, if only because of the fact of the difference in the attack.

Worthy of note are the crepuscular states in which epileptics tend toward escape (fugues, poriomania); they behave in an apparently orderly manner, but can fulfill the most fatal acts. If the attacks take place with frequency, in time this will lead to a notable apathy, which manifests itself especially in lack of feeling for one's neighbor (epileptic change of character); and at times finally degenerates into dementia.

b. Heredity

The so-called symptomatic epilepsy is almost always to be considered exogenous and hence not conditioned by heredity. There is, however, a familiar form (myoclonus epilepsy), which is definitely and predominantly conditioned by heredity.

"Genuine" epilepsy is considered a highly hereditary disease, but the form of succession is, however, not definitely established. The empirical hereditary prognosis is estimated in ten per cent of the progeny. Nevertheless, even in this matter there are yet unsolved problems.

c. Judgment

Because of their change of character, epileptics are at times truly dangerous persons; irritable, irascible, unpredictable, often excessively cruel, and inclined to commit terrible acts of violence (for example, arson).

Nero is supposed to have been an epileptic. On the other hand, among the epileptics are found persons gifted with great talent (Napoleon, Julius Caesar) and persons with an outstanding predisposition toward supernatural ecstasy (*morbus sacer*).

It is not impossible that authentic visions and mystical revelations can be united to epileptic symptoms (especially to the aura). On the other hand, it is also possible to have intervening diabolical influences in epilepsy.

Up to the present time, epilepsy has manifested itself as not yielding readily to psychotherapy. But psychotherapy has distinguished it from neurosis in the strict sense.

d. Pastoral Questions

From the personal standpoint, epilepsy is of little interest. It is only important to recognize attacks, since these can take place even in church, and to distinguish such attacks from any ordinary fainting fit, hysterical attack, etc.

C. PSYCHOPATHY

1. GENERAL VIEW

a. Concept

Since there is no recognized definition of psychopathy, we here consider psychopathy as a degenerative predispositon, for the most part congenital, more or less a deviation of character, psychic life and reactive capacity.

If the anomaly predominantly manifests itself in an inclination toward neurosis, then the term " neuropathy " is generally used. This concept is not opposed to that of psychopathy, but constitutes a particular case of the same.

This degenerative predisposition is often called inferiority. It is better to substitute for this term that of " burden," which implies a fact objectively proved and not a judgment of value.

b. Nature of psychopathy

The degenerative psychopathic predisposition constitutes the great zone of limitation between health and psycho-mental disease, from which new and diverse forms of psychosis and neurosis constantly originate. But even the host of social deviations (criminality, vagabondage, prostitution, etc.) always receives new impetus from these substitute groups.

In this sense psychopathy does not represent a disease, but only a general disposition toward very diverse diseases.

In the psychopath, the disposition toward various psychoses, neuroses and other anomalies of development can be found *in potentia*. One or the other of these dispositions can, but need not necessarily, develop.

Here, the external circumstances of life play a role that is not to be overlooked. But a greater part is perhaps played by the internal variations that take place in the life of the psychopath. Up to the present time, too little attention has been given to these elements.

A controversial question is that of participation of the will. If the first tendency toward the morally false attachment is fulfilled without the collaboration of a personal act of the will, then the will is always more strongly impeded, the greater the deviation is fixed: " By the first we are free, by the second we are slaves " (Goethe, " Faust ").

The judgment concerning the volitive faculty is diverse. In unstable psychopaths, the will is undoubtedly very weak. In other psychopathic forms, as also in hysteria, a vigorous and inflexible force of will is often exteriorly manifested. However, a deeper examination of the same does not manifest a true force of will, but only lack of intelligence and ability to benefit from instruction.

The fact that the dispositions of psychopaths are very often ambivalent must not be overlooked; there is in them the possibility of not only developing toward the erratic side, but often toward the superior side.

Only some psychopaths succeed in overcoming the negative tendency and give free impulse to the positive. Up to what point they can succeed by their own power, and up to what point they need other help, is a question that is still to be studied.

Some psychopaths never overcome their internal conflict. They remain "incurables" or "not susceptible to betterment." They therefore belong to the class of the miserable and oppressed, whose internal dissension makes them appear particularly in need of that help which only supernatural powers can furnish.

Whether the psychopath accepts or rejects the help and denies himself supernatural aid is almost always more decisive for his fate than for the mentally normal.

This knowledge is basic—as much for the understanding of psychopathy and mental disturbances in general as, in particular, for psychotherapy.

2. SYMPTOMATOLOGY

a. Physical characteristics

Some psychopaths manifest physical characteristics, i.e., so-called signs of degeneracy, among which are the following: adherence of the ear lobes; incomplete involution of the helix (the so-called darwinian ear); the conditions in which the eyebrows grow together (synophrys); diversity of color in a part or parts that should normally be of one color (heterochromia), as in the two irides or in different parts of the same iris; the peculiar position of the pupil; fissure of the iris (colobma); high palate; abnormal forms of the nasopharynx; palatine fissure, malformation of the palate, harelip, defect of teeth formation; abnormal growth of hair (hypertrichosis, *lanugo persistens*); pigmentation anomalies (vitiligo, *albinismus*); the presence of supernumerary nipples (hyperthelia); gigantism or nanism; defects in the development of the cerebral column (e.g., *spina bifida*) and of the extremities; excessive number of fingers or toes (polydactylism) or phalanges (polyphalangism); congenital dislocations (mostly of the hip), etc.

Physical deformities, especially in the sphere of the genital organs: wrinkling of the scrotum (*membrum circumvallatum*), cryptorchism, hypospadias, epispadias in the male, genital atresia or duplications of all kinds in the female; bisexualism (hermaphroditism or pseudo-hermaphroditism).

Of the enumerated symptoms, the manifest deformities are to be considered as serious degenerative signs.

The minor anomalies are of no importance when they appear as isolated forms. But when numerous symptoms or, at least, several symptoms, manifest themselves, then these merit attention. The degenerative signs merit attention but are not to be overevaluated. They are symptoms which, when prudently evaluated, can furnish indices, but nothing more.

Not every person who is a bearer of such symptoms is to be considered "marked."

b. Mental characteristics

The most evident characteristic of a psychopath is that of lack of balance, the disharmony of his dispositions. This disharmony may be limited to an incongruity between the physical and mental faculties, by which the sphere of contact between body and soul is more or less seriously altered. This disharmony manifests itself from infancy.

Psychopaths are often difficult to educate. They are often hypersensitive in regard to their own person (hyperesthetic) and hence insensible to the world around them. They have "problematic natures"; they are persons "who suffer from the world or through whom the world suffers." For the most part, they are aware of their "being different"; they feel that they suffer much from life and are little adapted to life (feeling of insufficiency); and from this arises a disturbance of their estimation of themselves (feeling of inferiority). On the other hand, the psychopath often feels an accentuated need of succeeding and of making himself worth while.

This need of making himself worth while impels him to compensate for his incapacity in one sphere by exaggerated effort in another sphere (overcompensation). Some, as a result, succeed in laboriously re-establishing their mental balance. The impulse of interior inquietude renders others capable of outstanding endeavour. Others yet go off the path, suffer shipwreck, and through resentment assume a hostile attitude toward society (asocial). Some become criminals, delinquents, give themselves to prostitution, or end it all by suicide.

Criminal psychopaths distinguish themselves through high intelligence, courage and decision; others are very cowardly. The prostitutes are often of weak mind. So-called moral oligophrenia, inasmuch as it is not based upon a state of defect, is to be rather ascribed to psychopathy.

In contrast to these morally inferior persons who are often not capable of betterment, there are also found, among the psychopaths, personalities who occupy an eminent moral and intellectual position and who are indefatigable workers and even geniuses.

Certain psychopathic geniuses have given to the world the greatest works of the spirit. The permanent value of their activities depends on whether they dedicate their aptitudes toward the service of constructive ideas; if not, they have a destructive effect.

A number of psychopaths—as a result of the lability of their emotions—tend, sooner or later, toward profound mental disturbance. From these the army of neurotics is recruited. Finally, in others, a genuine psychosis, partly of endogenous origin (" reactive ") and partly of exogenous origin, develops on the basis of the prepsychotic personality.

c. Psychopathic types

The different types cannot be completely enumerated nor clearly distinguished. The doubtfulness of any typology appears particularly evident whenever there is an attempt to describe the various types of psychopathic personality.

According to the most pronounced characteristic, we are wont to distinguish: the emotionally labile, the impulsive, the compulsive; the weak-willed, abulics, maniacs, eccentrics, the asocial, those seeking to be accepted, the precocious (" wonder children "), the fantastic, dreamers, utopians, demagogues, radical extremists, fanatics, misanthropists, the exalted. In the realm of religion, we encounter the sectarians, bigots, miracle maniacs, ecstatics, eccentrics, reformers, redeemers of the people, egotists, the irascible, the misled, the misunderstood genius.

A dangerous type of impulsive is the explosive psychopath who at times tends to unforeseen " short-circuit action." Often the effects are incalculable and ruin the agent for his entire life, prescinding from the harm inflicted on the neighbor.

The " changing " psychopaths manifest in a clear manner the

"two souls in their heart." And their extreme characterization leads to a type of double life; an exchange between the phases of a morally and socially irreproachable life and that of a corrupt life.

The disassociation of the personality can reach the point that, in each individual phase, there is lacking almost all consciousness of the other phases (Kundry-type).

Criminal psychopaths can be divided into two classes: the occasional delinquent, in whom the short-circuit action which is not premeditated is predominant; and the cases of inexplicable crimes interpreted partly as "nostalgic reactions" (for example, incendiary acts, murder of children entrusted to psychopathic maids) and partly as reactions to sexual phases (menstruation, puberty, climacterium).

The hardened delinquent arises from a psychopathic type of moral insanity; he has been precociously corrupted, is difficult to educate and, for the most part, is incorrigible.

d. Psychopathic monomania

At one time, by monomania was understood the mental anomalies which presented themselves in an isolated manner and manifested themselves in a single morbid direction, apparently leaving intact mental sanity in the other spheres. They were wont to be classified as psychoses, since it was not known how else to classify them and they were considered "monosymptomatic" manias.

The following were cited as "monomanias" of this kind: the morbid mania for theft (kleptomania); the morbid mania for drink of the so-called intermittent drinkers (dipsomania); the mania for stupefacients (narcomania); the morbid mania to start fires (pyromania); homicidal mania; a sexual monomania and the morbidly exaggerated and insatiable sexual mania (erotomania) called satyriasis in the male and nymphomania in the female.

The idea of monomania as a disease *sui generis* has been abandoned. The phenomena described are nothing but symptoms of a general psychopathic predisposition.

e. Sexual psychopathy

It is comprehensible how psychopathy can express itself in a particularly intense manner in the sexual life. A certain psychopathic component is at the basis of all the phenomena of *psychopathia sexualis.*

Sexual psychopathy can express itself either in an abnormal intensity of the instinct, or in the abnormal direction of the same instinct (perversions). The anomalies of intensity and direction of the instinct can be combined.

In regard to the forms of expression of *psychopathia sexualis,* we refer to what is contained under the section on *Sexual pathology.*

In regard to the question whether, in these cases, it is a matter of a disease or vice, what has been said concerning narcomania is here applicable.

In an individual case, it is at times difficult to fix the limits of the concomitant factors; yet, when it is a case of psychopathy and not of mental disease, personal fault can almost never be excluded. The co-operation of personal guilt must, for the most part, be admitted.

3. CAUSES—CONCOMITANT FACTORS

Once the nature of psychopathy is known, it is then possible to evaluate the importance of all the factors which co-operate in its origin. The following are to be considered as such:

(1) Somatico-biological factors (endogeno-hereditary);
(2) Social factors (exogenous, environmental);
(3) Ethico-metaphysical factors.

a. Somatico-biological factors

Mention has already been made of the physical characteristics, the so-called signs of degeneration, of certain psychopaths. For a time, great importance was attributed to the signs of degeneration, especially by the anthropologico-criminal school (Cesare Lombroso), which held the theory of the born delinquent (*il delinquente nato*).

It was partly based on the older theory of Gall (phrenology). The cranium of the delinquent was established from characteristics of the skull. In like manner, Lombroso sought to establish the characteristics of the brain of the delinquent. This theory excluded free will and was therefore absolutely deterministic.

The same danger prevails today in heredo-biology in attempting to explain the origin of psychopathy exclusively by hereditary factors. The importance of the somato-biologico-hereditary factors in the origin of psychopathy cannot be underestimated. In certain cases it can be more preponderant than other factors, but it is never the only and exclusive factor.

Considering the multiplicity of the psychopathic predisposition, it is impossible to show that the hereditary course proceeds in a determined manner.

It is possible that a simple and general psychopathy appears in the first generation, a neurosis in the second generation and a serious psychosis in the third generation.

Such a hereditary succession presents a degenerative tendency. Yet, on the other hand, a regenerative tendency can also be observed.

b. Social factors

Since the dispositions of the psychopath are often ambivalent, so it can be of decisive importance to his fate whether he grows up in external circumstances in which the good dispositions must necessarily be stunted or, vice-versa, the bad dispositions are repressed and the development of the good dispositions favored. The seriously degenerate psychopath will remain unstable even in a favorable environment, but will not sink as deeply as he would in an unfavorable environment.

The overevaluation of the social factor leads to no less a deterministic view than that of the overevaluation of the hereditary factor. These look at the matter justly but in a unilateral manner. The unilateral overevaluation of the social factor is as wrong as the overevaluation of the biological factor. The two must be perceived in the light of their reciprocal relations.

c. Ethico-metaphysical factors

It is, however, not sufficient to recognize the concomitant action of the biological and social factors.

The moral aspect of the problem has been neglected. We have already evaluated the moral factor when we expressed our judgment concerning the problem of hysteria. Even here, a unilateral orientation would be erroneous.

Psychopathy does not constitute exclusively a moral problem.

Otherwise, an injustice would be inflicted upon the diseased by burdening him with all the responsibility and by attributing to him the complete guilt of his aberrations. He has a more difficult life than others. But he is nevertheless responsible and cannot be completely exonerated from guilt.

His accountability can vary from full responsibility to that of diminished responsibility. But this responsibility is never fully removed; otherwise, his would no longer be the limited state of psychopathy, but that of mental disease.

In the matter of personal sin, the personal responsibility of the precedessors must be taken into consideration, and this, not only in the sense of heredity, concerning which we have already spoken, nor in the sense of original sin (cf. below), but also in that particular sense according to which the descendants are still participants of the good mental qualities of their predecessors just as, in the same way, they suffer from their transgressions.

Mental forces and irradiations can produce lasting effects. Mental acquisitions and productions are not lost. This goes as much for good as for evil. Thus the problem of the heredity of acquired characteristics, which seemed already resolved, appears in a new light.

Besides the personal guilt—which is never completely removed—we must take into account the imposing metaphysical factor of original sin.

Only one who has grasped its significance and realized the corruption of human *natura vulnerata* (*spoliatus in supranaturalibus—vulneratus in naturalibus*), will realize its importance for the uninterrupted occurrence of psychopathic deviations. This realization makes clear the limited possibility of removing psychopathy by means of eugenics.

In general, it is impossible to eliminate hereditary diseases; if we limit ourselves to those cases with an absolutely unfavorable hereditary prognosis, the number of cases would then be few and an eugenic effect could not be expected. New taints would follow from the reservoir of limited cases and psychopathies. But if the suppression is to be extended to all those limited cases in which the arising of new taints is possible, then where is one to begin and where is one to end?

Finally, it must be realized that, even by means of a radical criterion, one cannot completely eliminate all that is potentially pathological. One would eliminate, together with the pathological elements, a number of valuable aptitudes.

4. UNIVERSALISTIC CONCEPTION OF THE PROBLEM

Only the universalistic criterion leads to a satisfactory solution of the problem, since it alone takes into account all the co-operative factors and neither underestimates nor overestimates any of the factors.

This leads to the only just point of view regarding the practical consequences of theoretical knowledge. It removes itself from the optimism of the social eudaemonists, who see the solution to the problem exclusively in the elevation of the social environment. It likewise removes itself from the pessimism of hereditary determinism, which takes into account only hereditary disease, in which the germinative plasma is degenerated, and hence excludes any possibility of a correction in the sense of regeneration. Nor can the just view adhere to a naïve optimism which believes in the possibility of removing the origin of hereditary disease by suppressive means. Moreover, hereditary factors are only one of the tributary veins— the poisoned source is always the *natura vulnerata*.

On the other hand, it is not pessimistic to consider these damages incurable in the individual case, since full consideration is to be taken of the supernatural factor and the fact of redemption and grace, which overcomes every weakness and corruption of human nature.

Only by adopting this mode of consideration can we attain the conclusive crowning which is that of the universal treatment. And only this renders possible the solution to the problems of psychotherapy and leads to a removal of errors and erroneous psychotherapy and points the way to a true psychotherapy.

5. PASTORAL QUESTIONS

From the pastoral viewpoint, what has been said of hysteria can be said also of psychopathy.

The counsels which are to be given to the spiritual director by the doctor follow automatically from the universalistic mode of observation of Pastoral Medicine. These have been explained at the beginning of the section on general psychopathology and

N

especially at the end of the section on psychopathic predisposition.

In the observance of these principles, the spiritual director will find the proper middle road between optimism and pessimism; he will not be extremely confident, but will always evaluate psychopaths for what they are and will moderate their exuberant repentance and proposals without abandoning them to excessive hope. Above all, he will act with necessary reserve toward those who are not manifestly susceptible to betterment. However, the confessor should never become hard and rough—he must not break the " bent pipe nor extinguish the glimmering wick."

Despite the required reserve, he will enclose them in his heart as special children, having always an intimate sympathy for them and distinguishing among them the burdened and oppressed. Finally, in regard to those who do not seem susceptible to betterment, he should never lose hope that the power of the supernatural can still be effective even after all natural power has failed. Even here, the expression *gratia supponit naturam* prevails: grace is joined to nature. But this must not be misunderstood in the sense that in these tainted persons there no longer exists any fragment of nature to which grace can be joined or that grace presupposes the health of nature. Such an idea would again introduce the error of predestination in the modern dress of heredo-biology. Inasmuch as the pastoral treatment of psychopaths seems at first glance to require enormous sacrifice and little satisfaction, we must not completely forget those psychopathic natures in which—by reuniting intelligently all the active factors in a tenacious effort— the negative tendencies will be overcome and the positive tendencies will be nourished; a noble end for the spiritual director in union with therapeutic pedagogy and psychotherapy.

C. FUNDAMENTAL QUESTIONS OF PSYCHOTHERAPY

I. General view

1. THE NATURE OF PSYCHOTHERAPY

Psychotherapy is the intelligent activation of mental powers for the purpose of curing the sick.

In this sense, it has a decisive part in all the morbid processes.

This mode of considering psychotherapy has its basis in the acknowledgment of the principle: *anima forma corporis.*

In this latter sense, the doctor always makes use of psychotherapy —whether he treats physical illness or neurosis. True or genuine psychoses are, up to the present time, inaccessible to psychotherapy.

In a limited sense, psychotherapy is understood as the specific therapeutic method for functional and psychogenic disturbances, especially in the case of neurosis. One must not lose sight of the fact that the concept of psychotherapy is, in reality, more comprehensive. One cannot accept an obscure terminology which indicates by the same designation the simple treatment of neurosis and magical or supernatural intervention. The definition "activation of the psychic forces" is universal and includes all the psychotherapeutic phenomena within the natural order, from the treatment of neurosis to the confines of supernatural intervention. This latter does not pertain to psychotherapy.

Within this extensive realm, a clear distinction of concepts is necessary. In the sense here defined, psychotherapy plays an important role even in the cure of organic disturbances. It suffices to think of the course of virus pneumonia or of preparatory and follow-up treatment on the occasion of a serious operation. The course can decisively depend upon the mental constitution of the sick. This can, however, in turn be decisively influenced by the action and comportment of the doctor and by the environment, and this favorably or unfavorably.

2. THE PERSONALITY OF THE DOCTOR

The personality of the doctor plays an important role in the general therapy. Without a personal relation between doctor and patient which inspires confidence, the successful outcome is problematic. This relation does not imply a lessening of the necessary distance. On the contrary, removal of this distance can destroy confidence. In psychotherapy, the personality of the doctor is of absolute and decisive importance. But from this special danger can arise an element which can endanger the required distance. Psychoanalysis designates as "transference" the erotic attachment which can easily arise, especially between a female patient and the doctor. The internal fixation which results can be favorable for the purpose of a cure, provided the transference is interrupted at the proper time. Effacement of or passing over the confines is always dangerous and harmful.

However, the personality of the doctor is of still greater importance in another sense. In many cases, psychotherapy signifies an internal transformation. This requires that the doctor insert his whole personality. Here, of greatest importance, is the *Weltanschauung* of the doctor.

If the mental disturbances arise from those strata of the personality which are disturbed by deficient orientation of life, then the doctor is called upon to re-establish the proper orientation. His task becomes quasi-spiritual. This aspect can be fulfilled by him only when he himself is properly orientated.

The doctor should not be a substitute for the spiritual director but, on the contrary, should as little as possible deal with such problems. But today these present themselves more often than ever. Neurotics lacking faith seek, to their harm, the doctor when they are more in need of a priest.

In the majority of cases, the doctor cannot refuse this task as long as the sick do not go to a priest. Thus he is forced to exercise, for a time, the functions of a spiritual director. His work is crowned with success when the sick person, under his discreet direction, finds his way to the priest.

3. PSYCHOTHERAPY AND NEUROSIS— THE PURPOSE OF PSYCHOTHERAPY

Even though psychotherapy is not basically limited to the sphere of neurosis, this is its principal domain.

The predominant position of psychotherapy over all the other therapeutic measures is most impressively manifested when the neurosis is revealed as the effect of a deficient orientation of life. In such cases, psychotherapy not only can attain results, but we can directly affirm that it alone can attain a cure.

Psychotherapy must include the proper and adequate objective, and must make use of a proper method: the objective must be psychic conversion—the proper orientation of life—and the method must be adapted and subordinated to this objective.

The lack of this orientation is the most profound cause of neurosis and anxiety of life which characterizes our time.

If one succeeds in understanding that neurosis is—in many

respects—merely the expression of the fact that man has lost the real meaning of life, then the true task and method of psychotherapy will easily be comprehended.

Schultz distinguishes between "heterogeneous neurosis" (arising from situations harmful to life), strata neurosis, marginal neurosis, and, finally, nuclear neurosis. The latter affect the very core or nucleus of the personality and lead to serious personality defects, which present a difficult problem for psychotherapy. According to Schultz, neurosis is the effect of an unfruitful life. With reason, therefore, does Hengstenberg assert that neurosis can be considered a form of the proof of the existence of God (cf. Caruso, Daim). Thus there exist unknown relationships between certain heresies and the propensity for neurosis. Here we are to define neurosis as the expression of an unresolved conflict between the unconscious lower psychic strata, that is, the id, and the higher conscious personality. The object of psychotherapy should be, above all, to render conscious the unconscious roots of this conflict and, in this manner, to "abreact" the unconscious and disturbing elements (complexes), thus rendering them innocuous (psychocatharsis). In neurosis are found elemental psychic forces which are falsely bound together. The object of psychotherapy is that of loosening these false bonds and directing the patient in realizing the image of his personality. It is essential, in order to attain this end, that the anxiety manifested toward God be converted to a proper fear of God and that the resistance to God be eliminated. One who fights this "just battle" will more easily bear all the failures and repulses of life.

Neurosis can also be of fate, and when this is so, it must be borne willingly. Here is a task which offers the occasion of heroically overcoming oneself. Inasmuch as neurosis is the expression of conscience, it is comprehensible how the mentally solid person is almost never affected by a neurosis. Whether this is an enviable privilege is a question not yet decided. One who has obtained a clear insight into the nature of neurosis will himself find the answer to this question.

4. METHODS OF PSYCHOTHERAPY

The fundamental importance of method arises from what has already been stated. Method and end are not inseparable. They correspond in their essence. Hence a critique of the different psycho-therapeutic methods must likewise take their ends into consideration. The end or objective will be determined by the ideological orientation, and not to take this into consideration would make it impossible to form a judgment.

The following is only a brief exposition of the more important methods which have been proposed:

(1) Psychophysical methods:
   Rational methods and non-rational methods.
(2) Suggestive methods:
   Hypnosis and suggestion;
   Auto-suggestion;
   Persuasion.
(3) Analytical methods:
   Psychoanalysis.
(4) Individual psychology.
(5) Analytico-synthetic methods and psychagogic methods:
   " Complex psychology " (Jung).

In conclusion, an attempt is to be made to outline the object and method of a universalistic Catholic psychotherapy.

II. Special view

1. PSYCHOPHYSICAL METHODS

By psychophysical methods, we are to understand those methods of psychotherapy which propose to activate the psychic forces from the somatic aspect (psychosomatic). This can be effected in a " rational " manner and with the help of so-called non-rational methods. These latter not only do not direct themselves to reason, but tend consciously to exclude rational reflection.

In any case, their mode of operation makes difficult a fully rational investigation of their cause.

a. Non-rational methods

To these belong, above all, many quackish and pseudo-medical methods. Inasmuch as they are definitely fraudulent and deceptive, they cannot be called non-rational, nor can they be considered as psychotherapy.

" Popular medicine " makes use of several procedures which are extraneous to scientific medicine and which, from the rational standpoint, are to be considered quackish, but which nevertheless are, to a certain degree, able to mobilize certain forces.

Liek designates these methods with the word " magic." A rational explanation of them is impossible. These methods do not even belong to the realm of the marvelous.

To what extent certain psychotherapeutists who work with the "imposition of hands " and similar symbolical actions make use of non-rational methods or tend instead to obtain supernatural cures through prayer, is a question that will be studied later.

b. Rational methods

Here we are substantially concerned with the attempt to therapeutically influence the mentally disturbed, on the basis of scientific consideration, by a physical process.

As an example, we recall the treatment of war neurotics (the tremulous, agitated and paralytic) practiced in its time, which for a long period was also used in the treatment of so-called accident neurosis.

The primitiveness of the remedy corresponds with the primitive mechanism of the neurosis: the application of strong faradic currents which produced a pain sufficient to break the barrier and constrain the neurotic to abandon his resistance and attachment. The remedy, in the simplicity of its structure, corresponds to the use of blows on psychopathic children. In certain cases this is successful, but in many other cases its failure is inevitable.

The idea of exercising an influence upon the psyche by physical means is not erroneous. In certain cases, good results can be obtained when one sustains the altered psyche from the physical side. The following pertain to this method: exercise therapy, work therapy, the cures of repose in cases of neurasthenia from exhaustion, etc. Of special importance is physical therapy. This works not only through objective-specific therapeutic action but also through the co-operation of a subjectively psychotherapeutic component. This is of a complex nature.

Together with suggestive elements, there arise the confidence of the patient, his mental preparation and co-operation, and his willingness to get well.

Rightly understood, the psychophysical methods are, in reality, more complicated than they appear. They offer a probability of success only if applied in a manner which is not simply mechanistic.

2. METHODS OF SUGGESTION

a. Suggestion and hypnosis

Here we are to evaluate solely the use of these methods in psychotherapy and not their relation to the phenomena of parapsychology (for example, somnambulism, telepathy). Suggestion is the mental influencing of a subject through the power of another's will. We can imagine it as an irradiation. There are mental energies: thoughts, ideas, acts of the will. The reciprocal influence which people exercise upon each other through this means is a completely common daily phenomenon. Even the simple word and the printed word serve this scope. The possibility of reciprocal influence is the basis of every form of common life. Suggestion, in the strict sense, is the influence exercised in a particularly obvious manner upon another by means of the presentation of determined intellectual contents.

This can arise, exclusively, through thoughts or even through words (mental suggestion and verbal suggestion). It can be the operation of another person or that of one's own ego, which attempts to influence, by means of suggestion, one's own id (heterosuggestion and auto-suggestion).

Finally, it can arise in a state of consciousness or, more easily, by means of provoking an artificial state of sleep (trance, hypnosis), suggestion while awake and hypnotic suggestion. If the suggestive character of a determined measure is hidden from the patient, we speak of a masked suggestion. Basically, suggestion is possible in any subject, yet suggestibility is subject to notable differences of degree.

Suggestion takes place more easily in subjects of a labile nervous system in whom it is often easier to eliminate the critique of conscience. Yet it is often the psychopathic and neuropathic personalities who offer strong resistance (apparent strong wills), to suggestion and hypnosis.

Hysterical subjects are often difficult to hypnotize. Subjects of extraordinary high suggestibility are especially useful for hypnotic experiments. A cumulative increase of suggestibility also takes place in mass gatherings (mass suggestion).

The strong influence of suggestion also manifests itself clearly in the somatic effects of an influenced action of a purely psycho-spiritual nature. For example, one can, through purely suggestive means, provoke erythema and swelling of the skin.

The action of several superstitious therapeutic procedures (for example, "conjurings") is to be considered as suggestion.

In hypnosis an artificial state of sleep is provoked, in which suggestions are effected. For this purpose, a mental relation between the one hypnotizing and the hypnotized is required: so-called rapport. The diverse depth of hypnotic sleep (degree of suggestion) is indicated by the following scale: somnolence, hypotaxia, somnambulism. If in one of these degrees rigidity takes place, we speak of catalepsy. This is also present in hysteria and in catatonia.

If the hypnotic suggestion continues even after the subject awakens, we then speak of a posthypnotic suggestion or of "mandates." These can also involve, in certain cases, even a part in crime. It is, however, generally held that it is not possible, through the post-hypnotic mandate, to induce a person of solid moral principles to crime. The moral inhibitions exercise too strong a resistance. Such inducement is possible in determined circumstances only with persons of moral lability.

It is controversial whether one can be hypnotized against one's will. The question has a bearing in regard to those crimes in which the accused professes to have been "railroaded" into committing the act. If such a hypnosis takes place, it is scarcely comprehensible how during it a crime of carnal violence (stuprum) can take place. It must, in that case, be that internal resistance is lacking. But in the case of narcosis or serious alcoholism, such a possibility must, on the contrary, be affirmed.

As a psychotherapeutic method, suggestion has a very important role, especially in the form of hypnosis. Not all neurotics—or, better, not all the sick—are suited for this method.

It is controversial whether, to attain therapeutic success, a light degree of hypnosis is sufficient, or whether hypnotic sleep is neces-sary. But even concerning this point, a general answer cannot be given. Yet, since hypnosis represents for the nervous system an intervention that is far from being indifferent, we ought to use the lowest degree in which success is guaranteed. In general, when suggestibility is very great, a minor degree of sleep is sufficient.

N*

The degree of somnambulism must be avoided as much as possible. Still the hypnotizer does not always have control of the dose. The subjects of hysteria offer at times great resistance to hypnotism; but once this resistance is broken, they quickly fall into a deep sleep.

The situation is just as dangerous as the narcosis of hysterical subjects and alcoholics. It is difficult or impossible to hypnotize very excitable persons.

The accurate choice of cases is necessary for the success of the method. The doctor must know what he can expect from the procedure and must realize the limitations.

The methods seem to be most successful in those ailments which arise either from a purely psychogenic basis or those which are originally organic, but are superimposed by others of psychogenic origin.

But even pains of organic origin can often be notably mitigated in suggestible patients, and this even when a functional disturbance is such because the patient has lost confidence in himself and no longer trusts the function—as, for example, in various disturbances in walking and speaking and also in severe cases of vaginismus. If one succeeds in convincing the patient, by means of suggestion (hypnotic or awake), that he can walk or talk without any difficulty, then the barrier is broken. At times great success has been attained in the case of the stutterer.

Hypnotism is not free of danger. It should be exclusively reserved to the experienced specialist. Only he is able to weigh the pros and cons and judge and control every single phase. The prohibition of experimentations and hypnotic exhibitions in public is completely justified. In the hands of a competent person, the dangers are minimized but in the hands of an incompetent person, hysterical attacks, convulsive states, neurosis which can be of permanent harm, are very possible.

Late damages, that is, those which occur after a certain free interval, have not been observed.

b. Auto-suggestion and similar methods

Auto-suggestion tends to make the sick independent of the co-operation of suggestive influence exercised by another and places at his disposal the therapeutic forces of his own soul.

The forces of his spirit and will must subject to his control the subconscious mechanisms which foster sickness.

Just as, by auto-suggestion, damaging influences can arise—a process which is important in the case of hypochondria—so it is possible that a favorable influence can be exercised.

Auto-suggestion was formed into a psychotherapeutic system by the pharmacist Coué of Nancy (self-control by means of conscious auto-suggestion). This system was supposed to cure by suggestion not only purely psychogenic disturbances, but also organic diseases. The success of each case depends upon the measure in which the activation of psychic forces take place.

J. H. Schultz has proposed the designation "autogenous training" in order to indicate the control of the vegetative nervous system obtained by means of conscious training of the will and by means of "concentrative auto-relaxation." But this designation does not render an account of the complications of the processes.

The success obtained by several therapists who cure by suggestion shows that the possibility of affecting even the organic sphere by means of auto-suggestive activation should not be underestimated.

c. Persuasion

Persuasion (Dubois) also belongs to the suggestive methods. It consists in the appeal to the rational understanding of the sick. It attempts, for example, to make it clear to the person who is simply psychogenically sick that the sickness has no organic basis and, by so doing, to restore the courage to live and self-confidence. It seeks to persuade not so much by words as by conviction. By this means, the desired activation is fulfilled.

It is important to carefully select the cases adapted to this method. Otherwise, failures are inevitable. This method appeals to the intelligence, the *ratio*, of the sick.

Thus its efficacy is limited, since the method does not extend to the unconscious.

3. ANALYTICAL METHODS

It is a common trend of the analytical methods to manifest the elements that lie in the unconscious, that is, the elements of the profound personality. Insofar as they may be interpreted as pathological complexes, this disclosure should make them again accessible to the patient's consciousness. In this way, they lose their power to produce sickness or neurosis. They are "abreacted."

a. Cathartic methods

The cathartic method established by Breuer is based upon this fundamental idea. Breuer made use of hypnosis to reveal repressed complexes. His objective was to allow the patient through hypnosis to relive the disagreeable situation, the repression of which occasioned the emotional fixation.

A *vaginismus* of purely psychic origin which renders a woman incapable of fulfilling her matrimonial duty, could, for example, be traced in this way to its root. So, likewise, a purely psychogenic *hyperemesis gravidarum* or any other kind of hysterical vomiting.

b. Psychoanalysis

(a) *Doctrinal content*

Psychoanalysis, founded by Freud and his school, has further developed the cathartic method. It distinguishes itself especially in this: that, instead of using hypnosis, it accomplishes recollection with the aid of free association. Analysis is to be effected in the greatest physical and mental relaxation possible.

Both disturbed acts and dreams are important in leading to the unconscious.

The manifestation of "resistance" can give very important indications.

The "transference" which is established between doctor and patient can be made useful in the overcoming of the resistance. The provocation of a phase of affective reaction appears to be indispensable for a successful outcome.

Even a phase of hate (negative transference) can, through ambivalence, develop from transference. For the therapeutist the dangerous possibility is that of a possibility of a "contra-transference" which he fixes on the patient and eventually allows to pass over into "contra-analysis." In such a case, the therapeutist has lost the game.

When analysis succeeds, then the removal from the transference takes place in the final phase and the patient is liberated from the therapeutist.

If the patient is then capable of mentally standing on his own feet, the object of the analysis is fulfilled.

Analysis requires much time in order to fulfill its objective, at least many months, ordinarily a year, and often even more than two years (with one or two visits a week and of about one hour's duration).

In the recollection of the unconscious, psychoanalysis makes use of antagonism (resistance-transference) and above all of the dream as the *via regia*.

The interpretation of the dream symbolism is basically and definitely sexual. It is especially sought in an infantile sexual trauma.

The classical analysis has, in this sphere, used much effort in dividing the infantile libido into an oral, anal and genital phase, as well as into the phase of narcissism and that of relative auto-eroticism, and has employed the sexual interpretation of vital manifestations of the infant which, up to that time, were considered harmless (for example, the sucking of the thumb as equivalent to ipsation, etc.).

In regard to the relation between parents and children, a sexual interpretation has been given, and this partly in the sense of an incestuous disposition of the libido.

Hence the Oedipus complex plays an important role as the primary complex of every neurosis: the libidinous bond of the mother with her son, and eventually of the daughter with the father.

The occurrence of neurosis depends on whether and to what extent one emancipates oneself from this complex. This is most difficult for individuals who have fixations from infancy.

They create an elusive position through " regression into infancy " in the face of the demands of life.

Sublimation plays an important role in psychoanalysis: the energies of the libido which are not transformed into sexual activity can be sublimated into creative spiritual activity.

(b) *Degeneracy and abuse*

Many of Freud's doctrines which we have enumerated have been partly exaggerated and partly executed in a strange manner. A serious danger was found in " lay analysis ": the opposition of Freud to academic psychiatry gave occasion to the intervention of persons who were not doctors. A disagreeable form in which this tendency was manifested was the psychoanalytical circles in which persons of both sexes made their most hidden intimacies the object of their decadent entertainment.

Even serious medical analysts were not always free from abusing the methods. Reports concerning the early period of analysis show that strong sexual excitement was provoked in patients by inconsiderate procedure.

Many works of analytical authors of that era concerning religious questions contained a diabolical characteristic. (Reid and others.)

The nature of the gross interpretation produced the impression of obscenity and blasphemy.

(c) *Judgment*

The value of a method need not be judged on the basis of its degeneracy and abuses. No doubt psychoanalysis has given a valuable and positive enrichment to our knowledge.

Insight into the processes which take place in the unconscious has been notably deepened, and many of the sexual interpretations of psychoanalysis cannot be rejected *a limine*.

The exaggeration of considering the sexual correlations discovered by psychoanalysis as the exclusive factors in the origin of neurosis and even of unconscious mental life in general (as if—besides the sexual factor—there were no other concomitant factor) is to be rejected (so-called pansexualism).

The exclusive use of a deficient methodology in revealing the hidden side of the psychic life, bringing on a destructive effect without any constructive tendency, and thus offending against the dignity of man whenever transference is abused, is to be rejected.

Psychoanalysis is to be rejected when it is based upon a materialistic conception of the universe; when it is founded upon false fundamental presuppositions, as when it acknowledges neither the immaterial and substantial nature of the soul, nor the fact of the fallen state of human nature. It is to be rejected when it denies the immortality of the soul, the supernatural end of life and, with it, moral responsibility, and finally, when it is practiced by doctors who tend not only toward materialism, but also open atheism— who are, in fact, hostile to religion.

As long as psychoanalysis was dominated by this ideology, it represented a revolt of the underworld of the soul against the spirit, and Freud's words "Acheronta movebo" take on an increased symbolic meaning.

We are beginning, little by little, to acquire the necessary perspective for the proper evaluation of psychoanalysis. By examining it without prejudice, it manifests itself as a "euristic principle" of inestimable value. The importance of the unconscious, the relation of the Es to the ego and to the super-ego, the theory of repression, of psychocatharsis, of sublimation of the libido, etc., retain their importance.

Even the theory of infantile sexuality, despite certain repugnant elements, has a great instructive value. The theory of the libidinous character of the relations between parents and children, upon first sight strongly rejected, when calmly examined and reduced to its proper limitations, merits serious consideration.

But great prudence and precautions against an exaggerated interpretation of the concept of libido are indispensable. It is to be acknowledged without restriction that psychoanalysis, with its theory of the Oedipus complex, has come to coincide with the "archtype" of the psychic conflict.

As yet, psychoanalysis has not progressed beyond the sexual interpretation into a deeper metaphysical interpretation.

We have already attempted elsewhere to show that this is nothing more than the problem of original sin—the original cause of all guilt feelings, of every disease and of every disturbance of order; the rebellion against God, the Father of all (as the so-called "image of the father"), with the idea of possessing unlimited dominion over the "mother" (nature). This is the deepest symbolism of the Oedipus myth: hence, Oedipus is punished with blindness and deprived of the supernatural light of knowledge.

There is no further need of demonstrating the fullness of light that psychoanalysis will acquire through this knowledge nor of showing how its indisputable natural knowledge can attain its full cognitive value through this means. And inversely, it cannot be denied that the knowledge acquired through psychoanalysis can signify an inestimable benefit, even for traditional Catholic psychology (cf. Ringel, van Lun). It would be wrong to deprecate those elements of psychoanalysis which contain correct connotations. A proper knowledge of truth, wherever it is found, belongs to the totality of the knowledge of truth of all times.

Catholic science encounters in psychoanalysis an analogous situation to that in which St. Thomas found himself in regard to the philosophy of Aristotle, which was at first rejected as pagan and even anti-christian.

St. Thomas, by purifying the philosophy of Aristotle from the errors of paganism and by preserving the full richness of its truths —which were worthy of abiding as a *philosophia perennis*—incorporated Aristotelian thought in Christian philosophy, and rendered the latter one of the greatest possible services.

(d) *Pastoral questions: Analysis and confession*

Attention has been called to the definite analogy between the analytical method and confession. Without doubt such an analogy exists, but it is only peripheral. This manifests itself basically in psychocartharsis.

The liberating and purifying effect of verbal declaration upon the most secret wounds of the soul has been acknowledged. The things that are brought from the depth of consciousness, and which are acknowledged and expressed, lose much force. The elimination of the cramped state of the mind can effect an activation of psychic forces.

This realization has given occasion even in non-Catholic circles to a demand for the reintroduction of free, private confession. But psychoanalysis can in no way substitute for the action of authentic sacramental confession accompanied by the will to acknowledge one's sins before God.

The substitution of the doctor for a spiritual adviser is of questionable and doubtful advantage for the unbelieving (cf. above).

Above all, there are lacking in psychoanalysis the essential requirements for the action of confession: supernatural sorrow (contrition and attrition) and the firm purpose of amendment. Only a true conversion, added to these, forms the necessary basis for a real reconstruction of the psychic life.

The sacramental character of confession is essential: the mediation of the supernatural action of grace, based upon (1) the natural and visible fact of acknowledgment of sin before the priest (in the place of God) and (2) absolution.

Thus, even if the analogies, on superficial observation, appear stronger than the deep differences, psychoanalysis can never be a substitute for confession. It can, however, in unison with the super-natural means of salvation, be very valuable and, even, in certain cases and when rightly conducted, irreparable as a natural means.

Confession cannot and will not be a substitute for psychotherapy when psychotherapy is necessary. The object of confession is sin—that is, infractions of moral law which are conscious and freely willed.

The object of psychotherapy is, on the other hand, neurosis—that is, conflicts buried in the unconscious, between the "depth personality" and the ego.

Hence a clear distinction is necessary: not an *aut . . . aut* but a *tantum . . . quantum*.

It is therefore an error to hold that a Christian has no need of psychotherapy; for inasmuch as he is neurotic, he does have need of it, on condition that it is adequate in his case.

Otherwise, a stone instead of bread would be given to him.

4. INDIVIDUAL PSYCHOLOGY

a. Doctrinal content

The "individual psychology" founded by Adler belongs, because of its nature, to the analytical methods. Yet it occupies a very special place.

While Freud attempts to explain the nature of man and his deviations more from a causal standpoint, Adler strives to explain the same from a "final" standpoint and interpretation. This is sought in the relation of the individual to the community. In this is found the synthetic-pedagogic method, especially when the individual has to be removed from his deviating behaviour and be incorporated into society.

Adler tries to discover the "directive line," the "plan of life." According to his opinion, the "will to power" plays the most fundamental role. The "feeling of inferiority" spurs this at times in an intense pathological manner.

There arises the desire for compensation and, eventually, of over-compensation. When this fails, it leads, through excessive stress, to neurosis, to discouragement and, especially in "unadapted subjects," to resentment and an asocial state. The subject seeks even more to attain security. Hostile and asocial attitudes isolate the subject from society.

Besides the individualistic will to power, one of his most primitive impulses is the feeling of belonging in the community. Return to mental health comes through right order, and adjustment to the community. This gives mental courage to man and effects in him the consciousness of his self-worth.

The ideological basis of individual psychology is essentially as earthly as that of traditional psychoanalysis. It is closely related to socialism inasmuch as it overestimates the exogenous and environmental influences and underestimates the endogenous factors. Its harm is based on the fact that spiritual and supernatural factors have no place in it. It has been based on a purely social-eudaemonistic and utilitarian element. Religious and spiritual values were for it mostly an ideological superstructure which in many aspects was seen as nothing more than an escape from reality—hence the same thing that the ideology of the class struggle designated as "the opium of the people." Original sin is denied and all evil is considered merely a consequence of social influences.

From this arises a boundless optimism in regard to education, almost like that of Rousseau and the belief in an earthly paradise which man is able to procure of himself. The religious idea of the future life is considered in the same manner as in psychoanalysis—that is, as an "autistic wish-fulfillment."

Individual psychology seeks to educate man in the observance of the commandment of love for neighbor and thus to incorporate him into the order of the community. But if this does not tend, at the same time, to love of God, this striving, as a simple social system of education, remains in the terrestrial realm.

Among others, Ringel has shown how individual psychology can be useful in a Catholic psychotherapy.

b. Evaluation

Individual psychology, like psychoanalysis, has enriched and deepened our knowledge with certain definite observations. But even it has tended toward partiality and overevaluation of partial factors.

Hence, even it can attain only partial success and can never lead to a total comprehension and solution of the questions which proceed from it.

5. SYNTHETIC AND PSYCHAGOGIC METHODS

a. Complex psychology (C. G. Jung)

Among the methods which tend toward a comprehensive conception, that of C. G. Jung is to be especially noted. It was originally designated by its author as an "analytical psychology." Later, the designation "complex psychology" came into use. Its starting point was similar to that of the analytical methods.

Jung strove to take greater account of the endogenous, hereditary congenital factors. In the place of "free association" of psychoanalysis, he applied the "attempt of association" with the help of the "stimulus words": conclusions concerning deep psychic fundamental behavior were made from characteristic reactions.

The central idea of Jungian psychology is the "collective unconscious," the totality of the primitive psychic experiences of mankind. The dream offers an access to the research of psychic life. In the dream interpretation, Jung values the fact that in dreams the primordial instincts of humanity are manifested, together with fantastic activity.

According to Jung, religions are derived from the natural life of the unconscious mind and, in a certain manner, more or less adequately express this unconscious. He distinguishes two principal types: the extrovert and the introvert type. For the introvert, the contrast with the world, a contrast which can extend even to self-annihilation (prophets, martyrs), is characteristic.

In any case, Jung is right when he does not consider the totality of the psyche to be in the consciousness of the ego.

With regard to neurosis, Jung concluded that neurosis does not merely signify something negative, but also something positive. The patient must learn, not how to free himself from it, but how to bear it: what it teaches, its meaning and its purpose. Neurosis is a curative attempt of nature. The complete removal of neurosis would signify "purchasing the soul" for the patient, which is basically impossible since one cannot betake oneself from his own shadow.

What is manifested in neurosis is the part of the personality which is not recognized, which seeks to impose its recognition.

This curious theory of neurosis strives to point out to psychotherapists that they should tend toward the self-education of the patient. But, as we shall explain later, it seems to us that the problem of self-liberation from nervous illness can only be resolved in the sense of co-operation with the power of grace.

Jung does not stop at analysis, but requires the "guidance of the soul." Thus the "problem of guidance" is in the foreground of psychotherapy. It is already indicated in the "transference" of psychoanalysis.

For Jung, psychotherapy becomes psychagogic, and its object will be the discipline and strengthening of the soul. Thus analytical psychology will lead to psychosynthesis.

b. "German psychotherapy"

Included in the "synthetic tendency is the so-called "German psychotherapy," which is based upon the conception of unity of body and soul, in the sense that has already been criticized (Klages, Prinzhorn).

This trend, which required a psychotherapy colored by nationality, was introduced by Goering, Künkel and others. They made use essentially of the ideas of the psychoanalysis which they rejected. As a system or ideology, it does not offer uniformity. Heyer sees in the Christian doctrine of body and soul an antagonist of the "theory of totality" (Ganzheitslehre), since, not knowing the Scholastic doctrine, he holds extreme dualism as Christian doctrine.[1]

The designation "psychosynthesis" was used by Paneth and others in order to accentuate the opposition to psychoanalysis. On the other hand, it must be stated that a true synthesis is not possible if it is not preceded by analysis and that true psychotherapy never stops at analysis, but always tends toward a synthetic "construction."

The "construction" to which the German psychotherapy aspired—in accordance with the idea of individual psychology—was conceived as an "incorporation" into the community of folk and race, and the "construction" was crowned by this incorporation.

Certain authors associated with this trend tended toward the extreme in considering the doctor, in the service of the folk community, as the spiritual director of the future and believed that no other form of spiritual direction would be necessary (Grosschopf). However, certain authors have also acknowledged that, even from

[1] Cf. Schema (MSS. p. 289).

remote times, psychotherapy was realized in religion: the true "edification" is psychic construction. Had it not directed itself to God, it would have lost its meaning.

From this latter conception, it is only one step to the universalistic conception, to acknowledgment of the supernatural finality of human life, and to acknowledgment of the primary and fundamental importance of the supernatural community, without which ultimate assurance mental health would not be possible.

Only when the natural community is absorbed and elevated to the supernatural community of the Mystical Body is the path for a universalistic psychotherapy open.

c. Precursors of a universalistic psychotherapy

The way which leads to a universalistic psychotherapy has been already prepared. Ever more numerous and clearer are the voices which affirm that there cannot be an authentic psychotherapy which does not make the spiritual problems and the moral values of life the object of observation and which does not recognize that the essential task is that of re-establishing the order and harmony of this aspect of life. Thus Bezdek definitely required an ethico-therapy. Henri Baruk required a mental reconstruction on the basis of moral piety. Weizäcker, Tournier and others demanded a medicine of the complete personality (*médecine de la personne*). Bingswanger required the transformation of psychoanalysis into "existential analysis." The first important step in the direction of a universalistic psychotherapy was made by Victor E. Frankl.

He bases his "existential analysis" upon the freedom and responsibility of the human race. He seeks a "logotherapy" which does not treat the matter "from beneath," from the unconscious (id), but "from above," from the aspect of spiritual man.

If psychoanalysis has, with prejudice, designated only a "look from the depths," so the danger of only "looking from above" must also be avoided.

This danger would be present if "logotherapy" were to forget that it should merely complete and not repress the psychotherapy of the unconscious.

The accomplishments of depth psychology, as long as they are verified, can and ought to be incorporated and posited as a basis of a universalistic psychotherapy.

On the basis of these inferior strata, the therapy can be constructed on the spiritual foundation in the sense of "logotherapy." Then, and only then, can psychotherapy include the entire man, the complete personality.

In this sense, Caruso, Daim and others have already begun the construction of a universalistic psychotherapy.

6. UNIVERSALISTIC PSYCHOTHERAPY

Directives for a Catholic psychotherapy

If we take the concept of "catholic" in its fullest sense (καθ' ὅλου), it becomes self-evident that a Catholic psychotherapy must be universalistic and must include complete authentic understanding of all trends. This is by no means eclecticism (capricious selection), but is much more the principle of the entire and indivisible truth.

The universalistic mode of observation proper to Pastoral Medicine takes into account biological phenomena and social factors (predisposition and environment) as well as psychological and ethico-metaphysical aspects.

It completes the natural observation with supernatural considerations and thus crowns the same.

Even in psychotherapy this mode of observation can obtain correct and valid ideas, though these may be one-sided and fallible. It embraces all the elements of truth which have been discovered and gathered in all times and by all the researchers. And hence, it is catholic (καθ' ὅλου) in the literal and highest sense.

The following directive ideas arise for a Catholic psychotherapy: In regard to the method, any method which is not contrary to the Catholic concept of the essence of the soul, of the dignity and moral responsibility of man and his supernatural end of life, is permissible.

Hence the method can be selected according to the personal choice of the therapist or may even be adapted to the peculiarity of each case. There is no rigid system. All morally permissible methods have a place in a universalistic panorama. Therefore, there exists a notable adaptability in regard to method. The only condition required is that the objective be uniform and inflexible. Thus the universalistic Catholic psychotherapy has at its disposal all the knowledge, means and therapeutic recourses of all the psychotherapeutic trends and schools and makes use of them after prudent selection. It also leads to a complete mental hygiene. Moreover, it possesses special possibilities which no other of the numerous partial groups possesses.

It is very important to realize the proper value of these possibilities and to exhaust them in order to attain the therapeutic objective in the most complete possible manner. An example of such a possibility has been mentioned in reference to the treatment of nervous insomnia; the calming effect of prayer on nerves affected by excessive tiredness and too much vigilant thought. Here elements which act in a purely natural manner (calming rhythm) combine with supernatural actions. The purely natural factor can prevail in the case of a simple insomnia brought on through excessive fatigue.

It would be erroneous to attribute the effect solely to the soporific monotony, to the uniform repetition, which can be easily established in the recitation of the rosary when this becomes a mere lip prayer.

On the contrary, the calming effect of prayer on the soul is in proportion to the fervor that is present. Only a most incomplete effect is to be expected from prayer said with distraction.

However, there is also a metaphysical insomnia which arises from the deepest strata of the soul and which cannot be calmed. In this case, neither medicines nor physico-dietetic cures nor psychotherapy in the usual sense can be of any help. Here only the deep reorientation of the soul which directs the entire being to the true meaning of life—the reconciliation of the soul—can be of help. The object is the complete re-establishment of mental health. In order to attain this end, it is necessary to transform all the disharmony and conflicts which torment mental life into the most perfect possible equilibrium. Such an objective cannot be obtained by a mere step. In a great number of cases, it will not be attainable in a complete manner, and one must be satisfied with a partial success.

Hence if we succeed in drawing forth from each person what can reasonably be expected of him according to his predispositions and powers, taking into account his hereditary characteristics, pathological tendencies and the impediments which affect freedom of will, the task would in practice be fulfilled.

The ideal aspiration as such remains unlimited even if in the individual case it cannot be completely realized. However, in this regard, no concession is to be made. The fulfillment of the task requires both the co-operation of the patient and that of a zealous spiritual director.

The question of " self-liberation " from nervous (mental) ailments has been discussed in various ways by Catholic psychotherapeutists —as, for example, Bergmann. Here it must be distinguished whether by such a " self-liberation " is meant the overcoming of the illness solely by the patient's own power of will, or merely an initiation, without the co-operation of a third party, of a spiritual assistance, which consciously calls into effect supernatural means of overcoming the illness.

The first type of " self-liberation " must be considered problematic or at least very rare and difficult. It requires an unusual degree of will power—and it is the lack of this which characterizes the neurotic.

In most cases such attempts are similar to the attempt of Baron Münchhausen to pull himself out of the mud by the hair.

The mentally ill almost always have need of spiritual direction which, in turn, must have the proper objective. Otherwise it will be more harmful than none at all. It is possible, up to a certain degree, for a patient to attain proper orientation without depending upon spiritual direction. This consists in " personal co-operation " and, especially, in opening up the supernatural sources of power. Essentially this is not a " self-liberation " in the true sense of the word. Here the role of spiritual guidance can be assumed by a written or printed instruction or by the study of an appropriate book.

For an exact diagnosis, the doctor is indispensable. The therapy itself consists of two elements: medical and spiritual assistance. Both are necessary in conformity with the principle *ora et labora*. It is not right to omit either one or the other. The natural powers have been given to man for his use.

The natural plane in which therapy finds itself must be in harmony with the supernatural; then it will be possible to re-establish this harmony even in the soul of one in whom it was disturbed and destroyed.

As in the case of medical assistance the doctor is exclusively competent, so in the case of spiritual assistance only the priest is competent. This is to say that one must take account of the other and one must not work against the other. The collaboration of the two will be the more fruitful the more they complement one another and work together.

This collaboration will take place more completely the more

deeply the doctor is instructed on questions concerning pastoral and moral theology and the more thoroughly the spiritual director is instructed on those concerning psychopathology and psychotherapy.

If the doctor wishes to be "spiritual director," he himself must be well orientated toward the proper objective. He must also know and respect the limits within which he can be director and must know when he should concede to the priest.

The ideal is to have the two working together from the beginning: co-operation of the doctor and spiritual director toward a common end. This collaboration is natural in patients of Catholic ideology.

Today the greater number of patients seek the doctor first, even in matters which primarily pertain to the spiritual director. Psychoanalysis in its initial stages transformed the doctor into a "magician of a 'divinized' world."

The doctor instructed in Pastoral Medicine realizes his exalted mission. He refuses merely to represent the aspect of "magician." He must be an illuminated director. He must know when, after having directed the sick person little by little, the moment has arrived at which he can remove the bandages and show the patient the deep cause of his fall and where to find the true means of recovery. To recognize these deep causes is to acknowledge one's own fault.

The moment the patient can utter with deepest conviction the words of the Confiteor: *mea culpa, mea maxima culpa*, the rigidity of his soul is loosened. At this point, it is indispensable for the patient to see the spiritual director—if he turns away then, refusing to co-operate, rejecting direction, and closing his eyes to the truth, hope for his improvement cannot be great. The moment he rejects the remedy, he deprives himself of recovery.

If the doctor is capable of making the patient recognize the existence of supernatural sources of power and of pointing out the way to them, and if the patient follows these indications and makes use of the redemptive power of grace, and co-operates with it, then the victory is complete.

It is certain that the defect established by the psychopathic predisposition cannot be removed, but it can surely be mitigated. The deepest recesses of the soul can be transformed if the patient can utter with absolute faith and full consciousness of their importance, the words *Tantum dic verbo—et sanabitur anima mea!* The most strident dissonances of being will be resolved. Even if the patient does not achieve immediately the most perfect harmony, yet he will, little by little, lose his painful desperation.

An indescribable consolation and a strengthening of soul is found in the realization that before God there is no other justice, no other honor and value than unconditional dedication to the will of God. That there is no other justification than that acquired through the grace of redemption and its humble acceptance. And that there is no other " inferiority " than voluntary and conscious sin and rebellion against the will of God. The most miserable among those who suffer under the stigma of psychopathy and neurosis is ennobled by the realization that no external force can separate him from love of Christ, whose redeeming blood has flowed even for him.

The feeling of futility and depravity is transformed into one of assurance and realization that no one is excluded from the friendship of God unless through his own fault and the refusal of grace.

The disharmony of life cedes to an increasing equilibrium. The realization of one's worth, which was disturbed, is renewed. The patient realizes the true meaning of life and suffering, the exalted and inalienable dignity which, despite original sin and fallen and broken human nature, can never be taken from him. He realizes the power of redemption and salvation and the infinite value and dignity of the human soul. He can exclaim with the saintly Pope Leo the Great:

" Acknowledge, O Christian, your dignity: having been made participant of the divine nature, do not fall back into the former ignominy through unworthy relations. Remember of what head and body you are a member. Remember that you have been snatched from the power of darkness and have been brought into light and into the kingdom of God."[1]

It will transform him into a much more worthy member than he could have been without this elevation, since *gratia non tollit nec destruit, sed implet et perficit naturam.*

---

[1] *Sermo I de Nativitate Domini:* " Agnosce, O Christiane, dignitatem tuam: et divinae consors factus naturae, noli in veterem vilitatem degeneri conversatione redire. Memento cuius capitis et cuius corporis sis membrum. Reminiscere, quia erutus de potestate tenebrarum, translatus es in Dei lumen et regnum."

7. APPENDIX—THE IDEA OF A UNIVERSALISTIC PSYCHO-THERAPY IN DANTE'S DIVINE COMEDY

Instructed in the teaching of St. Thomas, Dante realized and resolved, in anticipation and in a prophetic manner, the essential problems of depth psychology and psychotherapy in his "Divina Comedia," although these were not posited as problems until six hundred years later.

a. Introduction

"In the midst of life's ways" ("life's turning point," Jung) the soul (Dante) finds itself in a forest full of horror and takes into account its position (the "frightened conscience," Luther). It seeks the exit, but cannot find it. A mountain beckons from afar, but the way is closed by three wild beasts: the panther, wolf and lion. They symbolize the human passions: inordinate sexuality, avarice and pride.

A helper or guide (Virgil) appears to the perplexed wayfarer. He has been induced by "illuminating grace" and "supernatural love" (Beatrice), through the intercession of the Mother of God, to save the lost soul.

Virgil represents natural reason. Dante entrusts himself to him as guide and submits himself to him without reserve. Symbolically, whatever is attributed to Virgil in his task is likewise attributed to the medical guide in psychotherapy.

Virgil demonstrates the only way of escaping error:

(1) First, the descent into the inferno. According to the "micro-cosmic" interpretation, this signifies the descent into the deepest recesses of the soul, and hence the phase of analysis.

(2) Then the laborious ascent to the Mount of Illumination, i.e., purgatory. This corresponds to the "synthetic" element of psycho-therapy, to the reconstruction of the personality. Once the summit has been reached, the task of Virgil as spiritual guide is completed. He leaves and cedes the further direction to Beatrice, the representative of the Church and the supernatural (grace).

(3) As a conclusion and crowning point, and under the direction of Beatrice, the way of salvation and perfection follows, and the soaring into the realms of paradise to the supreme *visio beatifica*.

The following is to be observed concerning the three phases of the journey:

b. Inferno

As we have already mentioned, it is a matter of a " microcosmic " interpretation: the descent into the abyss of one's own soul. The gate of hell, which is constantly opened, does not allow anyone to leave through the same way: its inscription threatens absolute desperation.

The descent into hell is accomplished through strata. At every passage from one sphere to another the diabolical powers try with always new forms of resistance to force the wayfarers to give up their journey. Virgil always succeeds in overcoming this resistance.

In the successive degrees of the infernal spheres, which become narrower the deeper one descends, the individual vices and evil inclinations of man and his sins become manifest; in the higher and wider spheres are seen, above all, the sins of human weakness and sensuality; in the deeper sphere, those of conscious rebellion against the established order of God, the sins of pride.

The strongest resistance is manifested in the confines between the higher spheres and the *basso inferno* (or deeper spheres). Here the underworld resorts to the use of all the powers of hell in order to impede the entrance. At this point, not even Virgil, with his natural powers, succeeds in overcoming the resistance. Here an angel—a messenger of the supernatural—must come to aid: without the help of grace, the Power of the Underworld does not give release from the way that leads into the *basso inferno*.

At this point, the following is to be observed: that psychoanalysis or purely natural psychotherapy can guide man only up to this point, but can go no further. It can reveal the abyss of sensuality and other sins of the senses, but nothing more. Hence it always remains in the external region. Only when the view into the *basso inferno* is opened does depth psychology in the strict sense begin.

Now the journey becomes step by step more terrible. Only with the help of " giants," symbols of the elementary forces of nature, can the wayfarer pass from the last step to the deepest abyss. Once the deepest recess has been reached, then no fire burns: the external ice or freezing denotes that every love and life is extinguished. There, in the deepest recess the wayfarers are constrained to look directly into the eyes of Lucifer, the metaphysical principle of evil itself, who appears as the horrid parody of the Divine Trinity.

They have reached the center of the earth (of one's own ego), "where all things lose their weight." They do not find, in this center, "God within themselves" but the "adversary" and the "caricature" of God.

It is impossible to escape from this notion. There is only one way out: in the immediate contact with evil, at the center of the earth, a "turn of one hundred and eighty degrees," so that what was above is now below. From this moment of "retraction" every step leads away from evil and later to liberty.

Here in a crevice flows a stream of water, gently at first, then increasing more and more: after the crossing of those infernal rivers of death (Acheron, Styx, Phlegethon, Cocytus), this is the water of life newly awakening. Far above the narrow shaft's opening, we see the light of a star, new hope.

c. Purgatory

After having left the exit of hell, the wayfarers find themselves at the point of the earth opposite that in which they found themselves when they entered. First, they have to wash themselves of the impurities of hell. Then they gird themselves with a reed—symbol of humility—and are exhorted by an angel—a messenger of grace—to pray and thank God and seek the necessary strength for the rest of the journey.

The ascent to the Mount of Illumination takes place again by degrees. In a succession which is the inverse of that of hell, a vice and the corresponding evil inclination are expiated.

In contrast to the preceding phase, the ascent from the deepest recesses becomes gradually lighter. At the entrance to purgatory, an angel sits before the gate, which symbolizes the tribunal of expiation. He makes the way free only after he has, with his sword, marked the penitent on the forehead with seven "P's" (representing sins). Little by little, as the penitent passes along, an angel cancels a "P" so that the journey is in this way made easier. The force of the inclinations which tend to drag one under is more and more overcome.

In the highest and ultimate degree—in contrast to that in entering hell—there only remains the conquering of inordinate sensuality.

The wayfarer must pass through a terrible fire; he draws back but Virgil incites him to this last trial of self-abnegation by indicating that Beatrice awaits him on the other side of the fire.

It is in this way that the last terrestrial part is traversed. Now Virgil gives up his function as guide. His words of farewell contain in a most complete manner all that a doctor, in the capacity of a spiritual director, can say to the patient after a successful psychotherapy.

Virgil now retires in silence and cedes the direction to Beatrice, who, from now on, appears always clear as the symbol, not only of celestial love but also of theology and, at the same time, of the supernatural—of grace itself.

d. Paradise

From the standpoint of psychotherapy the comparison would be terminated. But paradise—in its indissoluble connection with the two preceding ways—represents their necessary conclusion and crowning point.

The journey through hell and purgatory is directed toward this end. It would have no sense or purpose without this conclusion.

With the whirling from one celestial sphere to another, the perspective extends always farther and becomes freer; the panorama increases in height, the relationships in the situation are better comprehended until supreme perfection is reached in a *visio beatifica* which, in the contemplation of the divine mystery, recognizes the love which moves all things.

e. Summary

In conclusion it can be said that a true psychotherapy can follow no other way than that shown by Dante in the symbolic personality of Virgil, no matter what method is used. The question of the method, which in the first era of psychoanalysis appeared essential, becomes something definitely secondary in the face of the question concerning the end that is to be accomplished and the way that is to be followed. The end cannot be anything else but that designated by Dante—and there is no other way to attain this objective. With regard to direction, together with the details which cannot here be mentioned, it is seen that Virgil fulfilled his task with great mastery.

However, of greatest importance is the fact that Virgil, after fulfilling his task, had to step back and cede the continuation of direction through the supernatural realm exclusively to Beatrice, who alone sanctifies.

D. BORDERLAND STATES OF HUMAN MENTAL LIFE

1. GENERAL VIEW

a. Concept

By the designation " borderland states " of human mental life is here understood a conspicuous number of heterogeneous mental phenomena which lie partly between normal mental life and pathological mental life, and partly between phenomena which can be explained in a natural manner and supernatural phenomena. They cannot be classified under the concept of " normal " mental life, since they are not normal. They are strange to the ordinary mental state in which the majority of men find themselves. They therefore do not fall within the sphere of psychology in the strict sense—and they do not fall under the concept of psychopathology, since they are not to be considered morbid in the proper sense, even if they do deviate from the concept of normal since they are unusual.

We will here consider phenomena which are partly natural which, to date, have been little studied and seem mysterious. Other phenomena to be considered here are outside the sphere of natural investigation.

The heterogeneous character of the phenomena here considered is manifested in the fact that these phenomena extend from the confines of simulation, hysteria, psychopathy and superstition to genuine mysticism and true miracles.

b. Summary

The phenomena to be studied can be divided into two principal groups. To the first group—that of natural manifestations little studied—belong: non-rational therapeutic methods, the phenomena of parapsychology (telepathy, telekinesis and others), a part of the "occult phenomena," and the manifestations of pseudomysticism.

To the second group—that of borderland states of natural experience and the extranatural or supernatural—belong phenomena of authentic obsession, authentic mysticism, ecstasy, revelations and authentic miraculous cures.

Among the phenomena which cannot be explained by natural means, we can further distinguish two kinds: supernatural phenomena in the strict sense which can be explained only by the action of divine omnipotence; and extranatural phenomena which must be explained by diabolical influence.

In conformity with this, the first group of non-rational natural phenomena must be distinguished from the extranatural and supernatural phenomena.

2. NON-RATIONAL PHENOMENA

a. Non-rational therapeutic methods

We have already briefly mentioned the non-rational methods of psychotherapy. Here we consider therapeutic methods which are not limited to psychotherapy in the strict sense but which also have organic diseases as their object.

But even here the existence of a psychotherapeutic factor, at times decisive, is manifest.

These therapeutic methods embrace, in turn, the most heterogeneous practices, from undoubted fraud to the limits of supernatural phenomena.

Fraud does not really belong to the sphere of this exposition, yet we must make mention of it. It plays a real role as a therapeutic factor, since the faith awakened in the sick by it can contribute to the activation of mental powers. One speaks of the *pia fraus* of the doctor who, in determined circumstances, may be compelled to deceive the patient concerning the seriousness of his condition.

But even the vilest intrigues of fraudulent charlatanism can occasionally attain a successful outcome. Hence it can be seen from this how difficult it is to draw the limits where non-rational medical arts end and fraud begins. It is no less difficult to separate the concept of charlatanism from that of justified natural therapy, and this, in turn, from that of scientific medicine.

Liek designates all non-rational therapies by that word of many meanings—sorcery.

The history of medicine shows that in early times it was difficult to determine the limits between doctor and sorcerer, magician and medicine man. The doctor healed *verbis, herbis, lapide* (worthy of notice is the order of succession). We have already spoken of incantation. Another series of remedies could be assembled for study from the "heylsame Dreck Apotheke" (Paullini, 1714) through such superstitions as "headsman's medicine," and secret methods (love potions), up to the use of sex hormones extracted from the urine of the pregnant in modern hormone therapy.

There are methods in which it is difficult to determine the limits of the rational and non-rational elements.

Homeopathy in its fundamental idea has without doubt a scientific-rational basis, yet in conditioning its mode of action non-rational elements concur, perhaps in no small measure and hence in a greater degree than in "school medicine."

Biochemistry (Schüssler) strives to attribute all functional disturbances to lack of definite vital elements. But even here there can be a grain of truth; yet this method, in its outline and, much more, in its application, is with difficulty separated from doubtful non-rational methods.

In more recent times we encounter methods in which non-rational methods are mixed with rational methods which have not yet been studied, but which are susceptible to research—as, for example, "pendulum diagnosis," "iris diagnosis," diagnosis by means of light staffs (Zeileis), etc.

At times we encounter a curious mixture of psychotherapy and *Weltanschauung* (anthroposophic medicine), occasionally with sectarian tendencies (Weissenberger sect). More difficult to judge are the methods which almost touch the sphere of mysticism. The most difficult question is the following: Up to what point is it a matter of pseudomysticism, of conscious deception, self-deception, hysteria, etc., and up to what point can, at least, the co-operation of genuine mystical factors be possible?

There are the "health-praying sects" (e.g., Christian Science). They consider disease as sin or as the effect of sin, and this, not merely as the effect of original sin but in each case as the effect of personal sin. This generalization is false. The idea that there is no disease that is not in some way the effect of sin contains a grain of truth, but the truth is dangerously deformed. According to their opinion, any disease can be healed solely by means of prayer.

The obtaining of a cure with prayer should presumably be rather an obtaining of a cure with thought. Again, a grain of truth is mixed with fatal error. The error consists especially in this, that the duty of man to use his natural powers of intellect and will is neglected. In this there is an infraction of the civilized commandment of God: "Subdue the earth," as well as the Benedictine principle "*ora et labora*." It is not permissible for man to neglect either one or the other. In the sects which we have mentioned, man merely relies on the help of God and does not fulfill the duty imposed on him.

In recent decades, a great number of miraculous cures were reported which a Protestant pastor (Stanger) from the Swabian village of Möttlingen was supposed to have accomplished by the mere imposition of hands and prayer—and these were cures, not only of purely neurotic diseases but also of organic diseases.

Without doubt the reports concerning many of these cures is to be taken seriously, even if the majority of cases can be attributed to purely psychogenic factors and can be explained in a purely natural way. If such a supposition can ever be advanced, it is applicable to the method of "imposition of hands" more than to any other method. It is asked what does this imitation of the symbolical curative act of Christ signify: Does it awaken in the patient the realization that Christ is the doctor, or is it wont to communicate to the patient the magneto-therapeutic irradiation of the operator? In any case, we have here a case of two basically different elements concerning which it is not possible to make a clear distinction—which produces a surprising impression.

Since the possibility of an exact test or check is lacking, it is not possible to take a stand in establishing whether, in these cases, only a psychotherapeutic component intervenes or whether, at least in part, there is supernatural intervention. The latter does not seem basically inconceivable; otherwise it would have to be held that God could not, nor does He wish, to reveal His power outside the Catholic Church. Now, it has been proved that the Catholic Church has been authenticated in a singular manner, even by numerous miracles; yet there is no reason to hold that God cannot and does not wish to be revealed also through pious persons who are outside the Church.

b. Parapsychology—Occultism

(a) *Forms of manifestation*

The phenomena of occultism, or of parapsychology, are limited states of human psychic life in a twofold sense: they are on the border between normal psychic life and pathological psychic life and partly, perhaps, on the border between natural and supernatural phenomena.

Somnambulism and telepathy especially belong to the parapsychological phenomena which have been extensively studied in a scientific manner, and are accessible to investigation.

Occultism (occult science) is the theory concerning the occult powers of human nature and inanimate nature (microcosm and macrocosm).

Such powers allow man to perform actions and acquire knowledge without being bound to the limits of physical (causal in space and time) phenomena.

We speak of spiritism when there is an attempt to communicate with the spirit of the departed.

Somnambulism is the most profound degree of hypnotic sleep. It is characterized by a memory deficiency after awakening (amnesia). There is also a spontaneous somnambulism, found especially in the hysterical or psychopathic personality.

This latter is, without doubt, a limited pathological state (so-called " nocturnal walking "); *lunatismus*—sleepwalking during moonlight). Hypnotic somnambulism is characterized by an accentuated rapport, which is manifested in the " command automatism " on the part of the somnambulant. At times a cateleptic rigidity occurs. Posthypnotic reactions as well as sense deceptions have been described.

(b) *Evaluation*

On page 366, under *Special view*, suggestion was studied merely as a licit psychotherapeutic method. Here we are interested in evaluating the limited mental states associated with hypnotism. Here we meet with several serious preoccupations, the most important of which are the following:

(1) Hypnotism is a pathological state, or at least can provoke morbid states;

(2) The hypnotized places his will under the power of the hypnotizer; he is exposed to morally dangerous suggestions;

(3) Hypnotism, especially in the form of somnambulism, is intrinsically based on diabolical influences and is, therefore, illicit.

With regard to (1), according to the opinion of most authors (Libéault, Bernheim), hypnotic sleep is not distinguished from common sleep and therefore cannot be considered a morbid state. This viewpoint can be so with regard to the lighter degree of hypnotic sleep, but is not so with regard to somnambulism. This is to be considered a borderland state in which the pathological element prevails more strongly, the more the hypnotizer himself manifests abnormal characteristics (hysteria, psychopathy). In this latter case, the danger provoked by posthypnotic disturbances of the psychic life is greater.

With regard to (2), the extent to which a person is exposed to morally dangerous suggestions, especially in the form of posthypnotic commands, is in general considered insignificant. Yet even here the utmost prudence is necessary. An unstable psychopath in the hands of a hypnotizer without a conscience runs a very serious risk.

With regard to (3), the contention that hypnotism in se is based upon diabolical influences is definitely not correct. There is a use of hypnotism which is absolutely legitimate and which cannot be eliminated because of the possibility of abuse (*abusus non tollit usum*). But there is the possibility that an individual familiar with the secrets of demonology (" black magic ") can also use hypnotism for the purpose of the latter. Such a possibility is evident, since one cannot think of a more suitable method for such a purpose.

(c) *Doctrinal decisions of the Church*

In 1840 the Congregation of the Holy Office decided that the use of hypnotism or of magnetotherapy, as a simple application for physical remedies, is licit as long as it is not directed toward a morally illicit end.

A response to the Holy Office of July 26, 1899, specified the requisites for the liceity of hypnotic experiments under the previous assurance that those who perform the same have nothing to do with extranatural things.

Antonelli, on the basis of the opinions of *probati auctores*, arrives at the following requirements:

(1) That the disease to be healed by means of hypnosis cannot be healed by any other means or that it is of such a nature that only through hypnosis can a cure be expected;

(2) That the patient requests this therapeutic method on his own initiative or, at least, willingly submits to it;

(3) That the medical hypnotizer be a specialist, morally irreproachable and beyond all suspicion, and that hypnosis be effected by moral means;

(4) That the suggested ideas be morally unobjectionable and adapted to the nature of the disease;

(5) That hypnosis and suggestion be effected in the presence of a trustworthy person and that the rules of decency and morality be safeguarded.

(d) Telepathy—Clairvoyance

By telepathy is understood all the experiences in which psychic elements (ideas, sensations, feeling and volitions) are communicated from one mind to another other than through the known sense organs; while clairvoyance entails the relations obtained in the same manner between a person and an event or an object (Wasiliewski).

Subjects with telepathic or clairvoyant aptitudes are for the most part nervous and often hysterical. The psychopathic predisposition is more or less pronounced. Their assertions take place in a hypnoidal state (similar to a trance). In others, consciousness remains unchanged. The sessions of occultism strongly excite the mediums (Capellmann—Bergmann). The danger of severe nervous and mental harm is not to be overlooked.

Of the phenomena here mentioned, the most notable is that of clairvoyance ("second sight"). When this clairvoyance means seeing from afar, distinction is made between space and time—spatial and temporal clairvoyance.

To the phenomena already mentioned belong "prophetic dreams" (visions) and prophecies—as long as they are not based on deceit or diabolical influences. In the last case they belong to extranatural phenomena. Moreover, the possibility of supernatural visions is also admitted.

Among the phenomena in which mediums play a part, we mention so-called natural ecstasy and levitation—that is, suspension in air, unexplained by reason, of one's body or of determined objects telepathically influenced by a medium. In this latter case we speak of telekinesis.

The idea of natural ecstasy (in contradistinction to supernatural ecstasy) is questionable. It should be considered as direct contemplation.

(e) *Attempts toward an explanation*

It is very difficult to form a judgment concerning the phenomena which have been mentioned. The explanations already given are unsatisfactory.

"Animistic hypothesis" seeks to explain the phenomena by means of psychophysical energies which have their basis in the subconscious. Attempts to explain the phenomena in a purely materialistic manner—as, for example, the "theory of undulation" (Boehm)—are superficial, as is the attempt to transfer the same readily to the supernatural realm.

No doubt, even this is a matter of "borderland states" of the psychic life. Yet, in this, as in other cases, the Catholic researcher is obliged to seek, above all, a natural explanation and to extend it to the utmost in order to find a solution. We must remember that "unexplored" does not mean "not explorable" and far less "supernatural." There are still many forces of nature which we do not know. From this concept of phenomena to the universalistic concept is only a step, but certainly a decisive step.

At least for a part of the phenomena already mentioned, the more acceptable theory still seems to be that of electromagnetic or radioactive "irradiation." That such "irradiations" (emission of electrons) leave the body can definitely be supposed ("micro-oscillations," Rohracher). The electroencephalograph (EEG) is based on graphic proof of the waves due to the action of the cerebral cortex. And it can likewise be supposed that electromagnetic vibrations can, in determined circumstances, and when there exists a particular psychic disposition, increase beyond the normal measure. This capacity can be increased beyond the normal measure both on the part of the transmitter and on the part of the receiver. (Compare the receptive capacity for radioactivity and the phenomena of the divining rod; the capacity that many persons possess of feeling whether an electrical current passes through a conductor, etc.)

The intensified sensibility to such irradiations is called radio-esthesia (psychic radiosensibility). There is no need to give pseudo-mystical names to these irradiations, nor to relate them to an "astral body."

We are only at the beginning of new knowledge in the field of theoretical physics and we can suppose that many phenomena, today unexplainable, will eventually find a very simple explanation.

On the other hand, we must not lose sight of the fact that we move within a borderland sphere. That is the reason why we have proposed the designation "borderland states." The borders are easily surpassed. This can happen with regard to any of the phenomena here mentioned, at least in part. Genuine supernatural and extra-natural phenomena are distinguished from such limited phenomena, for the most part through determined and well-characterized signs.

(f) *Spiritism*

By spiritism is meant the systematic theory and practice of direct relations between living persons and the spirits of the departed. To it belong a series of phenomena of various types. The best known are the so-called movement of the table (knock-phenomena), writing under dictation of the spirit, and rendering the departed visible (materialization).

In accordance with these expressed forms, Antonelli distinguishes:

(1) *Spiritismus typtologicus:* The answers are given by means of a series of knocks;

(2) *Spiritismus graphologicus:* The answers are written by the medium after being dictated;

(3) *Spiritus invadens:* The spirit gives the answer through the mouth of the *medium invasum* (*instar instrumenti*);

(4) *Spiritismus videns:* The medium sees the spirit and effects it that the participants also see it;

(5) *Spiritismus materializatus:* The spirit is "materialized," i.e., makes itself perceptible, talks, etc.; this phase is also called reincarnation.

From this relation are excluded all the phenomena that can be attributed to fraud or illusion (auto-suggestion, hysteria, etc.). In

these cases, it is not a matter of true and proper spiritism. Authentic
spiritism demonstrates most clearly the import of the concept of
"mental borderland states."

On the one hand, purely natural presuppositions (medial predisposition) are required; and, on the other hand, in authentic spiritistic
phenomena, the boundary between nature and extranature is, without doubt, overstepped.

Moreover, even if so much deceit and fraud are found under the
title spiritism, yet there remain sufficient phenomena which cannot
be given a purely natural explanation.

The possibility of authentic spiritistic phenomena cannot be
doubted if, in general, one believes in life hereafter and if one
believes that it is possible to communicate with the spirits of the
deceased—for example, through prayer. If the possibility exists of
using prayer properly, then the possibility of abuse is not to be
excluded, and spiritism is therefore to be considered as such an
abuse.

With regard to the danger of spiritism, the same is true, and in
even greater measure, as holds for hypnotism and somnambulism,
both as regards physical and psychic dangers (moral).

Spiritism is not limited to the sphere of demonomagy, but in
certain forms is to be considered *maleficium*, as is black magic.
Hence the Church has severely forbidden all the faithful to actively
or passively participate in spiritistic sessions.

(g) Doctrinal decisions of the Church

As the Church once before took a position against the evoking
of spirits (for example, Pope John XXII in 1326), so was she alert
when modern spiritism arose in the nineteenth century.

On August 4, 1856, the Holy Office directed a long circular to all
the bishops on the abolition of the abuses of magnetism, which
was then very common.

After having declared licit, under certain conditions, magnetism
used for purely natural ends—for example, scientific, therapeutic
ends—the decree continues: "Even though the limits of the licit
use of magnetism have been clearly defined, yet the malice of men
has increased to such a degree that they, neglecting the lawful study
of the sciences and seeking, rather, extraordinary matters to the
serious detriment to the soul and also disadvantageous to civil

society, boast of having invented a new means of divination and prophecy." Then the decree disapproves seriously of the behavior, not always decent, of women who—in a state of magnetic sleep and clairvoyance—pretend "to see invisible things of all kinds and presume to speak of religion, and to evoke the souls of the departed, to interrogate them, to discover occult or distant things and to do similar superstitious things, without doubt for the purpose of obtaining pecuniary gains for themselves and their masters from these revelations."

Magnetism served as an introduction to spiritism.

Imported from America and always more widespread in Europe, the modern form of spiritism became in 1880 a veritable public calamity. Rome had to intervene repeatedly. Thus on April 2, 1864, the Holy Office prohibited all spiritistic writings. On March 30, 1898, the same Congregation forbade to Catholics any spiritistic experiment, any active or passive participation in spiritistic sessions.

Pope Leo XIII, in the Constitution "Officiorum ac munerum," prohibited the publication and even the reading and possession of spiritistic works. Accordingly, Canon Law states in canon 1399: "By law itself are forbidden: books which teach or approve of any kind of superstition, fortunetelling, divination, magic, communication with spirits, and other things of that kind."[1]

Thus the spiritistic writings are, without exception and definitely, prohibited to Catholics.

According to canon 2314, those adhering to spiritism incur *excommunicatio Sedi Apostolicae reservata.*

In 1917, the Holy Office to the question:

"Is it permissible to assist at spiritistic sessions of any kind, with or without the so-called medium, using or not using hypnotism, even when they conserve the appearance of honesty and piety; be it by interrogating the spirits, or listening to their answers, be it limited to looking on, even with tacit or expressed protestation that one does not wish to have any part with evil spirits?"[2]

---

[1] "Ipso iure prohibentur: libri qui cuiusvis generis superstitionem, sortilegia, divinationem, magiam, evocationem spirituum, aliaque id genus docent vel commendant."

[2] "An liceat per medium, ut vocant, vel sine medio, adhibito vel non hypnotismo, locutionibus aut manifestationibus spiritisticis quibuscumque adsistere, etiam speciem honestatis vel pietatis praeseferentibus, sive interrogando animas aut spiritus, sive audiendo responsa, sive tantum aspiciendo, etiam cum protestatione tacita vel expressa nullam cum malignis spiritibus partem se habere velle."

Answered:

" Negative in omnibus."

3. SUPERNATURAL PHENOMENA

a. Summary

In the treatment of non-rational phenomena, we had to evaluate a series of varied phenomena from the limits of deceit up to the border of extranatural phenomena.

In the same way, supernatural phenomena, recognized and confirmed and not subject to natural explanation, reveal the characteristics of " borderland states."

On the one hand, they reach deeply into the realm of nature, and on the other hand they touch the ultimate and supreme regions of true and genuine mysticism.

From the series of authenticated phenomena, we must here choose only those which present particular interest from the medico-pastoral standpoint:

(1) A great number of somatic phenomena of marvelous character (*prodiges biologiques*, Henri Bon). Among these, abstinence (inedia), " the miracle of blood," and stigmatization are of particular interest.

(2) The phenomena of genuine mysticism (ecstasy, vision, prophecy, etc.).

(3) The phenomena of demonomagy (obsession and others).

(4) Authentic miraculous cures.

b. Just and false criticism

The principle which must inspire a just criticism must be that of considering the supernatural character of phenomena as authenticated only in those cases in which a natural explanation does not suffice. Nothing is so disastrous as indiscriminating credulity. Just as disastrous is materialistic skepticism, since it does not wish to recognize reality.

"Exaggerated religious credulity tends to attribute a supernatural character even to those facts which do not possess it. Materialistic credulity . . . strives to lead all things back to the same explicative schema " (Bon).

The Catholic doctor, as well as the spiritual director, must know the scientific data which authorize him to express his opinion.

c. Parallel natural phenomena

In all four groups of phenomena described under somatic phenomena (mysticism, demonomagy and miraculous cures), we must distinguish the authentic supernatural phenomena from the numerous parallel phenomena of simulative character and supernatural only in appearance.

This distinction can be very difficult in the individual case and requires, besides medical criteria, a very exact knowledge of all the distinctive marks taught by mystical theology.

Of such purely natural parallel phenomena, we mention:

(1) Somatic phenomena. In complete abstinence from food or inedia, there are excessive material changes from hunger, with destruction of somatic substance, followed by death. This suffices to distinguish it from the supernatural phenomena in which no notable loss of substance takes place.

Moreover, in so-called artists of hunger, it is a matter merely of a limited fast for a certain time and not of an absolute fast. Otherwise it is assumed that there is fraud and hysteria. Such cases are here excluded. We also exclude all phenomena that permit a natural explanation, such as "miracles of blood," stigmatization, etc., especially to the extent that they can be included under the idea of "vicarious menstruation."

According to the predominant opinion, most cases of " bleeding hosts " can be explained in a purely natural manner through the presence of *bacillus prodigiosus*. Bon rightfully warns against any generalization.

The *bacillus prodigiosus* needs humid heat. In such conditions corruption of the hosts takes place. However, there are cases which cannot be explained in this manner.

In stigmatization, a distinction is to be made between authentic stigmatizations and those which can be explained in a purely physiological manner.

There are subjects who, either through predisposition (negative neurosis) or by means of a particular exercise (autogenous training), can attain control over the autonomous vegetative nervous system. They are able, through voluntary innervation, to control vasomotor nerves and the glandular nerves to the point of being able to produce and stop, at will, the flow of blood through skin and mucous.

They can also produce bloody sweat, bloody tears and stigmata. The " stigmata " can thus be provoked even through experiment.

For obvious reasons, the hysterical pseudo-stigmatists often have a predilection for the regions of the wounds of Christ.

Authentic stigmatization cannot be produced at will in any part of the body and it cannot be healed.

An attempt has been made to interpret a part of the hemorrhagic phenomena also as " vicarious menstruation." It cannot be denied that such a phenomena can be verified, but the explanation is problematic and not applicable to the phenomena which we are here considering and, above all, not applicable in general.

The same is to be said regarding the attempt to explain hemorrhagic phenomena by referring to the hypothesis of a hemorrhagic diathesis.

The above-mentioned capacity to dominate the vegetative nervous system is at times associated with the capacity for limiting or eliminating consciousness. In this way sensations of pain can be completely eliminated.

Some of these capacities are cultivated and taught esoterically by occult Oriental doctrine. (Yoga, fakirism.)

(2) In distinguishing between pseudomysticism and authentic mysticism, it will be a matter of essentially excluding fraud, illusion and hysteria. The distinction can, however, become very difficult (cf. below).

(3) In demonomagical states, the possibility of purely psychopathological parallel phenomena must always be kept in mind. It is interesting to distinguish true obsession (*obsessitas*) from hysterical mania as well as from obsessive delirium which corresponds to illusory ideas.

(4) Genuine miraculous cures must be rigorously distinguished from the parallel phenomena.

Cures explained in a purely psychogenic manner, especially when it is a matter of pathological symptoms of a purely psychogenic origin, are also to be considered as such. Even if in these cases we are not to exclude, in general, the co-operation of a supernatural curative factor, a cure can be accredited as inexplicable by natural means only on the basis of rigorous requirements.

The question of miraculous cures will be treated in detail in the following section.

d. Somatic phenomena

Besides the psychophysical phenomena, the most important of which have been here considered, Bon distinguishes further the somatic phenomena which are also associated with the "borderland states" already mentioned.

He brings together both the somatic and the psychophysical phenomena under the concept *prodiges biologiques*. Among the somatic phenomena of this kind, the following are considered:

(1) The fast, especially the absolute fast (*ieiunium absolutum*).

(2) The signs of the miracle of blood. Here belong: in living persons, the bloody sweat, the bloody tears; in the corpse, cruentation, liquefaction of coagulated blood; in inanimate objects, the appearance of blood in relics and images and bleeding hosts.

(3) Stigmatization, especially in the form of the reception of the wounds of Christ.

(4) Incombustibility; incorruptibility, luminous apparitions, levitation, etc.

In the evaluation of numerous cases, accurately assembled, Bon rigorously distinguishes, in each group of phenomena, between phenomena of this kind, which are explainable in a purely natural way and supernatural phenomena; and in these latter, he further distinguishes between diabolical phenomena and "religious" phenomena.

It is impossible, within the confines of this work, to consider, even in an abbreviated manner, the number of cases which have been historically authenticated.

(a) *Fast* (*Inedia*)

In the lives of the saints, a great number of cases of *ieiunium absolutum* have been authenticated.

Angela of Foligno (died in 1309), for twelve years; Catherine of Siena (1347-1380), about eight years; Nicholas of Flue (1417-1487), twenty years; Louise Lateau (1850-1883), for fourteen years (according to Bon).

Pope Innocent VII ordered the fast of Colomba Rietti to be placed under observation. Many other cases were subjected to watching. In recent times, the fast of Theresa Neumann of Konnersreuth was placed under the observation of the Franciscan Sisters of Mallersdorf.

The value of this vigilance has not yet met with general acceptance.

Absolute and prolonged fast must be considered as not explainable in a natural way whenever there is proof of its being absolute and when, after a long duration, there is no proof of an essential loss of substance and no notable harm to health.

The attempt to think even then that it can be explained in a natural manner and to establish the hypothesis that, in such cases, nutrition takes place through cutaneous respiration (*perspiratio insensibilis*) under the action of solar rays and electrical waves, is typical of the "credulity of materialism," censured by Bon, a materialism which prefers an absurd hypothesis to the possibility of a supernatural explanation.

Buchingir acknowledges the possibility of absolute inedia, yet he seeks a natural explanation in the sense of a "charging" of the organism by the forces of "cosmic vibration." He asks: Besides air and water, are fluid and solid corruptible matter really the only means of nourishment? When, however, he, in regard to Theresa of Konnersreuth, quotes the words of Holy Scripture: "Not by bread alone does man live, but by every word that comes forth from the mouth of God" (Matt. 9:4), he acknowledges the insufficiency of the attempt to explain absolute inedia in a natural manner through cosmic irradiation.

(b) *Signs of the miracle of blood*

Bon presents a complete synopsis of all the authenticated cases of bloody sweat and bloody tears from the lives of the saints. He distinguishes the cases which do not have a natural explanation (*cas religieux*) from those explainable by nature (*cas medicaux*). The explanation for the latter has already been considered in the section on parallel phenomena.

In recent times, such phenomena were again observed in a most impressive manner in the case of Theresa Neumann.

Signs of the miracle of blood on corpses have been reported in various forms: blood on corpses at a time long after death, which gave the impression of absolutely fresh blood; in ancient times, in the case of suspected homicide, it was called " ordeal."

Among the signs of the miracle of blood on inanimate objects, the following have been reported: fresh blood on the relics of saints, on hosts and consecrated wine.

Among the best known of the miraculous signs is the miracle of blood of St. Januarius, which consists in the liquefaction of coagulated blood preserved in an ampule.

(c) *Stigmatization*

In a wide sense, stigmatization is the spontaneous presentation of bloody wounds which are not susceptible to healing in the sense of ordinary cicatrization. In a strict sense, it is considered especially the appearance of the wounds of Christ: on the hands, feet, side and forehead (corresponding to puncture of the spine). The stigmata of the hands are usually in the middle of the palm and on the back of the hands.

According to the confirmation which Hynek could make concerning the imprint of the body of Christ upon the holy shroud of Turin (*Sacra Sindone*), the wound on the hand of the Redeemer must have gone through the wrist.

The wounds of the stigmatist do not therefore correspond exactly to the real wound of the Redeemer. One should not be surprised at this, since authentic stigmatization is not to be understood as a copy of the wounds of the Redeemer, but as a mystical proof of grace, whose purpose is, above all, to manifest to other men the mystical graces by means of instruments of election.

There are also " invisible stigmata "; these consist in sensations of pain in the places of the wounds. In some cases (e.g., Catherine of Siena), the invisible stigmata became visible after death.

We have already mentioned the natural parallel phenomenon

of false stigmatization and its possible explanation. It can be attributed partly to physiological causes and partly to pathological causes.

"Diabolical stigmatization," for which there is no natural explanation, is to be distinguished from fake stigmatization. Bon mentions examples and distinguishes:

(1) Stigmatization of divine origin;
(2) Stigmatization of diabolical origin;
(3) Stigmatization of unknown origin.

Among the well-known examples of stigmatization of supernatural origin, the following are to be mentioned:

St. Francis of Assisi received, in 1224 at the age of forty-two, the sacred wounds. A precise description has been handed down by Thomas of Celano.

The cases of St. Veronica Giuliani (1697); Catherine Emmerich (1774-1824); Domenica Lazzari (1830), authenticated by Ernst von Moy, at the University of Munich, and others.

(d) Levitation—Bilocation

By levitation is not here meant the homonymous phenomena spoken of in relation of "mediumistic phenomena" nor cases of pseudo-levitation of a physiological or pathological nature, but a transfigured elevation of the body corresponding to the Biblical account of the transfiguration of Christ.[1]

Such levitations have been handed down both from the Old Testament (Enoch, Elias), and from the lives of the saints (Joseph of Cupertino, André Hubert Fournet).

Of the levitation of religious objects, we mention here the miracle of the levitation of the ostensorium of Faverney (May 26-27, 1608). Besides miraculous levitations, some of evidently diabolical origin have been known.

e. Mystical phenomena

(a) Concept

The essence of genuine mysticism consists in the mysterious supernatural unification of the human soul with God (unio mystica)

[1] Matt. 17:1-9. Among the mystical phenomena, that of bilocation has at times been recorded—the simultaneous bodily apparition in different places.

and the capacity for direct knowledge (" vision ") which is associated with it. The theological basis of all Christian mysticism is the mysteries of the Blessed Trinity, the Incarnation of Christ, the divine Maternity of Mary, the mystically living Christ and the renewal of His expiatory death in the Holy Sacrifice of the Mass, the real Presence of Christ in the Holy Sacrament of the altar, and His union with man in Holy Communion (the mystery of the Eucharist).

Mystical union is the ultimate and highest degree of the mystical elevation of the human soul. This elevation can be manifested in different degrees and forms.

(b) *Forms of expression*

The best-known forms of manifestation are ecstasy, visions and revelations (private revelation).

Yet these forms are secondary. The primary form is the mystical elevation of the soul. Generally the secondary forms of manifestation are considered, by less well-instructed persons, the more important, since they are externally most impressive.

This is so, especially, with regard to the concomitant bodily manifestations which have been mentioned in the preceding section. These are, however, only accessory phenomena and not essential. This is so even with regard to the most impressive concomitant form, that of stigmatization.

(c) *Preparation—Degrees*

Mystical experience is, for the most part, associated with a certain preparation of body and soul. Here the close relation between asceticism and mysticism is apparent.

The preparation is the way of purification and illumination. To illumination belong interior vision and contemplation, which terminates in the " prayer of repose."

St. John of the Cross distinguishes various signs by which the soul can know whether it can give itself to passivity (not to be confused with " quietism," which excludes co-operation of the soul).

After mystical elevation, the soul is wont to fall into a state of aridity, which, after special elevations, reaches the " dark night of the soul." The higher and more blessed the mystical elevation is, the more tormenting is this intermediate state.

(d) Ecstasies—Visions—Revelations

Ecstasies (from ἔκστασις = to go out of oneself) are possible in different degrees and in different forms. The lowest degree is that of " exalted repose." There are degrees of ecstasy in which the bodily life seems extinguished and is not awakened until after the return of the soul from the state of ecstasy. At times ecstasies are characterized by visions and revelations. The visions can entail the sight of God, Mary and the Saints. They can effect a retrospective experiencing of events in the history of redemption (e.g., the Passion of Christ).

If the visions are associated with communications concerning present or future data, we speak of revelations. Yet these need not necessarily be associated with visions.

Revelations regarding individual persons are called private revelations. These are distinguished from prophetic revelations insofar as they do not essentially concern objects of the divine general plan of salvation.

Private revelations do not constitute an object of faith. Critique and reserve are not only justified, but required in their regard. Yet they can furnish valuable indications especially when, as individual stones, they build themselves into a reasonable image. For the most part, private revelations represent only fragments of a complete picture. They even appear to the one contemplating mostly in a shortened form. Even here we notice the phenomena of " displacement " and " condensation " which we have learned in the treatment of dream images.

Private and authentic revelations can be intrinsically true even if the details have been seen and reported wrongly.

Regarding the reproduction through human speech, the fact must be held in special consideration that the one making the revelation cannot reproduce the latter except by his own words, in a manner suited to the times in which he lives, to his personal outlook and degree of culture. Many discrepancies, errors and deviations are thus explained. A clear idea can often be obtained only by synoptically comparing many private revelations concerning the same object. Precise indications of the time must be accepted, for the most part, with the greatest prudence.

In general, authenticated and genuine private revelations are not always perfectly unequivocal and do not always exactly establish the details of time and place.

(e) *Pseudomysticism*

False mysticism (pseudomysticism) can imitate all the secondary concomitant phenomena of the mystical life so that it is often very difficult to distinguish it from authentic mysticism. What distinguishes it—the internal mystical experience—takes place in the interior life of man.

One is able to judge whether it is a case of pseudomysticism from certain characteristics. One of the most important characteristics lies in obedience, especially when it is a matter of mandates which limit or annul the influence upon the external world.

Psuedomysticism will, at any cost, act in the external sphere. The public is of great interest to it. Hence pseudomysticism will, at times, deceitfully imitate the virtue of humility. Pseudomysticism speculates on the credulity and the mania for miracles on the part of people. The mania for miracles is therefore often the worst adversary of genuine faith. Genuine faith does not seek nor pretend continuous " miracles."

Finally, there is also a pseudomysticism of diabolical character (mysticism of the devil, *maleficium*).

f. Diabolical phenomena

(a) *Fundamental principles*

The possibility of diabolical influences cannot be denied. Denial of this would be equivalent to a denial of the fundamental Christian doctrine of original sin and, with it, the doctrine of redemption and of the supernatural life of man. If, in denying this possibility, the modern era goes to extremes, so in past times there was no limit to the acceptance of this possibility. The periods of the mania for witches (suspicion of witchcraft, of commerce with the devil) are a warning example.

Demonomagy, black magic and diabolical possession were suspected. Exorcism was asked of the priest for the least reason. Historiography failed to mention the fact that this mania was rooted in the people as a residue of ancient pagan superstition and that the Church was forced to combat it with all her power. Meanwhile the processes against witches continued in non-Catholic lands up to the nineteenth century; Carpzov (Leipzig) alone confirmed twenty thousand death sentences against the witches, and the Jesuit priest Father von Spee protested against the witch mania.

The Church is as reserved in the recognition of supernatural processes and miracles as she is with regard to diabolical influences. It is important to realize the great circumspection with which the Church proceeds before deciding to admit authentic obsession and making use of solemn exorcism.

(b) *Forms of manifestation of demonomagy*

Demonomagy (black magic) manifests itself in various forms. Its exact recognition seems possible only to the initiated. It can only be surmised to what extent secret societies initiate the adept in a gradual manner to the ultimate secrets. Moreover, relatively primitive forms of black magic (fortunetelling, magic, crystal gazing, chiromancy) were preserved in folk superstition. In astrology and the related occult sciences, one could distinguish between a well-founded scientific element (cosmic influences, rhythm of life) and superstitions or diabolical abuse.

Demonomagy made use, by means of abuse, of true and correct knowledge and, finally, even of science. The abusive use of psychoanalysis, hypnosis, etc., were examples. Finally, it was not even afraid to form a caricature of Christian mysticism (mysticism of the devil), the most perverse form of which is the sacrilegious abuse of consecrated hosts in the " black mass."

(c) *Diabolical possession (Obsessitas)*

That true obsession exists is proved from the testimony of Holy Scripture. Christ mentions even evil spirits which can be removed only by means of prayer, temperance and fasting.

It is with reason that the Church confers, within the minor orders, the office of exorcism.

In obsession, the body and lower powers of the soul are under the influence of diabolical powers. The higher spiritual powers are basically free; free will is therefore not abolished, but undergoes a difficult test. If, with free decision of the will, man approves the sovereignty of the evil spirit, he can be transformed into a " demon in flesh and bones."

We distinguish between a *circumsessio*, when the assaults and temptations fall upon the obsessed person from the outside, and an *insessio* (obsession in the strict sense). The highest degree of possession by the devil is called *possessio*: the devil takes possession of man and his bodily organs and makes use of them as instruments deprived of a will. The devil speaks through him.

At times the voice is a voice other than the natural voice of the possessed person, and this manifests clearly that another speaks through him.

The victim suffers terribly, and during the pause between each attack he repels the demon. For the most part, he does not feel capable of praying or receiving the Sacraments.

It seems from trustworthy reports that there are cases in which, despite intermittent diabolical possession, the moral personality remains intact and, during the pause, the person is capable of a profound religious life. Also there are cases in which the taking possession of the organs by the devil, against the will of the person, represents a suffering which, in determined circumstances, can directly assume the character of expiation.

In regard to these examples, there are cases in which the entire personality is so radically changed that the individual appears to those around him as a " devil in flesh and bones " (he has the devil in his body); and still other cases exist in which a sexual component primarily dominates all thoughts and is, at times, manifested in vulgar obscenity and eventually associated with terrible blasphemy. Finally, others are overpowered by sexual representations which correspond to " commerce with the devil," for example, to that of *incubus* and *succubus*. It would not be erroneous to suppose that such representations rarely arise without the co-operation of the person.

(d) *Differential diagnosis*

States similar to diabolical obsession can present themselves in various mental diseases and even in hysteria and in the psychopathic predisposition.

The ideas of sinfulness which we encounter in cases of melancholy can, in certain circumstances, assume a corresponding coloration.

On the other hand, the " split personality " in schizophrenia can lead to states which resemble the symptoms of true diabolical obsession.

In all the diseases in whose course are presented symptoms with illusory ideas (paranoia, *dementia paranoides, dementia paralytica*), the picture of diabolical obsession appears.

In hysteria, a simulated obsession appears at times, and this because of the need of making oneself the center of attraction. The desire for the sensation associated with a solemn exorcism performed by the bishop, the publicity which extends beyond one's place of origin, and other similar factors, are elements which contribute to the formation of a grotesque pathological symptom.

"Neuroses of the devil" are not rare in psychopaths. It is possible in many cases that a diabolical influence intervenes, together with natural factors, or engrafts itself in a secondary manner. In fact, some expressive forms of psychopathy and hysteria constitute fertile soil for diabolical influence. The character changes of psychopaths and hysterical subjects are a *locus minoris resistentiae*. In this case, the individual factors are difficult to separate one from another. It is scarcely possible to establish where the natural factors end and where the diabolical begin. Even different degrees of co-operation from diabolical influences are imaginable. At the beginning the intervention can be modest and, little by little, take predominance, especially when the patient does not reveal any resistance and plays with the idea of obsession.

The distinction between authentic obsession and pathological symptoms can, in the individual case, constitute one of the most difficult tasks.

As in the past, nearly all extraordinary phenomena—even those of definite morbid origin—were considered diabolical, so that persons really sick became victims of injustice, so in the present all phenomena of this kind are, without exception, considered morbid. It is only rarely that the diabolical factor presents itself unequivocally and exclusively. Much more frequent are the *casus mixti* (De Tonquédec), in which the diabolical factor intervenes, at least as a co-operating factor if not also as a principal factor. This is more often the case than is realized. This co-operation is possible in the most varied expressive forms of psychopathy; in compulsive neurosis, hysteria and even in psychosis, etc. In such *casus mixti*, the distinction between the causal factors is much more difficult since they, for the most part, entwine themselves in an inextricable "bundle," so that—despite the most detailed and impartial examination—it cannot be decided definitely where the pathological factor ends and where the diabolical factor begins.

There are cases which present, both for the priest and the doctor, almost insoluble tasks.

The doctor himself cannot resolve the matter, just as the theologian cannot do so without the most exact knowledge of the medical aspects of the case. The two must collaborate.

(e) *Pastoral questions*

The Roman Ritual expressly prohibits the exorcist to assume any medical function on the occasion of exorcism.

Canon 984 of the Code of Canon Law states:

"The following are irregular by reason of defect: Individuals who are or have been epileptics, insane, or possessed by the devil. If, after the reception of orders, they become thus afflicted but later on are certainly rid of the affliction, the Ordinary may again allow his subjects the exercise of the orders which they have received."[1]

4. APPENDIX—OBSERVATIONS CONCERNING THE PHENOMENA OF KONNERSREUTH

In the case of Theresa Neumann of Konnersreuth, we find a large number of phenomena which have been mentioned in this book among the "borderland states." We find:

(1) The cure of serious diseases. The supernatural character of these is still considered doubtful by medical science, since it has not been definitely ascertained whether the disease was of an organic or purely psychogenic nature.

---

[1] "Sunt irregulares ex defectu: Qui epileptici vel amentes vel a daemone possessi sunt, vel fuerunt; quod si post receptos ordines tales evaserint et iam liberos esse certo constet, Ordinarius potest suis subditis receptorum ordinum exercitium rursus permittere."

The designation of "vel fuerunt" has its importance because of the danger of relapse. Only those who have become sick after having received priestly orders and are definitely healed can, under certain assurance from the bishop or the superior of the Order, be permitted to exercise the orders already received.

In order to remove abuse and scandal, the ecclesiastical code specifies, concerning the treatment of an obsession, that exorcisms can be made only with the explicit and special permission from the Ordinary (canon 1151, #1), and this permission shall be granted by the Ordinary only to a priest who is distinguished for piety, prudence and integrity of life (canon 1151, #2).

(2) Stigmatization;

(3) Ecstasies;

(4) Visions, especially of the Passion of Christ;

(5) Revelations;

(6) The hearing and repeating of an unknown language (Aramaic);

(7) Absolute fast.

On the question of the nature of these phenomena, medical science has failed to give an answer. It cannot but fail as long as it does not overcome positivism. Only by taking into account the aspect of the question which considers the principles, and not merely the facts, can the limits within which science is able to contribute its clarification be realized.

Lack of insight concerning this requisite is the reason why even some Catholic doctors have taken a stand that has proved regrettable. There is no sufficiently clear distinction between the primary question of whether it is possible that the nature of the phenomena is supernatural and the secondary question of how the individual case is to be judged.

In the case of Theresa Neumann, the following can be considered as demonstrated: stigmatization, ecstasies, visions, the hearing and repetition of the Aramaic language. The questions which are still controverted are:

(1) Was the disease of Theresa Neumann an organic or functional disease?

(2) Is the fast absolute?

Concerning the question of the fast, it is to be observed that the Franciscan Sisters of Mallersdorf have confirmed it. Admitting that they were victims of a fraud, we would have to suppose deception. But this supposition would contradict the established character of the other phenomena.

In regard to the supernatural character of the cure, the following is to be considered. The question whether the disease was organic or functional is relevant only as proof of the nature of the existing disease, i.e., as *motivum credibilitatis* and not for the supernatural character of the cure as such. There is no reason for the exclusion of the possibility of a supernatural cure in a functional disease. In the case of a functional disease, however, proof of a supernatural cure is, in certain circumstances, difficult almost to the point of being impossible. However, in the case of Theresa Neumann, the miraculous cure is merely one element in a series of numerous other phenomena.

At the basis of the attempt to characterize the disease as purely psychogenic and the sick person as hysterical, is a tendency to question the credibility of Theresa Neumann. Here arises the question: What is meant by hysteria? If hysteria is understood in the sense of degenerative changes of character (the desire for notoriety, egomania, mendacity, so-called *pseudologia phantastica*), then the establishing of the same would be a serious element of suspicion against credibility. But if, on the other hand, it is considered merely in the sense of " psychogenic " readiness to reaction, as a designation of symptoms of a purely psychic origin (functional, psychogenic) which lack an anatomical (organic) basis, then it is incomprehensible why hysteria, in this sense, should be an impediment to supernatural phenomena, revelations and graces. The strong mental and emotional capacity can be a natural requisite for mystical experience or, at least, favor it.

The study of the mental life of the saints suggests the hypothesis that hysteria, in the sense of functional disturbances and labile equilibrium of body and soul, does not exclude the highest moral perfection. Conceptually a " hysterical character " excludes sanctity, since the hysterical character never arises without the co-operation of personal guilt.

The question of hysteria in the sense of functional disturbance is important only for the " proving force " of the cure, but not for the credibility nor for the possibility of the supernatural character of phenomena.

The tendency to seek a natural explanation or to certainly exclude it has led to the demand for " clinical observation." Here arise the questions: What can, in general, be expected of it and what is the limit of the competency of medical science? Clinical observation can no longer clarify the question of the former disease, since a complete cure has taken place. Observation can serve in the confirmation of inedia. It is asked whether this is still necessary. The supposition of fraud can be excluded. Thus observation cannot but affirm the facts which, as such, can no longer be doubted—namely, the phenomena of stigmatization, of the ecstasies and visions.

For the question of the authenticity of the mystical phenomena, medical science can only supply positive data—but is not competent to give judgment concerning this question, since it lacks the adequate norms.

The competency of medical science is, however, more than necessary, as long as its representatives, who are orientated in positivism, do not know and much less accept the principal propositions of theology and the medico-pastoral standpoint.

Whatever the definite judgment concerning the case of Konnersreuth may be, the phenomena force every person to discuss and take into account the ultimate question.

They require a clear profession in regard to the question:

Basic acceptance or denial of the supernatural?

They also place science at the crossroads.

PART III

RELIGION AND
THERAPEUTICS
(DEONTOLOGY)

Religion and Therapeutics (Deontology)

Preliminary observations

We have reached the point where the ways and the spirits separate. Up to this point, in the consideration of various themes, it was possible and necessary to prove, with logical arguments, starting principally with a purely medical knowledge of facts, the agreement between rational knowledge, based on nature, and the supernatural, inspired doctrine of the Church.

In the study of "borderland states" it was not possible to adopt this method exclusively. At times we found ourselves in a borderland zone in which even the believer is free to form his own judgment concerning individual phenomena. In every case we can and should consider the natural foundation of the facts.

In the subjects which we are now to discuss, this methodical procedure no longer attains the objective. Even here, as before, we must proceed, above all, from purely natural observations—but the deduced conclusions are not based upon a rigorously logical proof. Here faith has the word.

To those who believe in the reality of the supernatural, the conclusion will be simply self-evident. Those who deny the supernatural and acknowledge only the visible and measurable world cannot be convinced through any demonstrative procedure. They will certainly deprive themselves of the only possibility of knowing the situation and of bringing light to a darkness which can never be clarified in any other way.

One who calls this resistance to the totality of certain knowledge "scientific" and considers, on the other hand, accessibility to the

419

same as "unscientific"—for such, the following is not written and, it is doubtful whether the following sections will be of use for him.

1. MIRACULOUS CURES

a. Fundamental principles

The possibility of miraculous cures—like the possibility of miracles in general—cannot be seriously doubted by the Christian. It has its basis in the omnipotence of God.

By "miracle" is generally meant a direct intervention of the supernatural in a natural process, so that the change of the affected process can no longer be explained in a purely natural way.

For one who has properly recognized the relation between the natural and the supernatural, especially the basic principle of the *analogia entis*, and has understood the fact of the ontological reality of the supernatural in relation to the natural, there can be no doubt that miracles are possible.

The believer "wonders" much less than the unbeliever, since he realizes with greater clearness the connection between the natural and the supernatural. To him the extraordinary change of direction in a natural process will not appear as a necessary motive of faith. Even without miracles, he believes in the reality of the supernatural and in the relation between the natural and the supernatural.

The concept of a miracle does not necessarily require that the natural laws be suspended for the time being. Yet God can without doubt reveal Himself in this manner.

The revival of a dead person when decomposition has already set in (Lazarus) is an absolute exception of natural law. God is Lord even over natural laws.

Not in all cases of supernatural intervention must the natural law necessarily be abrogated. Even when natural laws are apparently revoked, the question can still be asked whether it is only a matter of laws unknown to us or, in reality, of superior laws unknown to us taking precedence over the lower laws known to us.

The supernatural fastens itself with preference on the natural. Many miracles take place in an absolutely unobtrusive manner, without sensational and external phenomena.

A "change of direction" perceptible to the senses is not a necessary and essential characteristic of a miracle. The world around us is full of miracles which the limited senses do not perceive. They do not notice the grandeur of the innumerable invisible miracles which take place every day and which could be called *miracula intra naturam.*

b. Concept

(a) *Classes of miracles*—Bon distinguishes the following:

(1) *Miracula supra naturam;*
(2) *Miracula contra naturam;*
(3) *Miracula praeter naturam.*

As an example of the first class, Bon posits the revival of a dead person; as an example of the second class, the saving of the youths from the fiery furnace; for the third class, the sudden healing of a wound with an instantaneous formation of new tissue. Characteristic of the last type of miracle is lack of the natural course of time and of other physiological conditions for a cure.

(b) *Definition of the miraculous cure*

Only a process of cure which is not absolutely explainable in a natural way can be considered a miraculous cure. Theoretically it is not necessary that each case be exclusively a case of an organic disease in which pathological modifications that are well characterized, demonstrable and anatomically controllable are established. Even purely functional diseases can be cured through the direct intervention of the supernatural.

Yet in such a case the proof of a supernatural cure—namely, the confirmation that the cure is not naturally explainable—becomes very difficult, if not impossible. As has already been mentioned, we do not have any " positive " criterion for the confirmation of a miraculous cure, but only a negative criterion—namely, that it is not explainable in a natural manner. When the possibility of a natural explanation exists, then the formal acknowledgment of the cure as a miraculous one must be eliminated. The possibility of a natural explanation can always be posited in the case of purely functional diseases; even cases of a sudden cure of such diseases are possible without a supernatural intervention, simply by means of a phenomenon capable of activating the mental powers.

It can be a case of " apparent miracles " and of natural " parallel phenomena." Thus in cases of this kind, sensational as they may be—for example, the cure of hysterical paralysis and hysterical blindness—there is no reason to consider these as miraculous cures. Such cases must at present be excluded as a testimony of a miraculous cure, with prejudice to the possibility that even in these cases it can be a matter of a grace received and a prayer that has been heard.

c. The miraculous cures of Christ

The miraculous cures of Christ are to be judged according to different norms.

The norm which we are to apply at the present time to the miraculous cures that have been mentioned fails here, since we treat here of an absolutely unlimited grandeur. There is no need to deny that among the miracles performed by Christ, according to the tradition of the Gospels, we find miracles which admit of the possibility of a natural explanation. It is nevertheless a miserable effort to apply this norm to the miracles of Christ. Despite this, there are still many miracles which cannot be explained in a natural manner. It does not matter here whether one can consider the possibility of a purely psychogenic paralysis. Christ does not select His miracles from the standpoint of rational demonstrability. Christ speaks and acts as one " having power." In this respect, the healing of the paralytic (Matt. 9:1-3) is of special significance. Before healing him, Christ said to him: " Thy sins are forgiven thee." The Scribes said within themselves: " This man [who speaks thus, without Himself being God] blasphemes." They, however, did not realize the effect of an understanding faith, and had become hardened in their incredulity. Christ, " knowing their thoughts," answered: " Which is easier, to say, ' Thy sins are forgiven thee,' or to say, ' Arise and walk '? But that you may know that the Son of Man has power on earth to forgive sins. . . ," He said to the paralytic " Arise take up thy pallet and go to thy house."[1]

---

[1] Matt. 9:1-8:

" And Jesus, seeing their faith, said to the paralytic, ' Take courage, son, thy sins are forgiven thee.' And behold, some of the Scribes said within themselves, ' This man blasphemes.' And Jesus, knowing their thoughts, said, ' Why do you harbor evil thoughts in your hearts? For which is easier to say, " Thy sins are forgiven thee," or to say, " Arise and walk "? But that you may know that the Son of Man has power on earth to forgive sins '—then He said to the paralytic—' Arise, take up thy pallet and go to thy house.' And he arose, and went away to his house. But when the crowds saw it, they were struck with fear, and glorified God who has given such power to men."

Here every natural critical norm must fail—whether it is a matter of an "organic" paralysis or a "functional" paralysis—since the Lord of the natural and the supernatural speaks.

It would be a worthy and meritorious task to gather and assemble all the miraculous cures of Christ to show how they fit into the pattern of thought here displayed. It would contrast with so many deplorable attempts to explain these miracles from the standpoint of a hardened incredulity. But in this way, within these patterns belief might enter by means of an enlightened science (*scientia fide illuminata*). This refers not only to the miraculous cures of Christ, but also His Passion and death. Hynek has already made an important attempt in this direction.

d. Confirmation of miraculous cures

If the miracles of Christ are beyond all human norms, so today there is great need for unobjectionable standards for the reliable confirmation of recent miraculous cures.

Such confirmation, using scientific means, is an indispensable condition in offering proof of these miraculous cures. The first principle for the medical expert must be a "healthy skepticism"; he may only consider a thing to be "not explainable by nature" when, according to science, there is no possibility of a natural explanation.

He must be aware of the fact that he will render a greater service to the Church and the faith by giving at first, in a definite, given case, a negative vote which is very severe and which may, if necessary, be changed to an *emendatio in melius*, than, on the other hand, by giving a positive vote, easily extracted, which must later be retracted and which would cause an *emendatio in peius*.

Regarding the practical execution, we can refer to the system of the *bureaux de constatation* in Lourdes as a model. Its members work with a staff of doctors who are experts from the clinical and specialist aspect and who examine the cases expertly by means of all the modern clinical methods of investigation and record these data officially.

It is possible at any time to check the sketches, photographs, radiographs, microscopic preparations, etc.

Any doctor, no matter what his religious profession or ideology might be, can at any time freely enter and convince himself of the

P

exactitude of the method used by the bureaux. Among the cures which are not explainable by nature, which without doubt are very numerous, only those are " confirmed " and acknowledged which are absolutely unequivocal and definite.

In accordance with the principles developed above, Dr. Le Bec (according to Bon) indicates the following as means of proof for miraculous cures:

(1) Definitely confirmed severe tissue lesion, loss of substance before the cure;

(2) Sudden re-establishment within a span of time that is too short for a natural and medical cure;

(3) The permanent character and duration of the cure, the full re-establishment of the natural function, confirmed over a sufficiently long period of time so that one cannot speak of a simple improvement.

(4) The seriousness of a lesion or disease which in se, according to human experience, excludes the possibility of a cure;

(5) The relation between the biological phenomenon and the religious experience;

(6) The exclusion of the " nervous factor " (cf. above).

e. Summary

Doubt concerning the possibility of a miracle implies doubt of God and His omnipotence. Even in our day God reveals Himself through miracles and, besides extraordinary events, through numerous daily marvels. One must only will to see.

On the other hand, men through miracle-mania seek miracles and try to exaggerate things to a point which in reality is not the truth.

On no other occasion does the Church use such reserve and prudence as in the acknowledgment of supernatural events. She exhausts every possibility of natural science and all means of proof used by science before attesting to the authenticity of a miracle. She definitely knows that the supernatural is in se neither scientifically comprehensible nor penetrable. It is an object of faith (*objectum fidei*), and as such is not directly accessible to science, even if, according to the Catholic conception, natural, rational knowledge is sufficient in order to definitely know the existence of

God and of the supernatural (*certo cognosci posse*: Vatican Council).

Science can only confirm facts capable of laying claim to validity as "motives of credibility" (*motiva credibilitatis*).

Metaphysics is capable of pushing forward to the confines of natural rational knowledge and or perceiving the natural fundamentals of faith (*praeambula fidei*).

Mystical theology is called upon to confirm the norms of authenticity for supernatural phenomena.

These criteria make it possible to evaluate each case with the greatest rigor. Despite this, doubt continues to be raised against these evaluations, and this in the name of science.

One who does not will to see cannot be helped. The blind can suppose that light does not exist. Yet one should not expect to impose his opinion upon the person who sees and to set himself up as an authority.

2. METAPHYSICO-PATHOLOGICAL PHENOMENA

a. Concept

When we speak of metaphysical pathological phenomenon, we mean that, behind the visible world (*physis*) and its processes, there exists an invisible world (metaphysis—μετὰ τὰ φυσικὰ). Behind a visible pathological process there exists a "metaphysical" phenomenon. This definition is a deviation from the ordinary use of the term "metaphysical," and this is deliberate, since metaphysics as a science always remains within the confines of a natural rational cognitive faculty. But here "metaphysical phenomenon" refers to processes which extend beyond the natural order of being, partly toward the higher and partly toward the lower. That is the reason why it is not possible to speak of a supernatural phenomenon. Since here it is not a matter of things which belong solely to the supernatural order, to grace—but also of things which pertain to its opposite pole, to the realm of the devil. One may refer to it as extranatural, but it cannot be called supernatural.

There is lacking an appropriate term to indicate these realms, both of which are beyond human nature. In order to include in one term both types of phenomena, no better term has yet been found than that of "metaphysical phenomenon." Yet, there is nothing to keep one from accepting a more appropriate and more exact term.

b. Basic principles

The recognition or denial of a "metaphysical pathological phenomenon" depends—as in the case of miraculous cures—on whether one acknowledges an order of being which extends beyond what is perceptible to the senses. For one who denies this, a phenomenon which is beyond a physical pathological phenomenon can at most be a "psychic phenomenon," and this in opposition to the physical phenomenon. This does not answer the question, since both still remain in the natural realm. But one who basically denies the supernatural does not acknowledge that the human soul can go beyond the natural realm.

What is essentially important is the question whether a phenomenon in the natural order also corresponds to a phenomenon in the supernatural order.

Thus the question of the *analogia entis*—that is, of the relation of "correspondence" between the two ontological orders—again assumes the central place.

It is a matter, therefore, of knowing not only whether one simply believes in the supernatural, but also whether one is convinced of the relationship of correspondence between the ontological orders.

Without conviction of the *analogia entis*, belief in the reality of the supernatural can only lead to an absolute "supernaturalism," which has already been mentioned and which holds that disease is merely the effect of sin—not only collective, but also personal sin—and hence can be cured only by supernatural means.

Health would—according to this—be a sign of grace, of harmony with the supernatural—in the same way that in Puritanism external success in life is a sign of election. Thus in this question what is important is to decide also the other question; whether human nature was radically corrupted by original sin and hence can be saved only by grace, or whether some capacity to co-operate is still present—that is, to decide between the Catholic idea and that of the Protestantism extending from Calvin to Barth.

c. Practical importance

The question of the " metaphysical pathological phenomenon " is not a theoretical one, but rather a question whose practical importance in all the spheres of life is incalculable. Provided that first a person grasps the idea that for each and every deed of man, every *actus humanus*, there exists on the supernatural plane some corresponding reality, which throughout his activities he is overlooking— or wrongly evaluating—then the person begins to take a wholly changed view of the world and his own acts and intentions. He gains insight into a new world, one that is greater and more true.

We can bring out the importance of this realization by a few examples: Entrance into life—generation and birth—as well as exit from life—death—are elementary biological processes of human existence, the two extreme points within which psychic life takes place.

When our considerations go beyond the confines of physical existence, we will become aware of the fact that at the moment of birth as well as that of death, a very important metaphysical phenomenon takes place.

If, in conformity with the Scholastic conception, we see a " microcosm " in man, we infer—in a special manner—that something great takes place at death; an end of the world within the microcosmic realm; and at the same time, a " universal judgment." " If you knew what takes place at that time," says St. Theresa of death.

The practical importance of this realization for the doctor is obvious. One who has comprehended the essence of this phenomenon will never consider the *procuratio abortus* or euthanasia as disputable interventions.

If it is seriously understood that every mortal sin, every conscious denial of God, in reality represents a " spiritual death " by which the whole world topples, then it will be better realized how perseverance in sin transforms the entire structure of the human soul, whose abandonment to the world and all the material things of life comes as a gradual consequence.

When the renunciation is not complete and does not embrace the entire nature of man, it leads to a deep discord, to " pathogenic conflicts " of a kind to which the frequently cited words of Shakespeare apply: "More needs she the divine than the physician."

In a case of total renunciation, neurosis will not arise. When conscience is completely dead, and the soul is hardened, mental "health" remains—at times, exteriorly enviable and robust health. In reality, this mentally "healthy" individual is more to be pitied than the "sick" individual, who is still capable of a neurosis. For neurosis is then a sign of an inquietude toward God, but the apparent "health" of which we speak here is an expression of absolute separation from God.

d. Importance for the nature and meaning of sickness

This knowledge will make it easier to understand how important the understanding of a metaphysical pathological phenomena is for a deeper comprehension of the nature and meaning of sickness in general.

This question is closely associated with the meaning of suffering —a question that can only be solved satisfactorily through a Christian viewpoint, through the *philosophia crucis*.

Among the world religions, Buddhism does not neglect this question but cannot answer it satisfactorily. It remains an insoluble enigma. On the other hand, the *mysterium crucis* solves all the enigmas of the world and of life.

In the light of Christian doctrine there must be a reason behind every illness: a particular "home-seeking," a decree and guidance of Providence or, at least, a "permission," whose meaning is not always immediately comprehensible, but is revealed only later.

However, illness is never a matter of pure "chance," blind fate, or forced causal necessity, since the organism is assailed by definite microbes.

The microbes are present and are often ubiquitous. The question why one becomes sick and another does not cannot be solved absolutely and satisfactorily by the factors of constitution, disposition, etc.

Behind this question there is another—namely, why an individual in the same condition remains healthy over a long period of his life and becomes sick just at a critical moment.

This question occupies the central part in the "biographical" observation of sickness made by V. Weizsacker.

Hollmann, in a study replete with thought, has shown the connection between sickness and the crises of life. He has evaluated the social causal factors and the endopsychic, but has not advanced to the comprehension of the metaphysical active factors.

The decisive step is the following: whether, even in sickness, a manifestation of divine power and providence is acknowledged— and in definite circumstances, even a task for the sick or for those around him on the proper execution of which something decisive depends.

The question that is to be asked is this: "What does God wish to say by this sickness?" It is the question asked by Saul when struck with blindness: "Lord, what wilt Thou have me do?" (Acts 9:6).

The importance for psychiatry and psychotherapy of understanding these relationships has already been stated. But it is full of significance and cognitive value even in cases of organic disease.

It is again of decisive importance for the supernatural end of man's life, how the sick person adjusts himself to his suffering, how he answers the question: "What wilt Thou have me do?" what suffering does to him and what he makes of suffering. Many things depend on it, even from the standpoint of a purely natural development of personality.

The same suffering can completely suffocate the personality of one person and enrich another interiorly, despite the fact that the body is decaying. "He must increase, but I must decrease" (*Illum oportet crescere, me autem minui*); the more the physical man diminishes, the more the metaphysical man increases in the true and substantial and eternal being. The psychic effects of disease upon men is, therefore, diverse. Certain typical mental reactions and types of behavior correspond to the various bodily ailments, as they are well known and studied. (We speak of the psyche of tuberculosis, stomach or liver ailments, of the blind, deaf, of the "cripple-psyche," etc.) Yet there is no like reaction for all men, no typical "cripple-psyche." Rather, one accommodates his physical impediment to a task, whether by means of physical compensation or through mental development, while another becomes torpid in resentment and finally allows malice to take over. It is, however, an *actus humanus* —a free decision of the will—whether one attains reconciliation and love through the *mysterium crucis* or gives free reign to the *mysterium iniquitatis* and perdition.

It is the object here only to indicate the basic questions and to call attention to their importance.

The proper comprehension of these will also indicate the course to be followed by medical deontology.

3. RELIGION AND SICKNESS

What is most important for the question of the relationship between religion and sickness follows from what has already been stated. Sickness leads one sick individual to religion, and a new meaning of life is opened to him which, up to that time, had been hidden from him; another is hardened by sickness, opposes God, and is in discord with the world. The importance of religion for complete adjustment to sickness and for the activation of mental forces in attaining a cure now appears very essential.

Without doubt religion can be considered one of the most important mental curative factors. And when a cure is not possible, religion helps one bear sickness, offers an explanation, and helps one to be reconciled to suffering.

a. Religion and psychopathy

On the other hand, it is often objected—sometimes reasonably— that even the religious person often fails in sickness by anxiously attaching himself to earthly life when liberating himself from it should seem a gain to him (*cupio dissolvi*). There thus arises a discrepancy between theory and practice which even for other reasons seems strange.

In this connection, attention is brought to neuroses which often befall religious persons, as—for example—compulsive neurosis, and especially scrupulosity, etc. It is believed that it can be concluded that it is not correct to say that religion is always a therapeutic factor of great worth. On the other hand, it is often a pathogenic factor, at least, a factor which paralyzes the desire to be cured, especially in psychopathy of religious coloration, in mental masochism in which pain is sought and metaphysically evaluated through conversion into "mental acquisition of pleasure." There is no need to deny that there are cases in which the objections raised have a certain justification. However, what should be rejected is the generalization and the idea that the deviations mentioned are to be imputed to religion as such and that they are the products of religion. They are the product of psychopathy and nothing else.

The fact that psychopathy in religious persons assumes *in dubio* a religious "coloration," just as in certain psychoses which proceed with the formation of illusions the illusion appears religiously colored, will not surprise anyone who seeks to understand the nature of psychopathy and psychosis.

Moreover, it must be determined in the individual case whether the phenomena in their disagreeable forms are really found in persons of authentic religiosity or whether it is rather a matter of apparent religiosity which is purely external, from which sickness causes the mask to fall. Even in the latter case it is not necessary that authentic religiosity be absolutely missing or be denied. Rather, in many persons "the spirit is willing but the flesh is weak."

When these persons fail, one must not immediately take scandal and exaggerate the situation to the point of making it a public scandal which would give occasion for some to fall into error with regard to faith. One should, instead, consider—without prejudice—just how the same persons would react without religion.

This would definitely show that the mode of behavior is influenced by religion only in a favorable manner, since without religion the sick persons would be more seriously sick, more egocentric and more asocial.

Even concerning the type of inflexibility not rarely found in pious persons, we must say that interior flexibility does not pertain to religion nor to a particular type of piety, but is merely the expression of an anxious and narrowminded mental deviation which is partly egoistic and partly of the nature of self-justification and intimidation. It has nothing to do with religion as such, but is a species of faulty religious behavior which easily throws discredit upon religiosity, but with no greater justification than the other deviations which we have already mentioned.

The consideration of the same as typical of Catholic piety is both unjust and manifests a lack of realization and understanding. Moreover, authentic Catholicity is not narrowminded but extensive and complete, for true humility and true love of God have nothing to do with servile fear, but arise from true freedom and the grandeur of filial obedience to God, which has overcome the interior "world."

What this interior comportment signifies for the sick person

P*

requires no further explanation. It makes him free and also teaches him to overcome sickness.

This idea should not, however, lead to the belief held by certain Christian psychotherapists (Gebsattel and others) who contend that the Christian as such no longer needs psychotherapy. This would be so if the Christian, because he is a Christian, were immune to every possibility of being affected by neurosis. But, since the Christian *in statu viatoris* must suffer as the result of *natura vulnerata* and hence can also be afflicted with physical illness, it is also possible for him to be afflicted with neurosis.

In comparing confession with psychoanalysis, it must be stated that the two tasks are completely different and should not be confused. Just as psychotherapy can never replace confession, so confession is not meant to, nor can it, render psychotherapy superfluous whenever this is indicated for neurosis. Such erroneous ideas always result in a confusion of the task of the priest and that of the doctor; they suppress the boundaries of the two professions, and end in obscure ideas concerning a " priest-doctor."

b. Sanctity and sickness

If it can be supposed with definite reason that the " saint "—i.e., one who lives with God in the most perfect harmony that can be attained by man—will be, because of this, *ceteris paribus*, little disposed toward neurosis, it must not be forgotten that not even the saint on earth is immune from every *inordinatio* of the unconscious strata of the soul, from the onslaughts of the *angelus satanae*. Hence he must also, as St. Paul acknowledges, suffer " in his members under the double law." Despite his supplications, the *stimulus carnis* will not be removed from him: *sufficit tibi gratia* (2 Cor. 12:7-9). At times the attempt has also been made to subject the mental life of the saints to a critical examination from the standpoint of psychopathology. It must without doubt be admitted that even among the saintly figures there are some who are at the boundary line of mental " normality " and who present characteristics which can be considered pathological or hysterical. Even if this is so, such a confirmation signifies nothing more than a new page of glory. For if there are persons who are successful, despite serious impediments and mental burdens, so that the Church, after most severe examinations in the process of beatification and that of canonization, has recognized their heroic virtue, this signifies a double merit and a special victory of grace over dispositions which for a great number of people would become a fatality and would drag them to the depths.

Concerning certain characteristics which are encountered in the lives of saints and which at times seem abnormal, the following is to be considered: Among these are found those concerning whom the doctors of the Church say: " Admirandum quidem sed non imitandum " (They are to be admired but not imitated)—as, for example, the Stylites in their voluntary isolation. They are to be considered in general as " morbid."

If we completely prescind from the fact that from the grand figures of hermits of all times there emanates a strong force which opposes unbridled dedication to the world and represents a convincing exhortation tending toward the *unum necessarium*, even here the words prevail: *Si duo faciunt idem non est idem.*

If acts exteriorly similar receive their impulse merely from the need to be known or the masochistic tendency toward auto-lesion, then it would not be a case of sanctity but only of morbid deviation.

c. Attitude toward the problem of suffering

The same can be said, *mutatis mutandis,* concerning the attitude toward suffering and sickness, in general.

Flight into sickness, when one is faced with reality and the demands of life, is neurotic. Morbid pleasure in sickness can also be evident. Yet the desire of many saints to make expiation by suffering for themselves and others and thus to attain sanctity, cannot be considered masochistic. Such generalization reveals a great lack of understanding. The basic reason for such a devaluating idea lies in the incapacity to look beyond the terrestrial realm.

To one who looks at the matter merely in an earthly sense, health appears not only as a great value of life, but as the supreme good. Hence sickness must appear as something hostile to life, as something that paralyzes the capacity to live, as weakness and inferiority. Only Christianity has taught us to see in the sick, " the burdened and oppressed," to whom God is very close and to whom Christ has given His special love.

On the other hand, opposed to the earthly concept which sees in the sick nothing but a burden for society and opposed also to the spiritualistic concept which we have mentioned and which sees in sickness only sin, and in health a sign of election, there is the concept of Christianity according to which sickness and suffering can be signs of election and grace. According to this concept also, the sick are closer than the healthy person to the road that leads to God. " God does not live in the healthy body " (St. Hildegarde).

This formula may appear strange to those attached to this world, but its true meaning can be properly understood only *sub specie aeternitatis*. It is necessary to emphasize these things since at times, even on the part of Catholics, under the influence of erroneously interpreted eugenic ideas, a wrong meaning has been attributed to the words *gratia supponit naturam*—as if grace, in order to be efficacious, presupposes the health and integrity of nature, especially " hereditary health."

But this is definitely not true. The supernatural builds on the natural, as on a foundation (*supponit naturam*), and certainly the integrity of nature can contribute to a richer development of grace. Mental integrity or integrity of hereditary health is, however, not a presupposition of grace. Its action is not diverted toward it, but often tends toward a completely different way.

Mens sana in corpore sano does not mean that a healthy soul can inhabit only a healthy body, but means, rather, that it must be considered a special gift of grace that a healthy spirit also inhabits a healthy body: *orandum est, ut sit mens sana in corpore sano.*

That the narrow concept of sickness as sin or as an evil conditioned by heredity, or as something merited by the guilt of the progenitors, was rejected by Christ Himself is testified by the words which Christ spoke with regard to the cure of the person born blind (John 9 : 1-38). To the question " Rabbi, who has sinned, this man or his parents? " the Redeemer answered that, in this case, neither this man nor his parents had sinned, but the works of God were to be made manifest in him.[1]

That sickness and death are effects of original sin, of the fallen nature of man, needs no further explanation. This truth is for the Christian absolutely evident.

---

[1] John 9 : 1-3 :
" And as he was passing by, he saw a man blind from birth. And His disciples asked Him : ' Rabbi, who has sinned, this man or his parents, that he should be born blind? ' Jesus answered, ' Neither has this man sinned, nor his parents, but the works of God were to be made manifest in him.' "

d. Sacraments and sickness

Concerning the question of the effect that the means of grace and especially the sacraments of the dying produce upon the condition of the sick, there is not much to be added to what already has been stated.

About a decade ago, in a drama, the author of which was an unbelieving physician, a doctor was celebrated as a hero because he considered it his professional duty to forbid the priest to visit the seriously ill person in order " not to disturb " him.

It is difficult to think of a more deplorable lack of understanding of the situation. What disastrous effects such an idea has exercised had to be experienced by us when for years the care of souls in hospitals was impeded in an unhuman manner and spiritual comfort was denied the sick.

It is not necessary to explain in detail what it means for the sick to receive the sacraments and especially what consciousness of reconciliation with God means to the ill person.

It is also a known fact that in many cases, besides spiritual peace, there also follows a physical improvement, solely through the effect of the reactivitation of mental forces. It would, however, be completely wrong to see in the sacraments a kind of magical remedy. The sacraments are not this, nor is this their meaning.

Their meaning is directed toward the supernatural, toward the re-establishment of harmony between the natural and supernatural. Religion (*re-ligio*) means " reunion."

This interpretation directs us in comprehending the deep relation between sickness and religion.

4. DYING AND DEATH (THANATOLOGY)

In order to present the problems related to dying and death in accordance with the universalistic conception, we must even here start with the consideration that it is not sufficient to study their biological, physiological and pathological foreground without considering their varied social and legal relations and, above all, the great metaphysical aspects of the moment of death and the ultimate problems which death presents to man. Only then can we speak of a truly scientific thanatology.

a. Medico-biological problems

In order to define death from the biological standpoint, we must begin with the concept of life. Such a definition can only be a negative definition, i.e., the extinction of all the vital functions.

Biology recognizes the following as vital functions: assimilation and dissimilation; and in relation to these, reproduction, excitability and locomotion.

These functions are common to men and the animals and partly to plants. Life, and hence also the dying of man, is distinguished from that of other living beings in that the vegetative and sensitive functions are completed and elevated by the rational functions.

Generally speaking, the vital functions are not suddenly extinguished, but almost always in inverse succession to that of their appearance, in such a way that the rational functions first become extinct and the purely vegetative vital functions last longer. However, there are also cases which manifestly contradict this apparent order of nature; cases in which the spiritual functions manifest a notable intensification before and at the moment of death.

In conformity with this, extinction of life should not be considered a purely negative sign, for the death of man also reveals high and positive forces and values. The death of man is not the same as biological decadence and disappearance.

When we distinguish between physiological death (through consumption and decadence of forces) and pathological death (through sickness), we intend the same distinction as that made between natural death and artificially provoked (unnatural) death (through accident, crime, execution, etc.). Even pathological death is a " natural " death.

At times it is very difficult to determine the limits between life and death.

In primitive living beings it is not easy to definitely distinguish the phenomena of the " latent life," of the *vita minima*, from definite death. This latent life can be designated as the borderland state between life and death.

In man, still other limited states come into consideration; thus, even in authentic supernatural ecstasies, we encounter states with characteristics similar to those of death, and parallel natural phenomena are also observed in these cases.

Moreover, it is important to distinguish between death and the states of cataleptic rigidity which, at times, can be confused with real death because of their resemblance to death.

In order to differentiate precisely between life and death, it is important to know whether death was preceded by a long agony or a serious and long sickness, or whether death has come suddenly when the subject was in good health.

In the first case, the processes of postmortal decomposition (putrefaction, corruption) intervene much more rapidly and it is consequently possible also to establish in a shorter time the definite signs of death.

The symptomatology (semeiotics) of the end of life should not be limited to the agonal and terminal symptoms which immediately precede death, but must also take into consideration the more remote signs preceding death.

For the establishment of death, it is important to distinguish between definite and indefinite signs of death.

Only those which represent proof of the incipient cadaverous transformation can be considered definite signs of death. They include:

(1) Cloudiness and maceration of the cornea;
(2) Parchment-like exsiccation of the skin (parcheminement);
(3) Cadaverous marks;
(4) The odor of putrefaction and the phenomena of corruption.

Corruption and putrefaction are not to be considered the same.

"Fetid putrefaction" precedes corruption. It arises from the co-operation of saprogenous bacteria, under the development of gas and the exclusion of oxygen (anaerobian process). Corruption, on the other hand, is a process of oxidation and arises under absorption of oxygen (aerobian process).

The process of corruption to complete skeletization of the cadaver lasts, in a porous and air-containing terrain, from six to eight years.

Of practical importance is the question of apparent death and that of reanimation.

Without doubt the fear of apparent death and of being buried alive is greatly exaggerated. At times it has even assumed the character of a diffused anxiety psychosis.

With the laws which today regulate the inspection of cadavers and the autopsies ordered by health departments, the police, etc., this fear has become unfounded.

In the case of those who die in the hospital, if the diagnosis is not completely clear, a pathologico-anatomical autopsy is also provided. Of great importance is the recently used distinction between apparent death and relative death.

Apparent death (*mors apparens*) is in opposition to real death (*mors realis*), and relative death to absolute death.

We can speak of absolute death only when there is no longer any vestige of life in the body cells. Since this does not take place suddenly, absolute death must necessarily be preceded by a phase in which life still is present in the cells of the body. This phase is called relative death.

Relative death is not simply apparent death. It is a real death, even though a number of body cells still continue to live. No one doubts that a decapitated person is "really" and not apparently dead at the moment of decapitation. Also evident is the fact that when decapitation has taken place, all the cells of the body are not immediately "dead." It is therefore possible that consciousness is present for a moment after the separation of the head from the body.

When an apparently dead person is reanimated, it is not a case of revivification in the strict sense. Life was not really extinct in him and death did not really intervene. Consequently, even according to natural law, revivification is inconceivable when absolute death has already intervened. It is conceivable only as long as the transitory phase of relative death subsists. Hence the revival of Lazarus is to be considered a miracle against the laws of nature.

Revivification from relative death can be a masterful work of modern medicine, but it is conceivable within the limits of natural law.

We can illustrate this by an example: Latent life (*vita minima*), which is found in apparent death, can be compared to a reduced flame of a burner. The flame still burns, even though it can just about be seen; but it can at any time become full-flaming when fed with more gas.

In relative death, the flame is actually extinct. The wick and burner are still warm and surrounded by inflammable gas. A cataleptic process can, in definite circumstances, reactivate the process of combustion, not, however, when the burner is completely cold, i.e., in the case of absolute death.

For the practice of reanimation there arises the possibility of activating the cataleptic actions.

The following methods are available for this purpose:

(1) Administering oxygen (artificial respiration, inhalers);

(2) Injection of stimulants (intravenous, intracardial, intra-arterial);

(3) Transfusion with an admixture of adrenalin;

(4) Direct massage of the heart.

These biological problems are of great importance for Pastoral Medicine, with regard to the possibility of validly and effectively administering the last sacraments, especially Extreme Unction, even to the dead.

When it is a case of administering the *sacramentum olei* to a person who has died, the sacrament can be administered *sub conditione* within two hours from the moment that death has been confirmed by the doctor. The period of two hours must not be taken as the maximum time for the phase of relative death, but as the average time. As has been stated, much depends on whether death took place after a long illness and a long agony or suddenly and unexpectedly.

Even if the post-mortal administration of the *sacramentum olei sub conditione* can never be a complete substitute for a good preparation for death in full consciousness and a conscious reception of the sacraments of Penance and Holy Viaticum, yet it can be a comfort to the relatives of the deceased to know that the sacrament capable of removing the effects of sin can be administered.

b. Psychological problems

It is of great importance to the doctor and to the priest to acquaint themselves with the question: "What occurs within the dying person?" This is a question which leads directly to metaphysical problems and is associated with that of the "metaphysico-pathological phenomenon." It is also associated with physiological and biological processes that take place in a dying person.

Because of lack of direct experience and evidence, we know practically nothing concerning what goes on within the dying person. Yet clinical observations permit us to deduce certain conclusions with relative security. There is greater casuistry on this point than is generally known.

The idea is quite prevalent that when the dying person has apparently lost contact with his surroundings and can no longer speak and gives the impression that he is no longer conscious, he no longer hears and is not aware of what goes on around him. This is a false idea and can have disastrous effects if it is believed that one can speak freely in the presence of the dying person, since he "is no longer aware of anything." This, however, is certain, that in death more goes on within the dying than the healthy person imagines and that the last moments of life are those which can be of decisive importance for the dying and for his life after death.

This consideration makes it clear how senseless and evil is euthanasia and every form of shortening life, even if it hides itself under the mask of humanitarianism and compassion and is presented as "merciful death."

c. Social and legal problems

Death, considered from the purely natural standpoint, is not only a biological necessity, but also a social necessity and not merely an inevitable social evil. Under this standpoint, it has two aspects: the one seems to man hard and cruel, inasmuch as it seems to break the bond of a loving community; the other reveals itself, to one who examines the matter deeply, as beneficial and salutary.

It would remain rash on the part of medicine to pretend to proclaim the "battle against death" as its general and highest law. Supposing such a struggle should end in victory for medicine, then medicine would have to assume the function of the killer and would have to make use of euthanasia as a means at the disposal of the sovereign being who has made himself "lord over life and death."

If the prolonging of the average life span brings with it the serious problem of the old and of the decrepit and, with it, the problem of the distribution of the means of subsistence and of the "struggle for existence" between the generations, what insoluble social problems would arise if death did not create a place for the young and thus transformed itself into the essential factor of rejuvenation!

Numerous are the legal problems which are associated with death. The legal effects of death pertain both to private law and to public law.

The "right of succession" is based upon the Roman idea that inheritance sustains the personality of the deceased (of the testator): *hereditas personam defuncti sustinet.* Moreover, legal questions arise concerning the cadaver itself. Of great importance are the prescriptions of Canon Law concerning burial (canon 1203-1242, CIC).

Penal law contains dispositions for the protection of the cadaver and of burial places. It legislates against their profanation and against the removal of the cadaver without permission. Finally, civil law contains prescriptions on the declaration of death, the dissolution of marriage through death, rulings concerning persons killed in the same accident; concerning the drawing up of a will and intestate succession by inheritance (legal succession by inheritance without a will), etc.

We have mentioned here only the more important questions.

d. Ethico-metaphysical problems

The ethical norms which regulate one's actions and attitude toward death and the deceased are based on the right to life or, more precisely, on respect for life. One who does not have respect for death, has no respect for life and vice-versa. Finally, this respect is based upon respect for the Creator of life—but such a question belongs to the religious sphere.

Among the ancients, respect for death and the deceased was a basic law of purely natural ethics—namely, of "piety." In the "Antigone" of Sophocles, the prohibition of burial leads to conflict between the eternal law (unwritten) of natural right and the unjust prescriptions of positive right.

Since the time of Hippocrates, medical ethics has acknowledged respect for death and the deceased as one of the most important precepts for the doctor.

It has been reserved to our disturbed times to bury, even in this point, one of the norms of medical ethics most deeply rooted in human nature.

It has been materialistic-positivistic thinking that has led to such a profound degeneration of medical ethics. It is the purpose of Pastoral Medicine to overcome, by its universalistic mode of observation, this positivistic materialism and to renew respect for death and hence even for life, as the basis of medical ethics.

From the metaphysical standpoint, the most important question seems to be that of the meaning of death. It has the same significance as the meaning of life and the meaning of suffering.

The anti-metaphysical mentality of the times has so tended to falsify the essential meaning of this question that writers have even dared to speak of the "iniquity of death" and the "iniquity of suffering" (Mulford).

Nietzsche in particular prepared, under this aspect, the way for existentialism. The latter falsified the concept of the substantial being to the point that it saw this exclusively in the simple "existence," i.e., in existing.

For Scholasticism, the substantial being was the *esse* and not the *existentia*. Only in God alone do existence and essence coincide: He is His being: "I am who am!"

From the realization that even our limited, dependent and relative being is a participation in the absolute being of God, there arises, in the same way as from the realization of the immaterial substantiality of the soul, the comprehension of the immortality of the human *anima rationalis*.

e. Religious problems

Religion and theology teach us the ultimate and most profound truths about death.

Without their conclusive data, our comprehension of death would not pass beyond the most external periphery. These studies alone render possible the essential perspective.

If, from the biological and social standpoints, we have to acknowledge that death is a necessity, theology teaches us that in the original order of creation death was not to be; that it has entered into the world only through original sin as punishment for sin. Hence, from the standpoint of our original nature, it is something which should not be.

If we have then comprehended the doctrine of redemption through the death of Christ and His resurrection, then even for us, the mere immortality of the soul does not suffice, and we realize the depth and significance of the Christian dogma of the resurrection of the body.

Only thus will the *natura lapsa seu vulnerata* be again placed in its original state (*natura reparata*). Then the meaning of the body which the Church recognizes will be opened to a deeper comprehension.

In this realization, the significance of the sacrament of the dying will also be made manifest to us.

Whoever considers this matter once will conclude it to be one of the most important duties of a doctor at the bedside of the dying to make possible for the sick and dying the reception of these means of grace at the opportune time and not to hinder their reception in any way.

The highest and most profound things the Church can say concerning death and dying are made manifest not only in dogma and moral theology, but, above all, in the liturgy.

In this connection, we refer to the prayers for the dying, the Office of the Dead and the various Masses for the deceased, as well as, in a special manner, the moving Sequence of the requiem Mass, the "Dies irae."

Of the fullness and richness of the treasures of the liturgy, we here mention only the sublime words of the Preface for the Dead:

"Life, O Lord, will not be taken from Your faithful but only transformed; and after the destruction of the house of their earthly dwelling, an eternal home will be prepared."[1]

This consoling perspective suffices to give us the solution to the tormenting enigma of our transient existence. It alone makes it possible for us to overcome fear of death, this "primordial fear" of life, and it is this certitude which makes the apostle St. Paul say: "O death, where is thy victory? O death, where is thy sting?" For "death is swallowed up in victory"—the victory of Christ, who by His death has conquered death and by His resurrection has restored life.[2]

In conclusion, let us recall the substantial importance that this universalistic notion of death has for medical ethics and, in particular, for the duties of the doctor at the bedside of the dying.

5. DEONTOLOGY

Preliminary observations

Since the following will treat of professional medical morality, we must first of all answer the preliminary question: Is there a

---

[1] "Tuis enim fidelibus, Domine, vita mutator, non tollitur; et dissoluta terrestris huius incolatus domo, aeterna in coelis habitatio praeparatur . . ."

[2] "Ubi est, mors, victoria tua; ubi est, mors, stimulus" (1 Cor. 15:55)? "Absorpta est mors in victoria" (1 Cor. 15:54-55). "Qui mortem nostram moriendo destruxit et vitam resurgendo reparavit" (Easter Preface).

proper and professional autonomous ethics for the doctor, or are the general norms of morality a standard for him?

An autonomous professional medical ethics cannot be admitted, since the doctor is not excluded from the general moral laws, but is subject to them, as is everyone else.

a. Concept

Medical deontology is not the same as medical ethics. This latter embraces a series of very heterogeneous norms which, because of the nature and essence of the medical profession and partly in a variable manner and according to the times, regulate only the external proper conduct of the doctor within his sphere.

The reciprocal relation between the ethics of the group and deontology can be compared to that of relative ethics and absolute ethics. There is a relativism which does not recognize any absolute moral norm that is universally obliging, immutable and indissoluble, but holds that all norms are conditioned by the times and are changeable.

One type of such relativism is that which holds that all moral norms are merely dependent upon people and race.

Only those norms which claim an absolute validity not subject to the times, and which have their basis in the nature of the medical profession, come under the concept of medical deontology. They are related to the "order of the group," as natural law is related to positive law. Moreover, what distinguishes moral theology from ethics applies to a Christian deontology: the fundamentals of ethics are purely natural; but moral theology derives its authority and validity from the supernatural divine law. Its deepest root is love of God and love of neighbor, which is its consequence.

Just as in Christian juridical philosophy every right has its origin in God, so also with the higher moral norms which pertain to the medical profession.

b. Fundamental duties

(a) General view

The fundamental duties which the natural law imposes upon the doctor are considered in the first section of the "Corpus Hippocraticum" (ὅρκος) in the famous oath of Hippocrates (born about 460 B.C.).

The essential prescriptions of the Hippocratic oath hold for doctors of all times:

(1) Gratitude toward teachers;

(2) Defense of medical science and medical arts against any profanation;

(3) Unlimited dedication to the sick and suffering;

(4) Unconditional consideration of the right to life as sacred;

(5) Irreproachable conduct in sexual matters;

(6) Absolute secrecy.

The basic norms of the medical profession could not be formulated in a better and more universally valid manner.

This is so especially with regard to the rigorous observation of the right to life, including embryonic life: "Not to administer—even if this were requested—any deadly medication, nor to give counsel concerning the same."

And "I will likewise never give a woman an abortive means" (οὐδενὶ γυναικὶ πεσσὸν φθόριον δώσω).[1]

In these few words, euthanasia, even in the form of "death on request," and abortion are both solemnly condemned.

If we compare the condition of the last decades in regard to these matters, it would be difficult to speak of "progress." We must admit rather that the doctors of our time should be ashamed before Hippocrates and Hippocrates should be ashamed of them.

Hippocrates was a pagan, but even today—two thousand years after the Gospel of Christ has been announced—he can be considered a model for Christian doctors.

The same applies to the requirement of exemplary conduct of life from the sexual standpoint. It is not licit for the doctor—or the priest—to cause repugnance and scandal through illicit familiarity with a patient confided to him. This precept is explicitly extended to perverse sexual activity, with explicit reference to pederasty.

Even regarding the rigorous observance of professional secrecy, our generation can learn from Hippocrates, since in recent years this secret has sometimes been dangerously violated in favor of state authority (cf. below).

How seriously Hippocrates and his disciples took the oath is evident not only from the solemn invocation of all the protective

---

[1] πεσσόν : (1) From πέσσω (to cook)—cooking? (2) From πεσσὸς (stone)—eventually in the sense of "pessary" ("tampon"?); thus "abortive": (1) dynamic and (2) mechanical.

deities of the medical arts, Apollo and Asculapius, Health and Panacea but, more so, by the solemnity of the final formula:

"Now, if I carry out this oath, and break it not, may I gain forever reputation among all men for my life and for my art; but if I transgress it and forswear myself, may the opposite befall me."

(b) *Special view*

(1) *Medical professional secrecy*

Medical professional secrecy has often been compared to the seal of the confessional, to which the priest is held. As such, it constitutes the basis for the absolute confidence with which one who suffers in body or soul reveals to the doctor, as to the priest, the most intimate secrets when seeking counsel and help.

If this confidence is abused, then the basis for the relation between the sick and the doctor is shattered. However, medical professional secrecy cannot be completely compared to the seal of the confessional. The sacramental character of confession raises confessional seal to the supernatural level.

The priest sits in the tribunal of penance "in place of God." Here it is a matter of the salvation of the soul, while the other pertains to the healing of the body. Not only the health of the individual but also that of all men in general is entrusted to the doctor.

In certain circumstances, a conflict of duties can arise, as when danger to the health of other persons is involved. Consequently, when higher interests are present, limitations must be placed upon medical professional secrecy.

The question is reduced to that of establishing where these limitations are to be drawn.

The individualistic concept of the medical profession acknowledges no limitation whatsoever. In this, the following principle prevails without limitation: *Le secret médical—il est absolu—ou il n'est pas.*

The collectivistic concept starts with the principle that in any circumstance common utility must have precedence over private utility. The *bonum commune* must therefore always and in every circumstance have precedence over the *bonum privatum.*

This principle has been formulated as follows: "Only that which favors the common good, by remaining untold, has the right to medical secrecy; but what must be revealed in the interest of the people or state has no such claim."

In this is found the basis of the principle obliging the doctor to reveal hereditary disease.

In opposition to this, the following is to be mentioned: An exclusive and unilateral individualistic interpretation can lead to consequences which are no longer in any justified relation to the protection of the legitimate interests of the individual, especially when it is a matter of communicable diseases and diseases which are dangerous to the community.

If an appeal made to the intelligence and sense of responsibility of the sick proves useless, then, in defense of higher interests, the doctor should be authorized to act, after having warned the asocial patient of what duty suggests. In such cases, the doctor should not have to fear any penal sanctions; otherwise *summa iniuria* would result from the *summum ius*.

On the other hand, the unlimited collectivistic concept leads to the same consequences: *summum ius—summa iniura*. If medical professional secrecy is surrendered in favor of state omnipotence, then the *bonum privatum* is no longer protectively transcended by the *bonum commune*, but simply suppressed by the latter. It is consigned to it without defense.

In the last analysis, the *bonum commune*, properly understood, is thus not favored but endangered. Only the just equilibrium of interests between the private and public good serves the interests of both. The individual has the right to the protection of his legitimate interests, provided he has regard for the legitimate interests of others.

The infraction of professional medical secrecy by the unlimited authority of the state, which has been confirmed little by little in the last few years in some countries, has caused great fear that the future will bring a similar attack upon sacerdotal confessional secrecy.

Even in the question of medical professional secrecy, the necessity of finding the proper way between the two false ways seems imperative. This can only be found in the formula:

The rigorous guarantee of professional secrecy in the strongest possible manner and the renouncing of it only when higher interests are endangered and only when it is inevitable and absolutely necessary.

Even if the interests of the individual are limited in relation to the interests of the community, it is not completely permissible to forget that even the latter has its limits in relation to the inalienable rights of personality.

To completely divest medicine of its individualistic mission would have the same effect as the complete abandonment of one of its deepest roots—namely, of the direct relation between the patient who seeks counsel and the doctor who helps him.

(2) *The duty of the doctor to tell the truth*

The question is often asked whether the doctor is obliged to tell the patient the truth in all circumstances or whether, in certain cases, a certain *pia fraus* is allowed or even imposed; when the truth would submit the patient to a very violent mental shock and thus endanger his life. If we remember that the activation of mental forces can represent an important therapeutic factor, we can imagine situations in which it can be very convenient to keep from the patient the true seriousness of his condition, for the purpose of mobilizing all the forces in overcoming a crisis.

Medicine at times successfully makes use of a conscious deception—for example, when it substitutes indifferent means instead of giving narcotics to the patient.

But the question arises: Can a lie be permitted for a good end? As has often been stated, a good end can never justify an action that is in se illicit. Is the *pia fraus* a lie?

The simple *occultatio veritatis* is definitely not illicit *ex iusta causa*. It is, however, permissible for a doctor to have recourse to a *pia fraus* only when it can essentially contribute to the cure or improvement of the patient. In other cases, he is obliged to inform him—or, at least to inform his relatives—of the seriousness of his condition. This can especially be the case with regard to reception of the sacraments. The doctor to whom the earthly life seems to be the only good may consider himself justified in the holding back of the truth, even when death is certain. If he bases this on the principle: *salus aegroti suprema lex*, then it must be mentioned that his interpretation of *salus aegroti* is too restricted. The welfare of the soul is greater than material welfare. One is not permitted to endanger the welfare of the soul by a culpable omission in order to take care of material welfare, which is often only presumptive. The doctor who has comprehended what is implied in this matter cannot doubt for a moment. It is a higher duty which imposes on him the obligation of exhorting the patient, perhaps in an indulgent manner, to care for his soul in the situation of imminent danger. This does not mean that the doctor should cast a sentence of death in the patient's face. The main thing is to persuade the patient to call a priest to his side for spiritual comfort and to invigorate the mental forces of the patient by animating him with words of hope that the priest can help him.

If the relatives are understanding, the favorable effect of this action can take place more readily. Very often the patient himself is much more understanding than the relatives.

In any case, the doctor must remember that by not informing the patient, in any circumstances, of his serious condition in order not to " alarm " him, he often deprives the patient of the greatest benefit that can be given to the seriously sick and dying person. Even if the doctor is not bound by positive juridical duty, there is a duty of love toward the patient—that is, a duty of charity which obliges the Catholic doctor *sub gravi*.

More than one conscientious doctor could scarcely forgive himself for an omission in matters of less importance.

It is necessary to reawaken the conscience of the doctor even in reference to this duty.

c. The doctor at the bedside of the sick

Some of the duties of a doctor at the bedside of the sick have already been studied in the section on fundamental duties (*Medical professional secrecy; the duty of the doctor to tell the truth*). Those which remain to be mentioned are matters which should be spontaneously understood; but, as experience teaches, to mention them is not superfluous.

It is relatively easy to show sympathy and solicitude toward the sick when treatment presents a good chance of being successful, as in the case of acute illnesses which afflict young and otherwise healthy people and, above all, when a surgical operation allows one to hope for success.

The duty of charity and solicitude becomes much more difficult in the case of chronic disease, in hopeless cases in which all effort seems useless; when the care and assistance given to the patient constitute an almost unbearable burden for those around him, and the idea of a " useless life " can possibly insinuate itself.

These are cases which do not offer any glory for the doctor but which will manifest whether he considers his professional duties merely in an earthly manner or *sub specie aeternitatis.*

In these cases the idea of " euthanasia " may occur to the doctor under the seductive appearance of " humaneness "; it will be more human to shorten this useless suffering, to bring an end to useless torment, to remove the burden from the relatives. Or else, with a " patriotic " motivation : " No weak, humanitarian compassion : medical help to the full extent, but only for those who can be of use to the ' people.' "

Here the roads definitely part. For the doctor who has learned to think only in terms of this world, such a concept can logically arise. For the Christian doctor, who knows that even hopeless suffering has a deep meaning, that every moment can be decisive for the manifestation of grace and for the salvation of the soul, the thought of curtailing life even for only a moment is out of the question.

Physicians are expected to strive by all reasonable means, even extraordinary ones, to prolong a patient's life. It is a serious moral obligation to use ordinary means, and if the patient, for spiritual or temporal motives, requests extraordinary means, they must be supplied. In 1957, Pius XII declared that a dying person may be given drugs to remove pain and consciousness, even if this will shorten life. But such drugs may be used in this case only if no other means are possible and provided that their use will not prevent fulfillment of moral and religious duties.

d. The doctor at the bedside of the dying

On the other hand, the question has been raised whether the Christian doctor is obliged in conscience to artificially prolong the life of the patient in any circumstance, even when this would hopelessly prolong the torment. As an argument for this, it is adduced that each moment of life can be of decisive importance for the manifestation of grace.

In connection with this whole matter, it is to be mentioned that, for the Christian doctor, the principle that he is not lord of life and death always prevails.

God calls men from life when He pleases. Just as the doctor

should not provoke death, even a moment before death, so he cannot be obliged in conscience to use all possible means of artificially prolonging life if such do not and cannot have therapeutic value.

However, if we cannot speak of a general duty of this kind, so it may not be said that in the individual case such a procedure is unjustifiable if the motives are good. It would therefore be erroneous to deny this right to the doctor. *Ex iusta causa* even this can be justified.

Not to be confused with this is the question whether the doctor is basically obliged to make use of all the therapeutic possibilities.

In this matter, cases of presumed " useless life " have been considered, and with regard to "progressive paralysis" it has been asked whether it was sensible to prolong the life of a patient by therapy in which there was no certainty of an absolute cure. As an answer to this, Wagner—Jauregg has declared that it is the duty of the doctor to use all possible means of attaining a cure. It would be wrong for a doctor who feared to prolong a tormenting suffering, to abstain from applying therapy to those who could perhaps be cured.

This position taken by Wagner—Jauregg has received full agreement on the part of the Church.[1]

A discussion of medical deontology " at the bedside of the sick " must include something on the part of the doctor in " assisting at birth."

Concerning the negative aspect, with regard to certain illicit interventions, what is necessary has been stated in the section on obstetrical interventions.

Of the positive duties we here mention the duty of the Christian doctor to administer emergency Baptism to babies of weak vitality.

Even the aborted fetus is to be baptized after cutting open— if necessary—the embryonic sac under water, so that the required *ablutio corporis* can take place. In such a case, Baptism is administered *sub conditione*.

Not everyone knows that even a non-Christian doctor, that is, a non-baptized doctor, can validly administer emergency Baptism provided he associates with the act the intention with which the Church administers the sacrament of Baptism.

---

[1] " Osservatore Romano," May 15, 1936.

The doctor assists his fellow men at the moment of birth and of death—i.e., at the moment of entering life and at departure from life.

It is especially at the bedside of the dying that the particular conception of the Christian doctor's duty is manifested. That it is for him a definite duty to see to it that the sick have the opportunity to receive the sacraments at the proper time is evident from what has already been stated. But this is not the only matter.

The attitude toward death is completely diverse according to whether the doctor sees in death only the extinction of the vital functions or the transition into true and real life: *de morte transire ad vitam*; whether one believes that at death the curtain of the *comoedia finita* falls or the curtain really rises and the veils which hide the higher reality fall. It is with reason that the Church celebrates the day on which a saint died rather than the day of his birth.

Like life, death is a great mystery and the doctor who is present at a holy death experiences a closeness to God. Here we can only present, in a sketchy outline, some of the essential points of medical deontology. It is important that these questions be called to the attention of students at the beginning of their medical course and not elaborated and learned the hard way in a gradual manner during their professional career, often after they have long followed the wrong way.

Such an introduction to deontology as a preparation for the medical profession should begin during the first semester, before the student enters the hall of dissection for anatomical preparatory exercises. If right attitudes are inculcated early, then what in recent decades was considered among young medical students as a sign of " open-mindedness " fortunately becomes impossible: that is, a complete lack of respect for human cadavers, not to mention something worse.

These things are of greater and more serious import than is often considered. It is not realized what disturbances can arise in the soul of the future doctor.

Respect for death necessarily is bound up with a genuine respect for life. If this is lacking, then there can only be an unworthy fear of death. This respect should constitute the first law of medical study, just as at one time the words *mors ianua vitae* were inscribed on the entrance of an anatomical institute.

6. PRIEST AND DOCTOR

a. Historical view—The "priest-doctor"

In works on the history of medicine, attention is often brought to the fact that originally the priest and doctor were one person, the "priest-doctor." It was therefore concluded that medicine and religion had a common origin and belong to each other, as soul and body.

In this respect, reference is made to the priest-doctors of the past, the shaman, magicians, druids; to the healings through " temple sleep " (incubation), which have been likened to the cures in pilgrim places and places of grace, etc.; and to the medicine man of primitive people.

With regard to these historical prototypes, in recent times when it was presumed that materialistic rationalism was overcome in medicine by recourse to an explicit " irrationalism " and new natural myths, the idea of a priest-doctor was again invoked.

Truth and error are dangerously mingled in such ideas.

There is profound truth in the ancient close union between religion and medicine when this union is rightly understood.

A revival of the study of these questions and a realization of the benefits to be derived from the renewal of religious forces and the advantage for medicine through the reacquiring of religious convictions would be welcome.

There is, however, no need of recurring to old-fashioned and obsolete forms of a " magical " epoch in which natural demonology or the pantheistic concept of nature prevailed. The demand for a priest-doctor in an epoch which does not realize the contradiction in its tendency to laicize the priest more and more, and to strive more and more to give " priestly " tasks to lay people, is astonishing.

b. Limits of jurisdiction

In recent times, because of the progress made in psychotherapy, it has been stated that a time will come when the doctor will make the role of the priest superfluous and will assume his task of spiritual director.

This tendency, in an epoch of new irrationalism, has a singular analogy with that of the period of rationalism or of so-called

Josephinism, but in an inverse direction. Just as at present there is a tendency to transform the doctor into a spiritual director, so at one time there was the tendency to transform the spiritual director into a doctor.

In the past, some states expected the priest, especially in rural sections, where there were no doctors, to assume as a useful occupation the care of the sick.

The designation "Pastoral Medicine," which was introduced at that time, was applied to the necessary medical knowledge imparted to rural pastors (*medicina ruralis*).

This mixture of competency was opposed with the striking words: "A *pastor medicus* (physician-priest) is as absurd as a doctor who acts as a pastor."

In opposition to such tendencies, it must be affirmed with the utmost clarity that Pastoral Medicine, when its object is properly understood, has nothing in common with these tendencies. It rejects any attempt to confuse or exaggerate competency or jurisdiction and respects the competency or jurisdiction of the authorized priest and spiritual director. This is a "limited zone," and because of this, we must reject any transgression, any intrusion in the competency or jurisdiction of the spiritual director. The doctor cannot and should not try to be a substitute for the spiritual director.

Just as in a situation of necessity when there are no doctors (as in mission lands), the priest can, to the best of his ability, fill the gap, so the inverse substitution can also be made in case of necessity. But this is not too desirable, and it is completely wrong to desire it basically.

The doctor of faith today cannot always avoid taking the role of substitute for spiritual director with patients who have not yet found their way to the priest. The more seriously he fulfills his duty, the more satisfied will he be when he succeeds, through his efforts, in leading the patient to the point where, for the welfare of his soul, he entrusts himself to the only truly competent spiritual director.

We recall here the example of Virgil and Beatrice as representatives of the natural and supernatural guidance of the soul. However, in such cases, the doctor realizes that he is only a substitute temporarily filling a gap. He will not try to take upon himself the mission of a spiritual director.

This, however, seems to be essential: The more the limits between the two competencies or jurisdictions are respected, the more carefully are transgressions of the proper limits avoided and the more satisfactory and fruitful will the collaboration of both parties be, and this for the welfare of the patient and the progress of the case.

c. Spheres of common activity

(a) *Co-operation of the doctor in the canonical process*

Prescinding from the various points of contact in common activity, which result from the content of this work, we refer here to two important spheres which, up to now, were not systematically elaborated:

(1) The activity of the doctor as a medico-legal expert and adviser in the canonical matrimonial process, as well as in the ecclesiastical process on the occasion of a *causa beatificationis* and in ecclesiastical investigation concerning asserted miraculous cures, mystical phenomena, etc.

(2) The participation of the doctor in practical pastoral matters, in the sense of " medical aid on the part of the physician in the care of souls."

Participation in both spheres requires, on the part of the doctor, a deep comprehension of tasks regarding the care of souls.

(b) *Medical aid in the care of souls*

At present, it seems of particular importance to outline, according to a plan, medical aid in the care of souls, which, in a certain sense, is analogous with the activity of the missionary doctor.

Protestant missiological literature pertinently distinguishes between the "external" and "internal" mission. This distinction merits acceptance, since the idea of "internal mission" is not to be confused with that of the charitable activity of the Church.

The "internal" mission, in the sense in which we understand it, can, in the future, assume great importance in lands of European-American civilization, and can perhaps surpass that of the "external mission."

At present, entire lands are so separated from Christianity, vast masses of the people so lack the most fundamental knowledge of religion, that a completely new missionary method seems indispensable for the reconstruction of a genuine Christian culture.

Q

This opens up for the doctor instructed in Pastoral Medicine vast and very important spheres of activity.

Medical aid in the care of the soul can, at times, through the humane and charitable action of the doctor, open up for the spiritual director the way that leads to hearts which would otherwise remain closed.

The doctor approaches the person estranged from religion first as a doctor and helper in physical and social difficulties; soon after, in regard to the needs of the soul inasmuch as it can be an object of psychotherapy. Three circumstances justify today the necessity of medical aid in the care of the soul:

(1) Social conditions of want, especially in the large cities and their surroundings;

(2) Disorder in the sphere of conjugal and sexual life;

(3) Frequent and serious changes in mental life.

These factors define, at the same time, the principal spheres of activity of modern medical aid in the care of souls. It is not always possible to precisely to distinguish one from the other, and their reciprocal relations are very close.

Co-operation between doctor and spiritual director can develop in a twofold direction:

In the direction from priest to doctor in those cases in which the patient has need of the doctor's technical collaboration, counsel and help in regard to questions of Pastoral Medicine. This will be the case especially with patients who still possess a religious concept of life, which they obtained in their home. These are cases of co-operation of the physician in the care of souls, in the strict sense.

In the "internal mission," in the sense defined above—which, together with the care of souls, comprises the special social tasks of the doctor in the lay apostolate—it is practically always a matter of cases in which the doctor is first sought and the collaboration of the priest, in the direction of doctor to priest, should also be sought. These are usually cases of a psychotherapeutic character.

Important tasks also present themselves in the realm of social and charitable auxiliary service. Here the possibility of action on the part of the doctor in the free practice of his profession should not be overestimated.

It would be a fatal error to expect, in this sphere, results which the doctor cannot accomplish. His contribution must be co-ordinated, in an impressive manner, with the great social and charitable tasks. But he can be successful only within his limited sphere of activity. Left to himself, and faced with the social need of the masses of the large cities, he could do nothing but fail.

In labor groups, in charitable organizations directed by priests, the doctor, together with lawyers, educators, social organizations, etc., can contribute essentially to the overcoming of those difficulties encountered in the care of souls which are caused by physical, mental and social stress and which in the large cities have become mass phenomena.

Such co-operation in the service of *Caritas* can be successively maintained only if good will is based upon a power capable of transforming a proposition into reality. Otherwise the best intentions will be unsuccessful.

For these reasons, certain limits are found in the social-charitable activities of the doctor.

Within these limits however, especially in the realm of well-directed ecclesiastical organizations, in public and private welfare, he can fulfill a meritorious task.

In this respect, both doctor and priest must realize that *Caritas* cannot be and should not be an end in itself; it is nothing but the necessary complement of social justice—never a " substitute for a due but denied justice " (Pius XI).

One of the most important spheres of medical aid in the care of souls is that of matrimonial counsel. This does not refer primarily to the activity of consultors. The tasks of these latter are to be treated as another relationship, as the object of pastoral hygiene. Here it is primarily a matter of that type of counsel that any properly orientated doctor can give in the realm of his private professional practice and which he can offer in connection with medical aid in the care of souls. In this way, a greater number of people who do not seek out an organized marriage counsel board will be included.

This can be transformed into more extensive medico-pastoral counseling in which, when proper co-operation between priest and doctor exists, a greater number of cases will be directed from the priest to the doctor than vice-versa.

A matrimonial counseling action with a universalistic objective is not limited to pre-nuptial counseling but concerns questions pertaining to the contracting of marriage and extends also to intramatrimonial counsel concerning the conduct of the married couple.

A close collaboration between priest and doctor can be realized in regard to the numerous questions arising during the course of premarital instructions. This can be very fruitful when it is systematically organized. The doctor who is well instructed in Pastoral Medicine is not only in the position of being of valuable help to the priest, but as a lay apostle can collaborate in the moral restoration of the people.

Many of the difficulties and much of the disruption of marriage, and much biological, social and moral corruption could be averted if the doctor collaborated in renewing the conviction that personal happiness in marriage and the health of the progeny are more securely guaranteed when the laws of the Church are accurately followed.

This would be true eugenics in the strict sense of the word.

The encyclical "Casti Connubii" constitutes an immovable foundation and the determining guide for intramatrimonial counseling. Further details on this point are presented within this work. Questions concerning the physical and mental difficulties of marriage, those of periodic abstinence, sterility, *usus matrimonii*, etc., are mentioned only as examples.

The examples here quoted show what important tasks can arise in regard to the collaboration of the doctor and the priest in his capacity of confessor.

Here the entire sphere of the sexual life, even in its pathological forms, can be the object of medico-pastoral counsel. Since medical sexual counsel has at times assumed suspicious forms, it is necessary that the priest have at hand a competent and trustworthy counselor to whom he can confide his penitents, without fear that they will be led astray.

That such a fear is not always unfounded is manifest from the decree of Innocent III, who found it necessary to prohibit the sick any medical treatment which could endanger the health of the soul. Explicit reference is made to advising extramarital relations, counsel which apparently was given by doctors who justified this for reasons of health.

Another example of the important social-charitable tasks of the doctor is presented in his assistance to those "tired of living," in the counseling of depressed persons, and those despairing of life. An indispensable condition for obtaining success in the matter is that the work is sustained by an organization which is not only animated by good will but which is in the position to render practical aid. Hence the best way to attain this objective is that centers of assistance and counsel be sustained by a "central diocesan *Caritas,*" which operates meritoriously and successfully and this, above all, because it is led by one skilled in pychotherapy and Pastoral Medicine.

Only a few indications of a general kind have been furnished in order to illustrate the multiple relationship between priest and doctor. If we have emphasized here the tasks of medical aid in the care of souls, we have done so because of the importance these questions have assumed in our day. The doctor should be aware of the high and irreparable self-worth that he has to place on the scale. But he must remember that his task does not constitute an end in itself, insofar as he does not consider health the "highest good." Then he will also understand the grandeur of the missionary task of the present, whose purpose must be the reconquest of the lost masses.

Just as the "great decline" began with educated persons and has gradually affected the entire populace, so must the great return be initiated by the educated people to whom the masses look for a model. Their reconversion to Christian ways means likewise a renewed humanism. For that human dignity that had been trodden under because of a materialistic epoch and its unavoidable consequences, it means restoration to the true freedom of the children of God.

7. THE MISSION DOCTOR

a. Idea of the mission doctor

The idea of the mission doctor as a medical helper in the missions arose from the manifold physical needs which in mission territories call for the corporal works of mercy besides the spiritual works of mercy.

The example of the Redeemer Himself, who did not disdain to take upon Himself the physical needs of man, even though He knew that their spiritual needs were greater, and who nevertheless said: "Misereor super turbam" and thus *pertransiit benefaciendo,* has conferred on medical missionary assistance a motive and internal justification.

Its leading motive is more *Caritas* than the solicitude corresponding to mere natural aid: that *Caritas* which has its roots in the supernatural and presses us in the sense of the words: *Caritas Christi urget nos.*

Hence the work of the mission doctor is, much more than that of the ordinary doctor, ordained toward a disinterested life of sacrifice up to the complete alienation of one's person and is predisposed to unconditional service. It constitutes a lay apostolate in the widest sense of the word.

b. Historical predecessors

The holy evangelist Luke can be considered as the precursor of the modern mission doctor. He accompanied Paul, the apostle, in his long missionary voyages and Paul often makes mention of this: *"Salutat vos Lucas medicus carissimus"* (Col. 4:14); *"Lucas est mecum solus"* (2 Tim. 4:11).

As long as there is a mission, there will be, as there has always been, a medical missionary assistance for the suffering even if there have not always been mission doctors in the strict sense. The mission doctor, in the present meaning, is a result of the development of the last two centuries.

Originally the missionary was practically always alone and had to depend exclusively on his own capacity. Without the aid of a skilled doctor, he had to acquire for himself at least the basic medical knowledge, in order to meet physical needs—if he wished to satisfy the task of fulfilling the duties of the Good Samaritan.

c. Relation of mission doctor and missionary

The relation between the doctor and the priest has a profound basis and at the same time, is a very delicate one. Its right order demands a reciprocal understanding of the spiritual principles of each other's task. Greater demands are imposed by the relation between the missionary doctor and the missionary or the mission assigned to him. There is required a complete absorption into the service of the mission, and at the same time a knowledge of how one depends upon the other in the mission field is necessary. A deep understanding of the difficulties of both, and especially of the ultimate causes of these difficulties is also needed.

(a) *Personal union and respective incompatibility*

At first glance, it would seem that the ideal solution would consist in the union of the tasks of the priest and doctor in one personality sufficiently instructed in both: somewhat like a return of the " priest-doctor " whom history shows originally performed these functions.

It must not be forgotten, however, that it is very difficult to unite successfully in one personality the tasks of priest and doctor, the lives of each requiring the complete efforts of the entire personality.

Formation for the career would be prolonged beyond measure if one were to prepare well for both tasks.

In the past, the missionary has found himself in situations which demanded prompt and immediate action.

Basically it is still not desirable that the missionary assume the tasks of the doctor. Theoretically the principle of incompatibility of both tasks still remains firm.[1]

The Mission Council of Shanghai (1924) made the exercise of medical activity on the part of the missionary dependent upon the permission of the Ordinary so far as the latter was invested with required authorization from the Holy See. This permission can be conceded only to missionaries instructed in medicine and these cannot receive any compensation for their service.

(b) *Medical mission and medical missionary assistance*

There are basically two possibilities in which the doctor can be useful to the mission. These possibilities are expressed by the terms " medical mission " and " mèdical missionary assistance." In the first case, the doctor appears as " missionary doctor "; i.e., he is at the same time both missionary and doctor; his activity as doctor is itself a mission, whether he exercises his pastoral duties or limits himself to medical practice.

No matter what the attitude of the doctor might be, through his medical activity alone he works in favor of the faith, of the mission. The expression " conquest by healing " is the most emphatic expression of this idea. This follows from the concept which American Protestants have of the mission as a social Gospel, a concept which circumscribes the object of the mission within the sphere of social

[1] Cf. Conc. Sin., Nn. 754, 746, 747.

action, while, according to Catholic doctrine, social action should not and cannot be more than a missionary means.

The other concept considers the doctor nothing more than a doctor and a member serving the mission. The missionary task does not become confused with the medical, but remains unconditionally in the first and leading position. As close and deeply rooted as is the collaboration between the doctor and missionary, yet the spheres of activity are basically distinct.

The sphere reserved to the doctor is medical missionary assistance, which extends beyond simple and individual therapeutics. It embraces all of health and even social assistance. The doctor is here a doctor of the mission and not a medical missionary. However, his basic subordination to the mission does not imply any lack of evaluation in regard to his activity. It should only express the hierarchy of values, the subordination of the natural to the supernatural.

(c) *Present development*

Protestants have considered it of primary importance to interest doctors in the missions. It seems that at first difficulties arose because of the twofold position of the doctor as medical missionary. It can be that, from the pastoral standpoint, some doctors at times overstepped their limits and thus it was not always possible to avoid errors which did harm to the medical-missionary idea.

Only such personalities as that of Albert Schweitzer have been able to resist the pressure and tension of both tasks. But such personalities are an exception and cannot in general serve as a model.

The projection of the Protestant mission into the field of medical missionary assistance constituted an advantage for the Catholic missions insofar as the latter made use of the experience of the former and were able to avoid initial mistakes with greater facility.

(d) *Scientific formation of the mission doctor*

The scientific and basic formation of the mission doctor is the same as that prescribed for any doctor.

In consideration of the particular tasks and their spiritual and ascetical basis, it would doubtless be a most fortunate and fruitful plan if this general preparation could be administered, from its earliest possible beginning, by the sort of institute which, filled with the ascetic atmosphere of a seminary, could teach at the same time the scientific and spiritual fundamentals of Pastoral Medicine.

Besides the general scientific formation of the practicing doctor, of special importance for the mission doctor are the practical disciplines of clinical surgery, obstetrics, gynecology and pediatrics; also, that of neurology and of dermatology which he must know in a higher degree than the general practitioner if he is to practice successfully.

A knowledge above average is required in the field of ophthalmology, especially in the lands where trachoma is prevalent. And odontology must also be mentioned.

Among the theoretical branches which the mission doctor must know, besides general and social hygiene, are bacteriology, together with epidemiology (loimology, the science of contagious disease) and microbiology and parasitology. In this sphere, of special importance is a knowledge of tropical diseases.

If he does not want to be a failure, the mission doctor should have a knowledge of tropical hygiene and tropical medicine. We here mention only a few of the more important diseases which especially come into consideration. Malaria in all its various forms (especially tropical malaria), yellow fever, blackwater fever; amebic dysentery, the plague, cholera, typhus, typhus fever (*typhus exanthematicus*); sleeping sickness, entozoic diseases such as bilharziasis, filariasis; anomalous forms of tuberculosis, lues and gonorrhea; frambesia and, above all, leprosy.

The mission doctor should also have a knowledge of pharmacology and pharmacy since he must often be able to direct a pharmacy and prepare formulas. Leprosy, increased by the disorders and wars of the last decades, seems to have spread more extensively and constitutes a special problem for medical assistance in the post-war era.

A knowledge of indigenous medicine and its methods is of great importance for the mission doctor. This is important especially in a country of ancient culture and of uninterrupted medical tradition, as, for example, China.

Nothing can be more erroneous than an a priori rejection of the methods of indigenous folk medicine as irrational charlatanism. The European doctor will do well at least to familiarize himself with those indigenous methods which are not of common use in European medicine.

Q*

Finally, we must penetrate the most profound causes of the particular difficulties which confront both the native and the indigenous doctors.

(e) *Other problems concerning medical missionary assistance*

Of the problems not yet completely elucidated, we can here briefly mention only a few of the most pressing ones.

Concerning the problems of organization, that of the union between the missionary and the mission doctor, as well as the position of the latter in regard to the mission, has already been explained. We consider the mission to have the superior position, to which the mission doctor is subordinated.

In regard to union, we consider the relieving of the missionary from the tasks of health assistance and the division of labor as progress.

The circumstances are similar to those when the selected deacons served primarily to relieve the apostles, sent to preach the Gospel, from the social and charitable tasks. This division of labor should not be abandoned without a serious necessity.

We adhere basically to the principle of incompatibility according to which clerics and priests are forbidden by canon 139, #2, CIC, to practice medicine and surgery without explicit apostolic indult. Granted the extreme need for mission doctors and that this need will be increased in the future, there arises the problem concerning the new generation. It is assumed that part of the medical generation of the post-war era will seek new fields of activity and will be disposed to willingly exercise their profession in regions not yet colonized. Notwithstanding this fact, it can hardly be assumed that the greater number of these doctors will fulfill the intrinsic requirements necessary for becoming true mission doctors. This profession cannot be chosen as other professions or other types of specialization. For this, besides suitableness and natural inclination, there is required a supernatural call of grace no less than that required for a religious vocation.

How serious this self-examination should be before one definitely decides to embrace this mission is manifested by the custom of the medical missionary institute of Würzburg, which prescribes for the candidate a retreat of thirty days before he assumes a duty of ten years.

If one takes into account the increased number of persons required for this service, the problem of preparing new members, as well as that of substituting for those leaving, constitutes one of the most important of medical missionary assistance.

It is not a matter here of a secondary problem; the personal problem has become a vital question of medical missionary assistance and even of the mission itself.

Compared with this, the question of whether, for the profession of mission doctor, particular vows corresponding to those of religious Orders should be required, appears of less importance. It is recommended that one disregard in general the question of vows and concentrate on a solemn formula of duty, at least where doctors are concerned.

When it is a case of women doctors, the question of vows could be considered, provided these women are not already married. In no case should an obligatory precept be demanded. The same can be said concerning the question of the marriage of a medical doctor, although it seems the ideal that a mission doctor contract marriage, when possible, with a female mission doctor. Even though there are many reasons in favor of establishing a family in the mission territory itself, so there are many against this idea, and the conditions of the different regions do not permit a general norm.

In regard to the question of a medical missionary congregation which has attached to it a tertiary institute for the married, the best thing would be to leave the decision to a natural course and spontaneous development.

In regard to auxiliary medical personnel, the nuns (native and foreign) have basically fulfilled the task of caring for the sick in a capable manner, but besides this, there is still great need of experienced personnel in ambulatory service and social assistance, which in the long run must be definitely entrusted to the native auxiliary staff.

(f) Difficulties and obstacles

Medical missionary assistance as well as the mission itself has to contend with external and internal difficulties, resistance and obstacles of various types. Among the external difficulties, the necessity of mastering the language is to be especially mentioned.

It is often a matter not only of a language but of a number of languages, and for the most part it is a matter of mastering different dialects, etc.

Often one must also contend with the difficulty of acquiring a foreign medical diploma, the so-called "nostrification."

According to the legislative specifications of place and in relation to the lack or excessive number of doctors, such "nostrification" can imply a mere formality or the procedure can be extremely rigorous for the purpose of impeding an undesired immigration.

Acclimatization and both hygienic and dietetic adaptation play an important part in the life of the mission doctor. This difficulty is increased when the doctor has a wife and children with him.

Often Europeans who reside in colonial regions fall into sexual difficulties, through which they cause serious scandal and cast discredit upon the white race, creating, with the miscegenation problem, a social problem full of tragedy.

These difficulties before which so many Europeans succumb should not constitute a serious danger for the mission doctor, and he can, if he is not married, overcome these by means of a deep supernatural orientation. But he must realize that these problems are present and must know how to meet them.

Difficulties of a general character follow from the conduct of the natives toward the Europeans. The natives' attachment to ancient uses and customs, their basically "conservative" comportment, which becomes more resolute the more valuable are the treasures of an ancient civilization and of an ancient tradition which must be protected against the modern leveling, will—in general—render more difficult the position of the European, especially with the Asiatics.

This conservatism has been highly manifest, especially in China, and it makes the task of the European doctor more difficult in two aspects: It will be difficult for him to win the confidence of the sick; and, on the other hand, it will also be very hard for him to attain contact with the native doctors in the high degree which, in the interests of both parties, would be desirable for profitable effects.

The isolated pioneer mission doctor will experience these difficulties in a manifold degree, but these can be easily overcome when he can depend on a well-organized hospital.

On the other hand, the hospitals often encounter difficulties in the maintenance and function of an organized service.

In relation to the doctor of a missionary hospital, the pioneer mission doctor has to contend more directly with the psychological difficulties arising from the native population. The reasons for the great and varied resistance against the European doctor are not based merely on the fact that he—as a representative of a rational medical science in the midst of people still in the phase of a "magical" civilization and dominated by the influence of the medicine man and demon belief—often finds himself with his rational methods in a very difficult position before the non-rational methods of the medicine man and native folk medicine.

The difficulties which arise are definitely not to be underestimated, but if the mission doctor tries to adapt himself to the psyche and culture even of primitive people, without European arrogance, and if he respects the truly ancient culture and tradition, and if he succeeds in convincing the people that, in regard to surgical maladies and obstetrical cases, his is at times an easy and gratifying task, then such difficulties can, in time, be definitely overcome.

Much more serious are the difficulties which result from the position of the European in non-European lands. Just as the mission should tend, with all the means at its disposal, to form a native clergy, it must also tend, as its ideal, toward the formation of native doctors no less eminent for learning and experience, exemplars in their own life.

The more states attempt to take over control of health conservation and care, the less demand there will be for the services of medical missions, but accordingly it becomes more urgent to form a body of native Catholic physicians.

The mission doctor must always be aware of the principal causes of the difficulties which have been encountered and of the successes which have been of little satisfaction:

(1) In the first place, the schism within Christianity.

(2) The bad example that Europeans have often given to the natives, particularly in regard to sexuality, so that "civilization" has been transformed into a "syphilization"; alcohol, the furtherance of narcomania, etc., have contributed to this work of destruction.

(3) The economic exploitation and enslavement of the colonial people has often been associated with an inhuman maltreatment.

Instead of being a bearer of true culture, the white person

appeared as a representative of colonial imperialism and attempted, as much as possible, to use the mission for this purpose.

In view of these difficulties, the mission should, in the future, interest native Catholic forces in undertaking the tasks of the mission doctor. This problem has been indicated, especially on the part of the Protestant mission, by the term "devolution." Cardinal Lavigérie most consistently supported the need of forming a native missionary clergy.

There are very serious and considerable reasons in favor of such a solution of the problem.

(g) Questions concerning the future

In all parts of the world, states have tried to monopolize the entire field of health assistance and medicine.

Wherever colonies still exist, the colonial powers have applied this principle without consideration in the colonial territories.

"The more the principles of our civilization affirm themselves and the more the state undertakes moral functions and with them, social-hygienic assistance for all its subjects, so much the more must the mission limit itself to its specific sphere, i.e., the diffusion of the Gospel" (Schlunk).

This is so, unfortunately, not only for the mission territory but also for the pretension of the modern state in assuming the direction of all the spheres pertaining to health assistance, social welfare, education, matrimony.

In opposition to this there exists another possibility for the future; namely, that of the return of the people, the states and their leaders to the fundamental doctrines of Christianity as the only foundation for a reconstruction of a disorganized human society.

Christianity is the only foundation not only of the religious and moral life, but also of the political and social, spiritual and economic life of the people.

In every sphere, Christ is the "center of the world," and because of this, the motto omnia instaurare in Christo! is appropriate.

On this basis, the way that is to be followed in the future for the development of the mission and the mission doctor manifests itself. In order to announce the Gospel to all humanity, there is no other way than this, that Christianity, again united in faith, give the splendid example of love: "See how they love one another." Only such a Christianity can demonstrate that it seeks nothing but the good of the people by bringing them the light of faith without the least intention of exploiting them.

The idea of colonization as held in the past must be definitely abandoned and must give place to a mission of universal peaceful civilization sustained by the idea of a family of people in the kingdom of Christ.

Solely in the spirit of this idea of Christ the King can the mission be successful, and in this spirit all the difficulties which arise from the necessity of calling upon a generation of priests and missionary doctors who are foreigners by blood, fatherland and climate will be surmounted. And, in time, the greater number will be native doctors who are stable and united to the fatherland.

It is the task of both the doctor and the mission to bring it about that they make themselves superfluous.

Until then, the doctor has many tasks to fulfill which require an absolute sacrifice of himself and which cannot be fulfilled unless he is convinced by an act of grace that his vocation is a charism and unless he wishes to be nothing more than a servant in the work of the salvation of souls and the expansion of the kingdom of Christ.

CONCLUSION

Our exposition concerning the nature and purpose of Pastoral Medicine should show that Pastoral Medicine is definitely scientific and that it is also something more.

It is not only a science, but at the same time a mission: a vocation and mandate—above all, in the sense of an apostolate.

If we take this into account, it will be significant that the last section treats of the doctor and his activities in the mission. Today, a mission no longer necessarily involves going into distant lands in order to diffuse the light of the faith and the knowledge of truth. This light is in danger of being extinguished in the ancient Christian Occident; thus the doctor, conscious of his mission, finds, even in his fatherland, abundant mission work. He should not take this lightly and should have less confidence in his own capacity and knowledge than in the Spirit of truth. He must realize that there is need of a new spiritual apostolate to enkindle, with the light of faith, love of God and neighbor and thus to promote Christian life and Christian teaching, in the name of the Spirit whom we call upon to recreate all things and to renew the face of the earth:

Emitte spiritum tuum et creabuntur
Et renovabis faciem terrae!

SCHEMA

Representing the body-soul relation

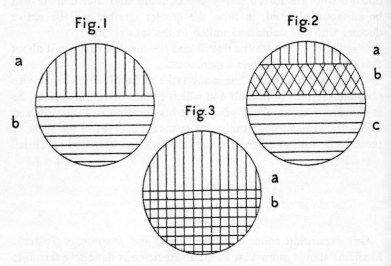

Fig. 1

Fig. 2

Fig. 3

Fig. 1. Body-soul representation of dualism: a=spirit or soul; b=body; each distinct.

Fig. 2. Body-soul-spirit representation of trichotomy: a=spirit; b=soul (psychophysical intermedia); c=body.

Fig. 3. *Anima forma corporis:* The immaterial spirit-soul (vertical) penetrates the entire body to the last cell, with a portion united to the body (b), but extends beyond it with a portion independent of the body (a). It forms a united, indivisible whole, yet portion (a) can be designated "spirit," and portion (b) "soul."

Bibliography

AUTHOR'S BIBLIOGRAPHY

Antonelli, Joseph, *Medicina Pastoralis in usum confessariorum, professorum theologiae moralis et curiarum ecclesiasticarum.*
  Vol. I, *Summula anatomiae et physiologicae humanae et teratologiae.*
  Vol. II, *Quaestiones physiologicae de primo, quinto, sexto decalogi praeceptis et de ecclesiastico coelibatu.*
  Vol. III, *De sacramentis baptismi et matrimonii.*
  Vol. IV, *De praeceptis ecclesiae super abstinentiam et ieiunium et de iis, quae referuntur ad graviter aegrotantes, moribundos, dubie mortuos et mortuos.*
  Rome, Pustet, 1932.
Niedermeyer, Albert, *Pastoralmedizinische Propädeutik.* Salzburg, Pustet, 1935.
——, *Handbuch der Speziellen Pastoral-Medizin.* 6 vols. Vienna. Herder, 1948-1952.
Pujiula, Jacobus, S.J., *De medicina pastorali.* 2nd edition, Turin, Marietti, 1953.

TRANSLATOR'S BIBLIOGRAPHY

HEREDITY

Cavanagh, John R., M.D., *Fundamental Marriage Counseling.* Milwaukee, Wis., Bruce, 1957.

Darwin, Charles, *Descent of Man.* New York, Crowell, 1871.

———, *Variations of Animals and Plants under Domestication.* New York, Appleton, 1898.

Dubois, Paul, *The Psychological Origin of Mental Disorders,* translated by Edward Richards. New York and London, Funk and Wagnalls, 1913.

Pearson, K., " On the Inheritance of the Mental and Moral Characters in Man, and Its Comparison with the Inheritance of Physical Characters." *Biometrika,* Vol. III (1904), pp. 131-190.

Popenoe, Paul, *The Child's Heredity.* Baltimore, Williams and Wilkins, 1929.

Scheinfield, Amram, *You and Heredity.* New York, Stokes, 1939.

Strecker, Edward A., *Fundamentals of Psychiatry.* 3rd edition, New York, Lippincott, 1947.

Tredgold, H. F., *Manual of Psychological Medicine.* Baltimore, Williams and Wilkins, 1943.

U.S. Army, *Outline of Neuropsychiatry in Aviation Medicine.* Washington, D. C., Technical Manual 8-325, 1940.

Sex and Marriage

Bruckner, P. J., S.J., *How To Give Sex Instructions.* St. Louis, Mo., Queen's Work, 1937.

Good, Frederick, and Kelly, Otis, F., *Marriage, Morals, and Medical Ethics.* New York, Kenedy, 1951.

Growing Up. New York, Benziger, 1939.

Harvey, B. C. H., M.D., *Simple Lessons in Human Anatomy.* Chicago, American Medical Association, 1931.

Healy, Edwin, F., S.J., *Marriage Guidance.* Chicago, Loyola University Press, 1948.

Juergens, Sylvester P., *Fundamental Talks on Purity.* Milwaukee, Bruce, 1941.

Keenan, Alan, O.F.M., and Ryan, John, M.D., *Marriage: A Medical and Sacramental Study.* New York, Sheed and Ward, 1955.

King, J. Leycester, *Sex Enlightenment and the Catholic.* London, Burns Oates and Washbourne, 1944.

Listen, Son. Chicago, Franciscan Herald Press, 1955.

Lord, Daniel A., S.J., *Some Notes for the Guidance of Parents.* St. Louis, Mo., Queen's Work, 1944.

Mother's Little Helper. Chicago, Franciscan Herald Press, 1955.

Pius XI, Encyclical Letter on *The Christian Education of Youth.* Washington, D.C., N.C.W.C., 1936.

——, Encyclical Letter on *Christian Marriage* (*Casti Connubii*). New York, America Press, 1931.

Pius XII, " Allocution to a Concourse of Women of Catholic Action, November 26, 1941." *Clergy Review,* Vol. XII (March, 1942), pp. 136ff.

——, *Moral Questions Affecting Married Life:* Allocution to the Italian Catholic Union of Midwives, October 21, 1951. New York, Paulist Press, 1952.

Vermeersch, A., S.J., *What Is Marriage?* A Catechism Arranged according to the Encyclical *Casti Connubii,* translated by T. Lincoln Bouscaren, S.J. New York, America Press, 1932.

Werth, Alvin, O.F.M. Cap. and Michanovich, Clement S., *Papal Pronouncements on Marriage and the Family.* Milwaukee, Bruce, 1955.

SPECIAL PROBLEMS—SEXUAL PATHOLOGY

Masturbation

Balsin, H., " Masturbation in Infants," *Journal of Pediatrics,* Vol. XL (1952), pp. 675-678.

Cavanagh, John, and McGoldrick, James B., S.J., *Fundamental Psychiatry.* Milwaukee, Bruce, 1953.

Flood, Peter, O.S.B., editor. *New Problems in Medical Ethics.* Westminster, Md., Newman, 1954.

Gagern, Frederick von, *The Problem of Onanism,* translated by Meyrick Booth. Westminster, Md., Newman, 1955.

Healy, Edwin F., S.J., *Medical Ethics.* Chicago, Loyola University Press, 1956.

Hildebrand, Dietrich von, *In Defence of Purity*. London, Sheed and Ward, 1931.

Huhner, Max, *The Diagnosis and Treatment of Sexual Disorders in the Male and Female*. Philadelphia, Davis, 1937.

Kanver, K., M.D., Meyer, A., M.D., and Park, E. A., M.D., *Child Psychiatry*. Springfield, Charles C. Thomas, 1935.

Kroger, William S., and Freed, S. Charles, *Psychosomatic Gynecology*. Chicago, Free Press, 1956.

Martindale, C. C., *The Difficult Commandment*. New York, Kenedy, 1927.

Odenwald, Robert, M.D., "The Problem of Masturbation," *The Priest*, Vol. II (January, 1955); Vol. II (February, 1955).

Oliven, John F., M.D., *Sexual Hygiene and Pathology—A Manual for the Physician*. Philadelphia, Lippincott, 1955.

Pratt, L., and Whelpton, P. K., "Social and Psychological Factors Affecting Fertility," *Milbank Memorial Fund Quarterly*, Vol. XXXIV (1956).

Vander Veldt, James H., O.F.M., and Odenwald, Robert, M.D., *Psychiatry and Catholicism*. New York, McGraw-Hill, 1952.

Homosexuality

Anomaly, pseud., *The Invert*. Baltimore, Williams and Wilkins, 1948.

Bergler, Edmund, *Neurotic Counterfeit-Sex: Impotence, Frigidity, "Mechanical" Pseudoşexuality, Homosexuality*. New York, Grune and Stratton, 1954.

Cory, Donald W., *The Homosexual in America*. New York, Greenberg, 1951.

Darke, Ray, "Heredity as an Etiological Factor in Homosexuality." *Journal of Nervous and Mental Diseases*, Vol. CVII (March, 1948), pp. 251-268.

Flood, Peter, O.S.B., editor, *New Problems in Medical Ethics*. Westminster, Md., Newman, 1957.

Glass, J. Duel, S.J., and Wright, C. A., "Sex Hormone Studies in Male Homosexuals." *Endocrinology*, Vol. XXVI (1940), pp. 590-594.

Gleason, S.J., "Homosexuality: Moral Aspects of the Problem." *Homiletic and Pastoral Review*, Vol. LVIII (December, 1957), pp. 272-278.

Hamilton, Gilbert, *On the Causes of Homosexuality*. New York, Legman, 1950.

"Homosexuality and the Law." *The Priest*, Vol. XIV (January, 1958), pp. 21-25.

Liebmann, S., "Homosexuality, Transvestism and Psychosis." *Journal of Nervous and Mental Diseases*, Vol. XCII (1940), pp. 65-66.

Moore, Thomas V., "Pathogenesis and the Treatment of Homosexual Disorders: A Digest of Some Pertinent Evidence." *Journal of Personality*, Vol. XIV (1945), pp. 47-83.

Odenwald, Robert, M.D., "Counseling the Homosexual." *The Priest*, Vol. IX (December, 1952), pp. 940-944.

Scholfield, Michael G., *Society and the Homosexual*. London, Gollancz, 1952.

Methods of Obtaining Semen Samples

Bouscaren, T. Lincoln, S.J., *The Canon Law Digest*. Vol I, Milwaukee, Bruce, 1934, pp. 156ff.

Clifford, J., S.J., "Sterility Tests and Their Morality." *American Ecclesiastical Review*, Vol. CIX (November, 1952), p. 365.

Doyle, Joseph, M.D., "The Cervical Spoon—An Aid to Spermigration and Semen Sampling." *Bulletin of the New England Medical Center*, Vol. X (October, 1948), pp. 225-231.

——, "Exploratory Culdotomy for Observation of Tubo-Ovarian Physiology at Ovulation Time." *Fertility and Sterility*, Vol. II (November-December, 1951), pp. 475-486.

——, "The Role of the Gynecologist." *Linacre Quarterly*, Vol. XXI (May, 1954), pp. 40-44.

Glass, S.J., M.D., and Lozarus, M.L., M.D., "Improved Fertility and Prevention of Abortion after Nutritional Hormonal Therapy." *Journal of the American Medical Association*, Vol. CLIV (March 13, 1954), pp. 908-910.

Kelly, Gerald, S.J., *Medico-Moral Problems*, St. Louis, Catholic Hospital Association, 1958.

Lynch, John J., S.J., "Some Moral Phases of Infertility Problems." *Linacre Quarterly*, Vol. XXI (May, 1954), pp. 53-63.

McCarthy, John, "A Lawful Method of Procuring Seminal Specimens for Sterility Tests." *Irish Ecclesiastical Record*, Vol. LXX (June, 1948), pp. 533-536.

McFadden, Charles J., O.S.A., *Medical Ethics.* Philadelphia, F. A. Davis, 1956.

Merkelbach, B. H., *Summa theologiae moralis.* Vol. I, 9th edition, Bruges, Desclée de Brouwer, 1954.

Noldin, H., and Schmitt, A., *Summa theologiae moralis.* Vol. II, *De praeceptis,* Westminster, Md., Newman, 1952.

Tyler, E., M.D., "Semen Studies and Fertility." *Journal of the American Medical Association.* Vol. CXLVI (May 26, 1951), pp. 307-314.

Artificial Insemination

Connell, Francis J., C.SS.R., "The Catholic Doctor." *American Ecclesiastical Review,* Vol. CXI (December, 1944), pp. 439-448.

Glover, William K., S.M., *Artificial Insemination among Human Beings.* Washington, D.C., Catholic University, 1948.

Holman, Edwin J., "Medico-legal Aspects of Sterilization, Artificial Insemination, and Abortion." *Journal of the American Medical Association,* Vol. CLVI (December 4, 1954), pp. 1309-1311.

Kelly, Gerald, S.J., "The Morality of Artificial Fecundation." *American Ecclesiastical Review,* Vol. CI (August, 1939), pp. 109-118.

McCarthy, J., "The Morality of Artificial Fecundation." *Irish Ecclesiastical Record,* Vol. LXVII (May, 1946), pp. 328-333.

McFadden, Charles J., O.S.A., *Medical Ethics.* Philadelphia, F. A. Davis, 1956.

Mahoney, E. J., "Artificial Insemination." *The Clergy Review,* Vol. XXV (June, 1945), 268-270.

O'Donnell, Dayton H., M.D., "Artificial Insemination." *Linacre Quarterly,* Vol. VIII (January, 1940).

Pope Pius XII, "Address to the Fourth International Convention of Catholic Doctors, September 29, 1949." *Catholic Mind,* Vol. XLVIII (April, 1950), pp. 250-253.

Impotence

Bouscaren, Lincoln T., S.J., and Ellis, A. C., S.J., *Canon Law Code and Commentary.* Milwaukee, Bruce, 1945, p. 526.

Cavanagh, John R., *Fundamental Marriage Counseling.* Milwaukee, Bruce, 1957.

Jorio, T. A., S.J., editor, *Theologia Moralis*. Vol. III, *De sacramentis*, No. 1178. Naples, D'Auria, 1953.

Merkelbach, Benedictus, O.P., *Quaestiones de Embryologia et Sterilizatione*. Liège, La Pensée Catholique, 1937, p. 93.

Niedermeyer, Albert, *Handbuch der Speziellen Pastoralmedizin*. Vol. II, Vienna, Verlag Herder, 1952, pp. 327-329.

Nowlan, E. H., S.J., "Double Vasectomy and Marital Impotence." *Theological Studies*, Vol. VI (September, 1945), p. 392.

O'Donnell, Thomas J., S.J., *Morals in Medicine*. Westminster, Md., Newman, 1956.

Stekel, W., *Impotence in the Male*. London, Vision Press, 1952.

Tanquerey, A., *Synopsis theologiae moralis et pastoralis*. Rome, 1920, Suppl. V.

Ubach, J., S.J., *Theologiae moralis*. Vol. II, Freiburg, 1926, No. 798.

Wiggers, Carl J., *Physiology in Health and Disease*. 5th edition, Philadelphia, Lea and Febiger, 1949, p. 1060.

Wouters, B., C.SS.R., *Manuale theologiae moralis*. Vol. II, Rome, 1932, No. 774.

PERIODIC CONTINENCE
(RHYTHM)

Cavanagh, John R., *Fundamental Marriage Counseling*. Milwaukee, Bruce, 1957.

Connell, Francis J., C.SS.R., "Questions and Answers." *American Ecclesiastical Review*, Vol. CXXVII (August, 1952), pp. 136-141.

Farris, Edmond J., *Human Ovulation and Fertility*. Philadelphia, Lippincott, 1956.

Griese, Orville N., *The Morality of Periodic Continence*. Washington, D.C., Catholic University Press, 1942.

Kelly, Gerald, S.J., "Rhythm in Marriage: Duty and Idealism." *America*, Vol. LXXXVII (May 3, 1952), pp. 128-130.

Knaus, Hermann, *Periodische Fruchtbarkeit und Unfruchtbarkeit des Weibes. der Weg Zur Naturlichen Geburtenregelung*. Vienna, Wilhelm Maudrich, 1934.

Latz, Leo J., *The Rhythm of Sterility and Fertility in Women*. Chicago, Latz Foundation, 1939.

McFadden, Charles J., O.S.A., *Medical Ethics*. Philadelphia, F. A. Davis, 1956.

O'Brien, Rev. John H., *Natural Birth Control without Contraception*. Champaign, III., Newman Co., 1938.

O'Donnell, Thomas J., S.J., *Morals in Medicine*. Westminster, Md., Newman, 1956.

Ogino, Kyusaku, *Conception-Period of Women*, translated by Dr. Yonez Miyagana. Harrisburg, Pa., Medical Arts, 1934.

Pius XII, *Moral Questions affecting Married Life: Allocution to Italian Catholic Union of Midwives*, October 29, 1951. New York, Paulist Press, 1952, pp. 13-15.

Schnepp, Gerald J., and Mundi, Joseph P., " Sociological Implications of Rhythm Method Practice." *Linacre Quarterly*, Vol. XIX (May, 1952), pp. 44-48.

Sturgis, S. H., " The Clinical Value of So-Called Ovulation Tests." *Bulletin of New England Medical Center*, Vol. XIV (February, 1952), pp. 6-12.

Control of Conception

Castellano, Marius, O.P., " Adnotationes ad Monitum S.S.C.S. Officii de 'amplexu reservato.'" *Ephemerides Iuris Canonici*, Vol. VIII (1952), pp. 341-345.

Cavanagh, John R., M.D., *Fundamental Marriage Counseling*. Milwaukee, Bruce, 1957.

Connell, Francis J., C.SS.R., " Answers to Questions." *American Ecclesiastical Review*, Vol. CXXIX (September, 1953), p. 197.

Dickinson, Robert Laton, *Control of Conception*. Baltimore, Williams and Wilkins, 1938.

Hering, Hyacinth M., O.P., " De amplexu reservato." *Angelicum*, Vol. XXVIII (October-December, 1951), pp. 313-345.

——, " Adnotationes ad Monitum de litteratura sexuali et de amplexu reservato." *Monitor Ecclesiasticus*, Vol. LXXVII (1952), pp. 568-585.

Himes, Norman E., *A Medical History of Contraception*. Baltimore, Williams and Wilkins, 1936.

Hurth, F. X., S.J., " De re morali." *Periodica*, Vol. XLI (December, 1952), pp. 251-269.

Kelly, Gerald, S.J., " Notes on Moral Theology, 1946." *Theological Studies*, Vol. VIII (March, 1947), pp. 97-117.

Lynch, John J., S.J., "Another Moral Aspect of Fertility Control." *Linacre Quarterly* (November, 1953), pp. 119-123

———, "Fertility Control and the Moral Law." *Linacre Quarterly*, Vol. XX (August, 1952), pp. 83-88.

McFadden, Charles, O.S.A., *Medical Ethics*. Philadelphia, F. A. Davis, 1956.

O'Donnell, Thomas J., S.J., *Morals in Medicine*. Westminster, Md., Newman, 1956.

Pius XI, Encyclical Letter on *Christian Marriage (Casti Connubii)*. New York, America Press, 1931.

Sieve, Benjamin F., "A New Anti-fertility Factor." *Science*, Vol. CXVI (October 10, 1952), pp. 373-385.

Wouters, B., C.SS.R., *De virtute castitatis*. 2nd edition, Rome, 1932, No. 118.

INVIOLABILITY OF HUMAN LIFE

Ficarra, B. J., *Newer Ethical Problems in Medicine and Surgery*. Westminster, Md., Newman, 1951.

Flood, Peter, O.S.B., editor, *New Problems in Medical Ethics*. Westminster, Md., Newman, 1954.

McFadden, Charles, O.S.A., *Medical Ethics*. Philadelphia, Davis, 1956.

O'Donnell, Thomas J., S.J., *Morals in Medicine*. Westminster, Md., Newman, 1956.

Pius XII, "Address to the Eighth Congress of the World Medical Association, September 30, 1954." *The Pope Speaks: The American Quarterly of Papal Documents*, Vol. I (Washington, D.C., 1954), pp. 347-359.

———, "Address to the First International Congress on the Histopathology of the Nervous System, September 19, 1952." *National Catholic Almanac* (Paterson, N.J., 1953 edition), pp. 64-70.

———, Address to the Sixteenth International Congress on Military Medicine, October 19, 1953. *Acta Apostolicae Sedis*, Vol. XXXV (1953), pp. 744-754.

Sullivan, Joseph V., *Catholic Teaching on the Morality of Euthanasia*. Washington, D.C., Catholic University, 1949.

MUTILATION

Ficarra, Bernard, J., M.D., *Newer Ethical Problems in Medicine and Surgery.* Westminster, Md., Newman, 1951.

Healy, Edwin, S.J., *Medical Ethics.* Chicago, Loyola University, 1956.

Kelly, Gerald, S.J., " Medical-Moral Notes." *Linacre Quarterly,* Vol. XX (November, 1953), pp. 116-117.

McFadden, Charles J., O.S.A., *Medical Ethics.* Philadelphia, F. A. Davis, 1956.

O'Donnell, Thomas, S.J., *Morals in Medicine.* Westminster, Md., Newman Press, 1956.

Pius XI, Encyclical Letter on *Christian Marriage (Casti Connubii).* New York, America Press, 1931.

Pius XII, " Address to the Eighth Congress of the World Medical Association, September 30, 1954." *The Pope Speaks: The American Quarterly of Papal Documents,* Vol. I (Washington, D.C., 1954), pp. 347-359.

——, " Address to the First International Congress on the Histopathology of the Nervous System, September 14, 1952." *National Catholic Almanac* (Paterson, N.J., 1953 edition), pp. 64-70.

——, Address to the Twenty-Sixth Annual Convention of the Italian Society of Urologists, October 8, 1953. *Acta Apostolicae Sedis,* Vol. XXXXV (1953), pp. 673-679.

SURGERY—PREVENTIVE AND CORRECTIVE

Clifford, John S., S.J., " The Morality of Castration for Carcinoma of the Prostate." *Theological Studies,* Vol. V (December, 1944), pp. 439-452.

Cunningham, Bert J., *The Morality of Organic Transplantation.* Washington Catholic University, 1945.

Flood, Peter, O.S.B., editor. *New Problems in Medical Ethics.* Westminster, Md., Newman, 1954. " The Marriage Hermaphrodites," pp. 50-57.

Ford, John, S.J., "Notes on Moral Theology: Marriage." *Theological Studies*, Vol. V (December, 1944), pp. 533-534.

Grossman, Herbert J., and others. "Surgical Separation in Granio Pagus." *Journal of the American Medical Association*, Vol. CLIII (September 19, 1953), pp. 201-207.

Hesseltine, H. Close, M.D., "Circumcision." *Journal of the American Medical Association*, Vol. CXL (May 21, 1949), p. 368.

Hinman, Frank, Jr., M.D., "Advisability of Surgical Reversal of Sex in Female Pseudohermophroditism." *Journal of the American Medical Association*, Vol. CXLVI (June 2, 1951), pp. 423-429.

Kelly, Gerald, S.J., "Notes on Moral Theology." *Theological Studies*, Vol. VIII (March, 1947), pp. 97-101.

——, *Medico-Moral Problems*. St. Louis, Catholic Hospital Association, 1958. "Organic Transplantation," pp. 22-28; "Vasectomy with Prostatectomy," pp. 35-41.

——, "Notes on Moral Theology: Fifth Commandment." *Theological Studies*, Vol. XI (March, 1950), pp. 43-44.

McCarthy, John. "The Morality of Organic Transplantation." *Irish Ecclesiastical Record*, Vol. LXVII (March, 1946), pp. 192-198.

Pius XII, "Address to the Twenty-Sixth Congress of the Italian Society of Urologists, October 8, 1953." *AAS*, Vol. XLV (October 8, 1953), pp. 674ff.

"Theology for Every Man: Does Moral Law Allow Kidney Transplants? " *Pilot* (Boston), January 22, 1955.

ABORTION

Dickinson, Robert R., *Control of Conception*. Baltimore, Williams and Wilkins, 1938.

Good, Frederick L., M.D., and Kelly, Otis F., M.D., *Marriage, Morals and Medical Ethics*. New York, Kenedy, 1951.

Heffernan, Roy J., and Lynch, William A., M.D., "Is a Therapeutic Abortion Scientifically Justified? " *Linacre Quarterly*, Vol. XIX (February, 1952), pp. 11-27.

Huser, Roger J., *The Crime of Abortion in Canon Law*. Washington, D.C., Catholic University, 1942.

Merkelbach, Benedictus, O.P., *Quaestiones de embryologia et de ministratione Baptismatis*. Liège, La Pensée Catholique, 1928, Q. IV, pp. 65-69.

Pujiula, Jacobus, S.J., *De medicina pastorali*. 2nd edition, Turin, Marietti, 1953.

Taussig, Frank J., *Abortion, Spontaneous and Induced—Medical and Social Aspects*. St. Louis, C.V. Mosby, 1936.

Treub, Hector, M.D., Van Oppenraay, R., S.J., and Vlaming, T., M.D., *The Right to Life of the Unborn Child*. New York, Wagner, 1903.

STERILIZATION

Bonnar, Alphonsus, O.F.M., *The Catholic Doctor*. 6th edition, London, Burns Oates and Washbourne, 1952.

Flood, Peter, O.S.B., editor, *New Problems in Medical Ethics*. Vol. III, Westminster, editor, Md., Newman, 1954.

Healy, Edwin F., S.J., *Medical Ethics*. Chicago, Loyola University Press, 1956.

Keenan, Alan, O.F.M., and Ryan, John, M.D., *Marriage: A Medical and Sacramental Study*. New York, Sheed and Ward, 1955.

Lehane, Joseph B., *The Morality of American Civil Legislation concerning Eugenical Sterilization*. Washington, D.C., Catholic University, 1944.

McFadden, Charles J., *Medical Ethics*. Philadelphia, F.A. Davis, 1956.

O'Donnell, Thomas, S.J., *Morals in Medicine*. Westminster, Md., Newman, 1956.

Pius XI, Encyclical on *Christian Marriage* (*Casti Connubii*). New York, America Press, 1931.

EUTHANASIA

Blakely, Paul L., " Mercy-Killing Turns Back the Clock." *America*, Vol. LC (November 4, 1939), p. 90.

Bonnar, Alphonsus, O.F.M., *The Catholic Doctor*. 6th edition, London, Burns Oates and Washbourne, 1952.

Ficarra, Bernard, M.D., *Newer Ethical Problems in Medicine and Surgery*. Westminster, Md., Newman, 1951.

Flood, Peter, O.S.B., editor, *New Problems in Medical Ethics*. Westminster, Md., Newman, 1954.

Ford, John C., S.J., *Mercy Murder*. New York, America Press, 1950.

Healy, Edwin F., S.J., *Medical Ethics*. Chicago, Loyola University Press, 1956.

Kelly, Gerald, S.J., *Medico-Moral Problems*. St. Louis, Catholic Hospital Association, 1958.

McFadden, Charles J., O.S.A., *Medical Ethics*. Philadelphia, F. A. Davis, 1956.

Neary, James T., "Euthanasia." *Linacre Quarterly*, Vol. VI (April, 1938), pp. 38-42.

O'Donnell, Thomas J., S.J., *Morals in Medicine*. Westminster, Md., Newman, 1956.

Sullivan, Joseph V., *Catholic Teaching on the Morality of Euthanasia*. Washington, D.C., Catholic University, 1949, p. 72.

PSYCHOLOGY AND PSYCHIATRY

Alexander, Franz, *Psychosomatic Medicine*. New York, Norton, 1950.

Alexander, Leo, M.D., *Treatment of Mental Disorders*. Philadelphia, Saunders, 1953.

Allers, Rudolf, *The Successful Error*. New York, Sheed and Ward, 1941.

Anastasi, Anne, and Foley, John P., Jr., *Differential Psychology*. New York, Macmillan, 1949.

——, *Psychological Testing*. New York, Macmillan, 1954.

Arnold, Magda B., and Gasson, John A., S.J., *The Human Person*. New York, Ronald, 1954.

Boring, E. G., *A History of Experimental Psychology*. 2nd ed., New York, Appleton, 1950.

Braceland, Francis J., *Faith, Reason and Modern Psychiatry*. New York, Kenedy, 1955.

Brennan, Robert E., *General Psychology*. New York, Macmillan, 1952.

Bruno de Jésus-Marie, C.D., *Conflict and Light*. London, Sheed and Ward, 1952.

Carroll, Herbert A., *Mental Hygiene*. New York, Prentice Hall, 1951.

Castiglioni, C., *La Psicologia Neoscolastica del Card. Mercier*. Brescia, La Scuola Cattolica, 1936.

Cattell, J., *Psychology in America*. New York, Science Press, 1929.

Cavanagh, John R., and McGoldrick, James B., S.J., *Fundamental Psychiatry*. Milwaukee, Bruce, 1953.

Curran, Charles A., *Personality Factors in Counseling*. New York, Grune and Stratton, 1945.

———, *Counseling in Catholic Life and Education*. New York, Macmillan, 1952.

Demal, Willibald, O.S.B., *Pastoral Psychology in Practice*, translated by Joachim Conway. New York, Kenedy, 1955.

Dempsey, Peter, O.F.M.Cap., *Psychology for Everyone*. Westminster, Md., Newman, 1953.

Deutsch, H., *The Psychology of Women*. 2 vols., New York, Grune and Stratton, 1944.

Dobbelstein, H., *Psychiatry for Priests*, translated by Meyrick Booth. New York, Kenedy, 1954.

Donat, J., S.J., *Psychologia*. Barcelona, Herder, 1944.

Doniger, Simon, editor, *Religion and Human Behavior*. New York, Association Press, 1954.

Doob, Leonard W., *Social Psychology*. New York, Holt, 1952.

Duffey, Felix D., C.S.C., *Testing the Spirit*. St. Louis, Herder, 1947.

English, O. Spurgeon, and Pearson, Gerald H. J., *Emotional Problems of Living*. New York, Norton, 1955.

Flood, Peter, editor, *New Problems in Medical Ethics*. Westminster, Md., Newman, 1954.

Frobes, Joseph, *Compendium psychologiae experimentalis*. Rome, Gregorian University, 1937.

———, *Cursus brevior psychologiae speculativae*. Paris, Lethielleux, 1933.

———, *Psychologia speculativa in usum scholarum*. 2 vols., Freiburg, Herder, 1927.

Gannon, T., *Psychology: The Unity of Human Behaviour*. New York, Ginn, 1954.

Gardeil, H. D., O.P., *Introduction to the Philosophy of St. Thomas Aquinas*. Vol. III, *Psychology*, translated by John A. Otto. St. Louis, Herder, 1956.

Gemelli, A., "In tema di rapporti tra Psicologia e Filosofia," *Riv. Fil. Neo-Scholast.* (November 28, 1936).

Hall, G. S., *Founders of Modern Psychology*. New York, Appleton, 1912.

Hughes, Margaret M., *The People in Your Life.* New York, Knopf, 1951.

Hurlock, Elizabeth B., *Developmental Psychology.* New York, McGraw-Hill, 1953.

Jersild, Arthur T., *Child Psychology.* New York, Prentice Hall, 1958.

Kanner, Leo, M.D., *Child Psychiatry.* Springfield, Ill., Thomas Press, 1957.

Klubertanz, G. P., *The Philosophy of Human Nature.* New York, Appleton, 1953.

Lindworsky, Joannes, *Der Wille.* 3rd edition, Leipzig, 1923.

——, *Experimental Psychology,* translated by H. de Silva. New York, Macmillan, 1931.

——, *The Psychology of Asceticism,* translated by E. A. Heiring. London, Edwards, 1936.

——, *Theoretical Psychology,* translated by H. R. de Silva. St. Louis, Herder, 1932.

——, *The Training of the Will,* translated by A. Steiner and E. A. Fitzpatrick. Milwaukee, Bruce, 1929.

McCarthy, Raphael, C., S.J., *Safeguarding Mental Health.* Milwaukee, Bruce, 1937.

Magner, Rev. James A., *Mental Health in a Mad World.* Milwaukee, Bruce, 1953.

Mayer, Michael, S.J., *Psychology.* London, Longmans Green, 1900.

Michotte, Albert, *Miscellanea Psychologica.* Louvain and Paris, 1947.

Misiak, Henry K., and Staudt, Virginia M., *Catholics in Psychology.* New York, McGraw-Hill, 1954.

Moore, Thomas Verner, *Cognitive Psychology.* Philadelphia, Lippincott, 1939.

——, *Driving Forces of Human Nature and Their Adjustment.* New York, Grune and Stratton, 1948.

——, *Dynamic Psychology.* Philadelphia, Lippincott, 1926.

——, *Nature and Treatment of Mental Disorders,* 2nd edition, New York, Grune and Stratton, 1951.

——, *Personal Mental Hygiene.* New York, Grune and Stratton, 1944.

Noyes, Arthur P., M.D., *Modern Clinical Psychiatry.* Philadelphia, Saunders, 1939.

Nuttin, Joseph, S.J., *Psychoanalysis and Personality.* New York, Sheed and Ward, 1953.

Overholser, Winfred, and Richmond, W. V., *Handbook of Psychiatry*. Philadelphia, Lippincott, 1947.

Raeymaeker, Louis de, *Le Cardinal Mercier et l'Institut supérieur de philosophie de Louvain*. Louvain, Nauwelaerts, 1952.

Schneiders, A. A., *Introductory Psychology*. New York, Rinehart, 1951.

Stafford, J. W., " Psychology at the Catholic University of America." *American Catholic Psychological Association Newsletter* (1953), 3rd suppl., No. 1.

Stern, Edith M., *Mental Illness*. National Association for Mental Health, 1951.

Vander Veldt, Rev. James H., and Odenwald, Robert P., M.D., *Psychiatry and Catholicism*. 2nd edition, New York, McGraw-Hill, 1957.

Walters, Sister Annette, and O'Hara, Sister Kevin, *Persons and Personality*. New York, Appleton, 1953.

White, Victor, O.P., *God and the Unconscious*. Chicago, Regnery, 1953.

Woodworth, R. S., *Contemporary Schools of Psychology*. Revised edition, New York, Ronald, 1948.

Index

~~~~~~